THE QUEEN HER LOVER AND THE MOST NOTORIOUS SPY IN HISTORY

THE QUEEN
HER
LOVER
AND THE MOST
NOTORIOUS
SPY
IN HISTORY

Roland Perry

ALLEN&UNWIN
SYDNEY·MELBOURNE·AUCKLAND·LONDON

ALSO BY ROLAND PERRY

Fiction

Programme for a Puppet

Blood Is a Stranger

Faces in the Rain

Non-Fiction

Horrie: The War Dog

Bill the Bastard

Last of the Cold War Spies

The Fifth Man

The Fight for Australia

The Changi Brownlow

The Australian Light Horse

Monash: The Outsider Who Won a War

The Programming of the President

The Exile: Wilfred Burchett, Reporter of Conflict

Mel Gibson: Actor, Director, Producer

Lethal Hero

Sailing to the Moon

Elections Sur Ordinateur

Bradman's Invincibles

The Ashes: A Celebration

Miller's Luck: The Life and Loves of Keith Miller, Australia's Greatest All-Rounder

Bradman's Best

Bradman's Best Ashes Teams

Don Bradman aka The Don

Captain Australia: A History of the Celebrated Captains of Australian Test Cricket

Bold Warnie

Waugh's Way

Shane Warne: Master Spinner

Documentary Films

The Programming of the President

The Raising of a Galleon's Ghost

Strike Swiftly

Ted Kennedy and the Pollsters

The Force

Victoria's Secret

First published in 2014

Allen & Unwin
83 Alexander Street
Crows Nest NSW 2065
Australia
Phone: (61 2) 8425 0100
Email: info@allenandunwin.com
Web: www.allenandunwin.com

Cataloguing-in-Publication details are available
from the National Library of Australia
www.trove.nla.gov.au

ISBN 978 1 76011 075 8

Internal design by Nada Backovic
Set in 11/12 pt Bembo by Midland Typesetters, Australia
Printed and bound in Australia by Griffin Press

10 9 8 7 6 5 4 3 2 1

MIX
Paper from
responsible sources
FSC
www.fsc.org   FSC® C009448

The paper in this book is FSC certified.
FSC promotes environmentally responsible,
socially beneficial and economically viable
management of the world's forests.

Dr Leon Levin, Professor Ed Byrne, Professor James Sarros
and Dr Anne Sarros
For their support

'Victoria was lame and unable to stand upright,' yet 'bent on marrying nobody but Lord Elphinstone.'

ROBERT BROWNING

CONTENTS

PREFACE

In 1993 and 1996 when I was interviewing ex-KGB agents (on camera) in Russia, it was revealed that Anthony Blunt, a British double agent working for the former Soviet Union, had microfilmed a cache of royal correspondence and sent it all to KGB headquarters. At the time I was researching two books: *The Fifth Man,* about Victor Rothschild, a member of the infamous Cambridge spy ring that had included Blunt; and *Last of the Cold War Spies,* about Michael Whitney Straight, the American member of the ring. I assumed that the important royal letters concerned the Duke of Windsor and his correspondence with Hitler and the Nazis. Two of the ex-KGB master-spies—Yuri Ivanovitch Modin and Vladimir Barkovsky—emphasised that the royal letters were important. For one thing, the KGB could have used them to blackmail the royal family. For another, Blunt's passing them on to his Moscow masters meant he had something over his palace masters and his MI5 superiors. It was subtle and unspoken. At no point did Blunt ever threaten anybody but all concerned in British Intelligence and at the palace tiptoed around him for 30 years, from when MI5 first became suspicious of him in 1949 until his knighthood was taken from him in 1979.

One element of the correspondence that the KGB master-spies hinted about was Queen Victoria's disclosures to her daughter concerning a love affair she had had before she met Prince Albert. Research established this was the thirteenth Lord Elphinstone. I spent many months poring over the 309 massive files in his archive in the Asian section at the British Library in London. (Library staff estimated that a full review of this archive would take six years.) The files appeared to have been intermittently 'vetted' or 'edited', the last 'review' being in 1982. The problem with this filleting of letters is that events and other information overtake the files. New and related data over time gives more meaning to the original retained information. Coupled with speedy internet searches, crosschecking, and access to other related files (for instance, in India where Elphinstone spent so much time), there is no hiding from, or prevention of, fresh perspectives and often insights and revelations. Short of destroying all the files, vetting can never avoid increased perception.

While working on this story I came across an Englishman claiming that he was a direct descendent of Queen Victoria and that she had had a bastard child while in seclusion at Ramsgate between September 1835 and February 1836. If true, the father of this mystery child—allegedly born in late October 1835—had to have been Elphinstone. I was sidetracked by this undertaking for over a year of exhaustive research. But there was no direct evidence of this illegitimate royal birth. I had DNA checks done on the Englishman making the claim but the results showed no direct link to the royals or Elphinstone. After checking of files—births, deaths and marriages, wills in England and Scotland, and a myriad other documents over six generations—there was nothing definitive linking this claimant to either Victoria or Elphinstone. Not even the Mormons, who bought up church parish registers in the UK and elsewhere going back to that time, could assist. (The Mormons' motive for acquiring these records was to baptise everyone on the registers into their church to boost their claim to having huge numbers.)

There was a great deal of circumstantial evidence that a child, who had been adopted into an impoverished London servant family in 1836, did have enormous wealth, mainly property, settled upon him in most unusual circumstances in a long-running cover-up. This person died in 1919, aged 83. His son died in 1968. Post-1968 that property, worth about £3 billion, was fraudulently distributed after relatively small payments (worth just £3 million) were made to descendents of that original adopted child. These payments were enough to buy off or prevent anyone in the family investigating the fraud, except for the one individual: the Englishman to whom I was introduced.

I may return to this story. A little distance and time will make it an enticing project.

I am most grateful to Yuri Modin, and (the late) Vladimir Barkovsky, both of whom were formerly Moscow controls running the British spies recruited mainly at Cambridge University, England, in the 1930s, 1940s and 1950s. I visited them in Moscow several times and they were unfailing in their courtesy and assistance. They both indicated at the beginning of our conversations that they would not provide information that was not already known by Western intelligence. I was happy with this; it put me ahead of anyone else in the Western media, and the data collected allowed me to probe deeper. Several journalists, including Philip Knightley and the late John Costello, were helpful with information.

Thanks also to those who offered comments and insights, including Dr Leon Levin, Dr Anne Sarros and Diana Georgeff. Jack Grossman, the documentary filmmaker who accompanied me to Russia, died in May 2013 but not before he read and offered advice on this book. His encouragement was always a mainstay and great support for me in my books on espionage agents and also this current book.

My thanks also to publisher Sue Hines at Allen & Unwin for her support on six books.

A word on the 'style' of the book. I call it 'non-fiction with occasional dramatisations and reconstructions'. This is similar but not the same as a television or film script-writer writing on a non-fiction subject and re-creating some scenes based on correspondence of the participants, interviews and other sources. Such stories and re-enactments are daily staple diet for television and film. The book writer can vary this film-script writing approach to make an otherwise complex narrative more accessible, digestible and comprehensible for the reader while keeping the subject's integrity intact. The key is to do at least as much research as one would for an academic or non-fiction project. This approach leads to the writer facilitating comprehension of a subject rather than simply regurgitating dry facts. I believe in the axiom that there are no dull topics, only dull writers.

Professor Roland Perry OAM, BEc., F. Monash
Writer-in-Residence, Monash University.
May 2014

1

A Princess
in Peril

Sixteen-year-old Princess Victoria was in a terrible state. Her mystery illness had lingered for several months by mid-October 1835 and her physician, Dr James Clark, had been unable to give a convincing opinion in his consultations with her at the family's hideaway resort at Ramsgate on England's east coast. The 51-year-old Scot, who had qualified at the respected Aberdeen University, was not the finest diagnostician. He had spent most of his working career as a naval surgeon and rarely attended to women. He had joined the household of the widowed Duchess of Kent—Victoria's 49-year-old mother—in April 1835 at the direction of the duchess's brother Leopold, King of the Belgians. The young princess's illness had been this earnest doctor's first real challenge since attending to the Kents. He mulled over a variety of ailments. Clark had examined her in late August in her bedchamber with her lady-in-waiting Baroness Lehzen present. He asked the princess to remove her clothes. She lay grim-faced on her back, naked but for underwear.

Glancing over his spectacles at the princess, Clark mumbled in his broad brogue that her 'tummy' seemed a bit bloated. He ran his fingers over her stomach and pressed here and there causing Victoria to wince. Clark asked her about her complaint that she was having a problem going to the lavatory.

'That's the trouble,' Victoria said in a frustrated tone, 'I can't go at all, doctor!'

Clark motioned for Lehzen to help Victoria dress.

'I believe you have constipation, pure and simple, my lady.'

'But you thought it was a bilious fever a month ago,' Lehzen proffered.

'You even thought I might have typhoid!' Victoria said.

'God knows you may have it still, my lady,' Clark said, his authoritative manner intact, 'but you *are* having trouble with constipation.' Before the others could protest, he added: 'You must have a daily dose of physic before breakfast. I will personally make up some for you today.'

'Physic?' Victoria frowned.

'It's a laxative,' the doctor said. 'You should be right in a week or so.'

Clark departed. Victoria said to Lehzen: 'I shall never let a doctor examine my body again!'

When Victoria collapsed soon afterwards, Clark was in London. Lehzen begged the duchess and the comptroller of the Kent household, 49-year-old John Conroy, to bring Clark back to Ramsgate urgently.

'No, that would be ridiculous!' the Duchess of Kent had scoffed. 'Such a summons would cause an unnecessary noise in London.' She was thinking of her brother-in-law King William IV, himself ailing. He had often voiced his disapproval of the way Victoria was being treated by her mother and tall, handsome and stern Conroy. The latter had emerged as the main culprit in the eyes of King William and those close to unfolding events.

Conroy, formerly an Irish officer in the British Army, was a philanderer and seducer who seemed to have a peculiar grip on the Duchess of Kent. He acted as if he were a strict father to Victoria. Over time, especially by late 1835, people whispered about his 'proximity' to both women. Rumours circulated: was he Victoria's father? The duchess's husband, the Duke of Kent, was believed to have been impotent late in his life. Was it possible that in 1819 the fiercely ambitious Conroy and the poor and avaricious duchess had coupled secretly to produce a child who would be claimed as the duke's? The child would be in line for the throne—and there would also be an increased annuity from the Privy Purse for them. If true, it would mean that Victoria was a bastard, ineligible to become queen. The speculation was understandable yet, without the science to decide paternity, it was little more than court tittle-tattle. More likely, the stout, doubt-riddled and indecisive duchess simply needed a strong man like Conroy to run her royal household, and he used his innate political skills to manipulate her.

King William had been irritated all through 1835 by the way Conroy and the duchess had paraded the princess up and down the country. They stayed with aristocrats, and opened everything from hospitals and parks to porcelain works and flower shows. Conroy insisted that a royal salute be fired whenever they passed by, an honour normally reserved for the monarch; King William had considered this the height of presumption. He was the reigning monarch. Why should the heir apparent be sent on tour as if the Kent household was already in Buckingham Palace? King William outlawed all salutes other than for him or Queen Adelaide. William was aware too that the 'unscrupulous and vain' Conroy was urging that he be appointed Victoria's private secretary and the duchess be made 'regent' if the king should die before Victoria turned eighteen, the prescribed age for crowning a monarch.

As Victoria grew more ill, the last thing the duchess wanted was a prying monarch, with his court and, indeed, the press demanding to know if Victoria—the next in line for the throne of England—was seriously ill. The duchess had contacted Clark about Victoria's collapse, but he remained unconcerned. The duchess became worried. She consulted Conroy, suggesting a local doctor should be called. Conroy was against it.

'It will be politically dangerous,' he warned. He too was worried about leaks. If the outside world learned or heard rumours that the princess was ill enough for a *local* Ramsgate physician to be called, then the king would soon be informed. But Victoria had deteriorated. In desperation, Moses Montefiore, the owner of the Townley House, the estate at which the Kents were ensconced, was contacted. He recommended a doctor friend, who came in the middle of the night. Victoria had become delirious. Rather than examine her, the intimidated local medico suggested rest and departed hastily. Even Conroy by this time was beginning to fret. He could see his hoped-for career evaporating. If Victoria died, he would be left with his wife, their two daughters and an impoverished duchess, who could not afford to keep him running her household. His machiavellian dreams of running a royal court were slipping away with every shorter breath the princess took.

Lehzen had witnessed Victoria's mood swings, hunger and growing plumpness over the past three months and dared to consider the possibility that she was heavier not just from overeating. She was aware of her charge's dalliances with one particular member of the Royal Horse Guards while out riding in London's parks. It was most unlikely but possible that she was pregnant to him. Lehzen had turned a blind eye to those assignations. Clark finally bustled back to Ramsgate and Lehzen begged him to examine her again.

'The scales then fell from his eyes,' Lehzen noted. Clark never expressed, but probably thought, that the princess may well have been pregnant. (Although rumours that the princess was pregnant abounded at this time, especially as she was secluded and putting on weight, no concrete evidence emerged that supported this theory.)

By late October 1835 Victoria's mental state reached a low point. She sat in her study looking forlornly at her diary, which sat on her large desk.

'I can't bring myself to write anything!' she lamented to Lehzen, 'I haven't touched it for weeks! I have written in it every day since I was 12, and now. . .'

Her voice trailed off. She sobbed.

Lehzen held her. 'There, there, my darling princess,' she said, 'you'll get back to it, in your own good time; when you have the strength.'

'I feel my life—my hopes for the future—have come to a crashing, horrible end!'

'My dear, you are but sixteen! This is one travail of many you will face as queen. You will overcome it!'

'I've let down everyone,' she cried.

Conroy burst into Victoria's apartment the next morning clutching a set of papers. Victoria was sitting in a chair, dozing, a book in her lap.

'You are required to sign these,' he said, standing over her.

'What?' she asked, startled.

Conroy thrust the papers into her hands. She began reading. They were legal documents that, if signed, would cause her to relinquish her position of 'monarch' to her mother, who would become 'regent', on King William's demise. This would apply whether or not Victoria had turned eighteen before King William's death. Conroy would be Victoria's private secretary. In effect, she would be passing all the intrinsic power and position of the monarch to her mother, leaving Conroy to pull all the strings, including those of the monarch's purse as dispersed by the treasury.

Victoria threw the papers on the floor, just as Lehzen entered the room.

'I shall not sign. Never!' Victoria said. Conroy picked up the papers and took several steps towards her.

'You are not fit to be a monarch,' he declared. 'You have proven this through your continued immaturity and your stupidity!'

'I shall be queen in my own right!'

'You are too irresponsible! You know nothing of government, of affairs of state, of parliament.'

'I shall learn, but not with your help or that of *the duchess.*'

The skeletally thin Lehzen moved close and stood between Conroy and the princess.

'I think you should leave,' Lehzen said. 'The princess is not well enough for this!'

Conroy stormed from the apartment.

After the confrontation, Victoria fell into a deep depression and lost weight too rapidly. She wept most of the time. She was listless. Her hair began to fall out. Her condition weakened further. Clark medicated her but nothing could revive her spirits. At the beginning of November, after hardly leaving her bed for weeks, Lehzen coaxed her to sit at a desk in her bedroom and attempt to write a diary entry. Lehzen opened the diary and placed a pen in her hand. Victoria seemed barely able to lift it.

'I...just...can't think what to say...I'm confused...' she whispered, seemingly exhausted from the thought of writing. At that moment, Conroy entered with the papers she had rejected a week earlier. He pushed her diary out of the way to put the papers in front of her.

'Sign these,' he ordered. 'You must sign over the regency to avoid a public disaster. Already there are rumours about your *behaviour.*'

'No!' Victoria said.

Lehzen pushed her way between Conroy and her princess, blocking him. A shouting match ensued. Conroy rounded on Lehzen for not strictly monitoring her movements.

'You fool!' a furious Conroy yelled at Lehzen, 'you let this stupid child out of your sight. It's your fault she was led astray—'

Conroy manhandled Lehzen, trying to force her out of the way. Showing surprising strength for one so thin, she held her ground. Victoria slumped in the chair, overcome with the shock. Conroy backed off, with Lehzen screaming at him to leave.

He was relentless. He returned the next day with the sharp-tongued lady-in-waiting Lady Flora Hastings and the duchess, who began with cajolery, but descended into harsh words for her daughter. Conroy confronted Victoria a third time. Lehzen once more interposed herself between the three abusers and her delicate charge.

The forceful interventions by Conroy created further lassitude in Victoria that stopped her from writing. She turned instead to something that would tax her brain less—sketching. She loved her crayon work, and she had more than a modicum of talent.

Victoria sat in front of her dresser mirror, contemplating her appearance. She drew a self-portrait. There was both pain and beauty in the result. The large eyes in the sketch were sad yet most attractive. The drawing took her much longer than normal as she drank in her own despondent reflection. But the exercise calmed her and generated her first signs of revitalisation. Victoria's only joy from the illness was her dramatic loss of weight. She had slipped to barely 44 kilograms, a loss of approaching 16 kilograms in just a few weeks. Her cheekbones were evident, appearing through a pale face, her chin sharper. Other features became prominent, especially sensuous lips. She had captured her youth on paper but the eyes reflected anxiety. They were clouded windows, suggesting experience that had aged her. Perversely, she liked what she saw. She would keep this one drawing of herself forever, she decided. Victoria had sketched herself before. Most other portraits had been torn up or discarded. She could never be considered an exceptional, conventional beauty, yet she was attractive. She had a vibrancy and drive. Even as a child, her bearing was confident. Victoria also had extraordinary and precocious sex appeal and charm.

The sketch lifted her self-confidence for the first time in weeks. She found herself drawing two people—herself and a Horse Guard captain—riding in a field. Then she outlined a further drawing, this time of the two horses in the first sketch, but they were riderless and grazing. This whimsical, even cheeky, second effort left the whereabouts and activity of the riders to the imagination.

2

THE LOVER

T he thought of one person gave her a rudimentary strength that allowed the fragile girl to cling to her sanity, just, in those dark days of late 1835. This was her lover, the dashing Scottish captain of the Horse Guards: the 28-year-old, tall, thirteenth Lord (John) Elphinstone. Reflections on this lean Highlander were on her mind during and after the prolonged illness. She was in love. He was her first. Their secret relationship had been blissful and, considering the exacting 'Kensington system,' the rigidly protective regime at Kensington Palace, it had also been defiant. It had been implemented in 1825 by Conroy to protect, cosset and restrict Victoria. The palace became a mini-fortress, making it difficult for anyone to enter without invitation.

The near-incarceration was exacerbated by the palace's location in a small hamlet, cut off from London by fields, parks, country lanes and market gardens. Yet Kensington's prison-like disciplines brought out the stubbornness, wilfulness and defiance in Victoria as she blossomed into mid-teenage years. This left her open to seduction from a more mature, experienced person offering everything her guardians were not. The princess and Lord Elphinstone had met a year earlier, and assignations had occurred throughout 1835. Despite the Kensington system, there had been plenty of opportunity for this 'attachment'. If she found an excuse to visit Windsor Castle, always chaperoned by Lehzen, Victoria might find him there, where he was often stationed. If she ventured to the fields and gardens near Buckingham Palace, including Green Park and St James's Park, there was a chance she might encounter him. There were balls, dances and parties that a select few of the titled members of the Horse Guards would attend. There was also the occasional innocent-looking rendezvous at church on Sunday. The churches St Martin-in-the-Field and St James were two favoured meeting places. It was her solo, short-term 'disappearances' while being chaperoned by Lehzen close to Kensington Palace that led to suspicions and even more rigid rules.

Lord Elphinstone, a carefree aristocrat, had been drawn to Victoria. Their love and care of horses had been the initial common denominator. Ever since she could remember, she had been enchanted by the Horse Guards, whom she saw as her 'knights in shining armour'. Their steeds with their plumes, prancing and procession were always thrilling to observe. Victoria first became aware of the young Scot when he joined the Guards as a cornet, aged eighteen in 1826 after being educated at the Royal High School, Edinburgh, and centuries-old Eton College, Windsor, the most elite school in the empire. She was not yet seven. He was made a lieutenant in 1828 and captain late in 1832, when he turned 25 and she was an impressionable thirteen-year-old.

In the same year, Elphinstone was appointed a Lord of the Bedchamber, a courtier in the royal household of King William IV, which in effect made him an appointed 'good friend' of the monarch. Elphinstone became the most popular individual in King William's court. Lady Granville remarked in 1832 that he was 'the most amiable, loyal person I ever met'. The best-known diarist of the time, Henry Greville, could be brutal and scathing about everyone from monarchs and politicians to the public and press. When it came to assessing Elphinstone at close quarters, his pen was dripping not with invective but high praise. 'A more perfect gentleman never existed,' he wrote, 'or one more full of sterling qualities.'

Elphinstone's duties included guarding King William in his bedchamber, and waiting on him while he ate in private. The role even included assisting the king with his dressing. At 25, the thirteenth lord also became a Scottish representative in the House of Lords. It all added up to a formidable, attractive, imposing figure: a man close to the monarch and who had inherited land in Scotland at age 21. He was considered to be a man of independent means with the extent of his riches being a debatable point.

Elphinstone became, at least subliminally, the father figure, dream lover and friend Princess Victoria had never had. Her own father had died when she was eight months old. More prosaically, Victoria was simply having too much naughty, forbidden fun. Their relationship was furtive, restricted and not just sexual. They enjoyed each other's company. Victoria was in need of more mature male company, or at least an attractive male she could look up to. The fact that she was in her youth and he was twelve years older was not unusual for the time. Elphinstone was a liberating influence in the near-imprisonment imposed by Conroy and the duchess, who had a vested interest in her remaining untouched in any way by those outside their control.

Young Victoria had long been aware of her mother's desire for her to marry a royal, preferably one from Prussia. The 'eligible' English royals were too poor, debauched, slack or amoral. There were no likely royal Scots. Even if 'high-born' and wealthy, the Highlanders were often too wild, unpredictable and uncontrollable. And manageability was what the duchess and Conroy (who hated Scots) wished. The duchess and Conroy feared Elphinstone, a strong character with liberal views, who would not be pliable. He was also neither German nor royal and therefore on several counts they considered him not ideal for marriage with Victoria. The previous twelve Lords Elphinstone—landowners, warriors and military class—reached back to 1510 when the peerage was created for Alexander Elphinstone. He had been one of more than 10,000 Scots killed three years later in the biggest clash ever between the Scots and the English, at the Battle of Flodden in the north of England. The thirteenth lord's strong character, wealth, background and good looks, made him feel inferior to no man, station or court. In his eyes, and those of several other Scottish families, the royals from Germany's House of Hanover who now ruled the British Empire were johnny-come-lately foreigners and inferior to their own breeding. There would never be a sense of inferiority or complexes in dealing with the interlopers.

It was just this demeanour that attracted the young princess and had drawn out her amorous instincts and Hanoverian characteristics. She and he had discovered her lusty soul. She was precocious in the bedchamber (and in the outdoors) and always, unusually hungry for satisfaction. Modern psychiatrists would diagnose her as exhibiting characteristics of a manic depressive, who often needed intense bedroom theatrics. Perhaps, more simply, she had a very healthy libido.

By 3 November 1835, Victoria could, without Lehzen's aid, sit at a desk and write to her Uncle Leopold. She had gushed over him as a father figure of sorts despite or perhaps because of his effete nature. His flamboyance had attracted and amused her. Leopold wore 7 centimetre platform shoes to cover for his lack of height and, for his vanity, a feather boa, rouged cheeks, thick make-up and extravagant wigs.

The princess was still weak. She struggled to hobble a few paces. She remained thin and her hair continued to fall out. Lehzen cut most of it off, leaving Victoria nearly bald. Clark took control in an attempt to restore his image as a competent physician. He prescribed a 7.30 a.m. daily dose of quinine, dissolved in wine to make it more palatable.

'This will counter your fever, pain and inflammation,' Clark informed her. 'I'm afraid you'll have to conform to a strict diet: potato soup for lunch at midday; boiled mutton, rice and jelly for dinner. The aim is for a daily balance of carbohydrate and protein, with a little sugar. Your natural weight will return, daily and gradually.' In this, Clark proved correct. He and Lehzen urged her to occupy her mind with knitting. Victoria found herself producing baby bonnets and booties.

Rumours and gossip were part of court life. By early 1836, King William IV heard of the plight of his niece, Victoria. The scuttlebutt was that she was being abused by her mother and Conroy, who were pressuring her over regency. King William was unfazed when he heard a wild rumour about Victoria giving birth, such was her isolation. He himself, from his younger days as the Duke of Clarence, had had ten illegitimate children (five sons and five daughters) to the comic actress Dorothy Bland, known as Mrs Jordon, a name that had given rise to his own observation that he had been 'bathing in the River Jordan'. There were respectable and not-so-respectable FitzClarences and other illegitimate families scattered throughout England's royal landscape. There was no stigma attached, only admiration for his (former) reproductive prowess. More important than any outrageous rumours was William's detestation for John Conroy. The king was angered to learn that he and the duchess had pushed the girl to the limit about signing over the regency in the expectation of his own death before Victoria's eighteenth birthday. William hated his brother's wife for keeping the loving niece, whom he adored, from him. He asked his court spies to discover if a birth had taken place and, if so, the identity of the father. William, a cantankerous man, yet one of strong character, would not spoil Victoria's chances of being crowned queen by making her plight public. Instead, he considered a little royal mischief.

The king's secret investigation did not reveal a royal bastard but had found the identity of the princess's lover, for whom she was pining. Those in and around the court whispered only one name: *John Elphinstone, the thirteenth lord*. Young poet Robert Browning, who mixed in court circles, noted that Victoria was 'lame and unable to stand upright,' yet 'bent on marrying nobody but Lord Elphinstone.'

'A romance hung around this nobleman,' Scottish biographer William Fraser wrote. 'He was a favourite of King William IV. When Queen Victoria was about sixteen, Lord Elphinstone was a handsome young guardsman, and it was currently reported and believed that the youthful pair had formed a mutual attachment.'

Victoria refused to tell her mother or Conroy her lover's name, fearing that they would take action to have him banished in some way.

But she yearned to make contact with him. The chance came in late February 1836, when Clark felt she was well enough to visit St James's Palace. She wore her grey *broche* coat trimmed with roses, which young Aunt Louise (Uncle Leopold's wife) had sent from Paris. It was Sunday and she attended church, knowing that her lover, Lord John, would be there. Victoria used Lehzen to pass word to him that she would be in attendance. They had not seen each other for five months. It was to be a heart-stopping moment for both. Elphinstone had a sketchbook with him. Sitting across the aisle from Victoria, he spent most of the one-hour service drawing her. The Duchess of Kent noticed. She was stunned. When she saw the two chatting coyly outside the church, she knew who Victoria's lover was and she was furious.

Later, in the princess's quarters at Kensington Palace, the duchess confronted her daughter. Victoria was still recovering from her multiple ordeals, including an undiagnosed 'fever' and depression. Yet she was strong enough to resist her mother with even more defiance.

'I shall continue to see him!'

'You are forbidden.'

'I want to. I will marry him!'

'He is not royal. I will not allow it.'

'I do not care. I shall be queen. I will marry whom I choose.'

In the argument that followed the duchess pointed out that the scandal that would surely erupt if they were to attempt to marry would mean Victoria would never be queen. This struck a nerve with Victoria, who had been groomed for the throne and was close to that attainment. Her eighteenth birthday was just 21 months away and the king's demise was perhaps even closer.

Still Victoria was rebellious and bold. She *would* marry Elphinstone. She would break with the tradition of the near-incestuous intermarriage of European royal families. The duchess was shocked at her daughter's intransigence and disobedience, which was near-mutiny for the household. Such a tryst of Hanover and Scotland would wreck her plans for the *right* kind of royal marriage. The confrontation led to the princess proclaiming her intentions to Lehzen and even Flora Hastings, the duchess's close friend, who sided with the duchess and Conroy against Victoria, often with spite. After this, it promised to be a house divided. The duchess moved to have Elphinstone banned from the princess's presence, even in church.

This tactic heralded a battle between the king's court and the Kents. King William had the scandal confirmed and he supported Elphinstone without equivocation. A close friendship had developed between them over the four years the Scot had been a Lord of the Bedchamber. King William's first move was to invest him as Knight Grand Cross, Hanoverian Order. This order of chivalry was peculiar to the House of Hanover and had been instituted by the previous monarch, George IV, when he was Prince Regent in 1815. A limited number were given out and King William bestowed it as his highest personal honour, a 'reward' for Elphinstone's friendship, *and* a clear indication he would be happy if the Scot married his niece. The monarch would have understood that the thirteenth lord's non-royal blood would make it difficult for him to become Victoria's husband, yet King William was doing much to give this match a chance to happen. At the very least, he was determined to spoil the plans of his sister-in-law.

The duchess countered by stepping up the search for an eligible young foreign prince. Soon after Elphinstone's investiture, she scheduled as fast as she could the visits of two Coburg cousins, sons of her second brother, Duke Ferdinand of Saxe-Coburg Koháry. There was an element of desperation in these invitations. The duchess knew that one prince, Ferdinand, was en route to Portugal to marry Queen Maria da Gloria, but they had yet to meet. The duchess made sure that the duke was aware of Victoria's availability and a glorious picture of her suitability was painted in dispatches. Young Ferdinand's long itinerary was diverted to the Channel and by boat to Dover. King William was obliged to meet and fete the visitors, but the duchess upstaged him in hospitality by putting on two lavish balls, one in fancy dress, at Kensington Palace. The princess enjoyed the company of young people, something denied her in the rigid system. She loved partying and being the centre of attention. She was attracted to Ferdinand.

The princess's affair with Elphinstone had made her experienced far beyond her years. She was sixteen but wrote with the insight of someone mature in matters of character and sensuality. She thought the brothers 'very *new* in the world,' which was her coded way of saying they were acting like immature virgins. Yet she enjoyed their company and Victoria could also afford to be generous in her professed affections. Ferdinand was betrothed. He was unattainable. Augustus was available but rejected and they departed after two weeks. It seemed far too sudden for the princess, who was allowed for those fleeting flirtatious moments to feel wanted, even though her heart was elsewhere. The contrived meetings and the concept of the planned marriage were irksome and left her feeling alone and miserable. 'Now they are quite gone,' Victoria wrote on 2 April, 'and no one can quite replace them.'

3

UNSUITABLE
SUITORS

K ing William, with his various illnesses, knew he was losing his
battle, or serious competition, with the duchess to have his choice
win the princess's hand. He was nearly 71 and suffering now from
chronic, incurable asthma. His time was running out. King William
knew that the odds were stacked against Elphinstone; once he died,
there would be little chance of the Scot marrying his niece. But he
was prepared to do anything to spoil his sister-in-law's plans. In May
1836 he invited the Prince of Orange and his two sons to visit from
Holland. This created panic with King Leopold, who could not stand
the thought of a Dutchman winning the race for Victoria. Belgium had
recently broken from the Dutch nation and there was a deal of enmity
between the neighbours on the North Sea. The Prince of Orange and
his two sons arrived in London in mid-May and were given stepped-up
royal treatment by the king. He threw a ball for the Netherlanders at
St James's Palace and also invited Victoria's cousin, young blind Prince
George, Duke of Cambridge. Now there were three possible partners
for Victoria.

Prince George made no impression and Victoria didn't care for the Netherlanders whom she told Leopold she found dull and plain.

Leopold was emerging as the most important influence in this ever-more frenetic game of courtship. He was in regular written communication with Victoria. He claimed to her that on his recent visit to Ramsgate (in late September, early October 1835), he had been direct in his discussions with Conroy about his pushing too hard for the position of private secretary, and the duchess as regent. Leopold was trying to give the impression that he was on Victoria's side but the fact that Conroy had ignored him and pushed her even harder was not discussed. Nevertheless, Victoria, relieved to have any powerful male support her, was grateful to the ingratiating Leopold, who stood to gain much from his connection to the princess when she was crowned—and she wished to please her uncle. Whomever he sent as possible suitors would be given a very good 'audience'. Victoria had not mentioned Elphinstone to him, although he already knew of at least the rumours about the Scot, who was the main block to Leopold's own plans. Victoria's heart was with Elphinstone, the monarch's Lord of the Bedchamber. The fact that he was forbidden fruit and not allowed near *her* bedchamber only enhanced her longing for him.

Leopold connived with the duchess to send their nephews Ernst and Albert, sons of their brother Ernst, Duke of Saxe-Coburg Gotha, to visit. All the focus, the adults hoped, would be on Albert. His older brother, Ernst, would inherit his father's domains. Albert would inherit very little beyond his title. A marriage with an English monarch would be a heaven-sent gift for the German house. King William heard of this move and asked Irishman Lord Palmerston, the foreign secretary, to delay, even prevent, the visit of the Coburg cousins. Palmerston—nicknamed 'the mongoose' because of his sharp nose and tight eyes—pointed out that he could not stop the duchess's brother making a private visit.

Frustrated, William then demanded that the visitors be lodged in a hotel and not Kensington Palace. William had control over all the royal palaces and had been annoyed to learn that the duchess, without his consent, had taken over seventeen rooms at Kensington, which were suitable for just such a visit. Conroy and the duchess refused to accommodate William's whims; they did accommodate the two German princes. Leopold was relieved and expressed disparaging views about King William. He was setting up the princess against William and his choices as opposed to those of the duchess and himself.

Victoria was responding as if she were gullible and ready to accept one of their offerings. Despite her precociousness, she was yet to master the byzantine ways of international royal intrigues and squabbles. She was restrained by her thoughts of a future with Elphinstone yet this did not stop a competition developing into a crisis; a huge contest over which male would be joined in holy matrimony with the future monarch of the world's most powerful nation. Britain was approaching its zenith as an empire and, in parallel, enormous change was on the horizon. Democracy was growing. Reformation of parliament and extension of the vote was always under review. New ideas kept coming up in Fleet Street with *The Times* leading the way and living up to its sobriquet, 'The Thunderer'. Writers and poets were setting a pattern and there was a deeper current of thought about equality and opportunity, two social virtues still in their infancy but developing. Even the City of London was not immune to reform and attempts to end abuses. No-one quite knew how this would affect the monarchy. Diminished power was one obvious implication, yet influence still sat with the monarch, who had to be more mindful about how he or she used or abused it as social and political enhancements occurred and the empire expanded.

While the German cousins Albert and Ernst were making their way along the Rhine, other matchmakers and candidates emerged. The Duke of Brunswick was mentioned but he was regarded as a 'Byronic Desperado': too much of a romantic playboy to be taken seriously as the prince consort. The Duke of Wellington, 67, perhaps the most famous man in the land after winning the Battle of Waterloo against the French 21 years earlier, decided to play cupid also by supporting her blind cousin, Prince George. Victoria liked him more than any other cousin, but any advances fizzled. The princess was saying very little except to her diary and closest confidantes. The ordeal stressed her, especially when her mind over a partner was fixed. The pressure was so intense that she felt 'extremely crushed and kept under'; she 'hardly dare say a word.'

Advice came from several quarters. Victoria's maternal half-sibling (one of two children of her mother's first marriage), Princess Feodora of Hohenlohe, then 28, wrote a prosaic appraisal of the German cousins en route to Victoria. Feodora, whose powers of observation were inferior to those of her much younger half-sister, thought Ernst had a better nature, while Albert was more clever and handsome. She asked Victoria to let her know what she thought of them. This helped build an expectation despite Victoria presenting her well-trained impassive exterior. Her emotions were with her uncle's choices. Like a slick horse-trader, Leopold was presenting two possible purchases, leaving it to her to feel she had a say as to which one she preferred. Victoria was so well disposed towards Leopold that she felt the urge to please him. She would see the best in the lads, whatever her deeper feelings.

Albert and Ernst arrived early afternoon on 18 May 1836. Albert was pleasing to her in many respects. He was as tall as Ernst, but broader of shoulder and better looking. Albert's nose was 'beautiful; his mouth sweet' and his teeth were good. After appraising the physical side favourably, she dissected his character. She agreed with Feodora that he was smart and bright but it was the charm in his sweet expression that delighted her most.

Above all Victoria sought *expression*. She wanted a confident, strong husband; someone with flair to complement intelligence; an individual with a deep interest in politics that might balance her own ambivalence towards certain aspects of the affairs of state. She had found all that in Elphinstone; she would accept nothing less in any other possible suitor. Victoria also looked for someone with a slice of daring in his political views. Elphinstone had had the best of schooling for the time and education had become one of his pet topics.

Elphinstone was appalled at the lack of funds given for public education—and he had supported abolition of slavery in 1833. The impressionable, cosseted Victoria had never really considered the ramifications of such reform issues until Elphinstone opened up her mind. Elphinstone, a liberal, had been drawn into politics over the Reform Bill of 1832. He believed in a much wider voting franchise. Only 440,000 people out of a population of seventeen million met the voter qualification. Seats in the Commons were allocated disproportionately. Some constituencies were over-represented; others had hardly anyone overseeing their interests. Through patronage, corruption and bribery, the Crown and Lords 'owned' about 30 per cent of the seats ('pocket' or 'rotten' boroughs). This gave them significant influence in the Commons, and in the selection of the prime minister. Elphinstone held an unpopular view in the Lords, but his thought was that, if the Commons were created by a wide franchise there would be a more dispersed equity in the nation's development and less disgruntlement in the population. People would feel they had some stake in the nation's progress and wealth. In 1830, Elphinstone had been inspired by Prime Minister Charles Grey, a Whig, who had been determined to reform the electoral system. Grey had had a high-powered cabinet, which included one former prime minister, Viscount Goderich, along with Lord Melbourne, Lord Russell, Lord Derby and Lord Palmerston (all future prime ministers). They fought for two years to pass the Reform Bill, which was more symbolism than substance. As liberal statesman John Bright put it: 'It was not a *good* Bill, but it was a *great* Bill when it passed.' Many 'rotten' boroughs remained. The 'new' system created by the Bill still excluded millions of the working class.

Women were not even considered anywhere as eligible voters, an odd state of affairs given that it was highly likely that a woman, Victoria, would become queen of the nation. Despite the trend to diminish the monarch's powers, Victoria could use her constitutional right and considerable influence to have an impact as both a figurehead and dynamic leader in her own right. An anomaly, even an absurdity, in the system that excluded women was the fact that as princess she did not have a vote. As queen, she would not vote anyway, but she would have more say than anyone in the way the country was governed (apart from the prime minister), its international relationships (apart from the foreign minister) and its moral values (alongside the Archbishop of Canterbury).

All Elphinstone's attitudes and attributes were part of the princess's idea of her future husband. She would have her ears open to the *minds* of the two unsuspecting and callow Coburg princes but she was also concerned first with the *physical*. After her experience with an ideal type so early, she would not accept someone who had no attraction for her. She noted that, where Ernst was dark, Albert had big blue eyes and light brown hair about the same colour as hers. Victoria delighted in their cultural interests. The two princes were both passable at the piano; they made time to observe and comment on prints. Victoria sat beside them as they drew sketches. Albert was appreciated more in everything. He was more reflective, more talented and wittier and had an adolescent flair for the histrionic. Once more Victoria's capacity to make judgements was evident. She praised both the young cousins (Albert was a few months younger than her, Ernst a year older) as if she were a doting aunt. They were so serious and yet happy, as expected in the young. Albert, who could do little wrong in her critical eyes, won extra points for his devotion to and fooling around with her beloved dog, Dash.

But Albert did not measure up in some areas. He was not a strong lad and was unused to staying up late. He needed his early bed-time and was bemused by Victoria's desire to dance until dawn. He could not keep pace on 20 May 1836 at St James's Palace, when a formal dinner lasted until 2 a.m. The next afternoon there was a drawing-room reception with a receiving line of an exhausting 3900 people. Pumping endless hands was not Albert's forte or wish. A salubrious dinner and concert followed. He fell asleep during his meal, resting his face on the table next to, but not quite in, his untouched soup bowl. He slumbered again at the late-ending concert. On 23 May, the day before Victoria's seventeenth birthday, he felt ill at a grand dinner at Kensington Palace and went to bed at 7 p.m.

The next day, perhaps through nerves or illness or both, Albert reported he was still feeling poorly but he just had to turn up for the big party at St James's Palace in his cousin's honour. Victoria thought Albert looked sickly. After two dances he looked as if he might faint and he went home. On 25 May, he stayed in his room, perhaps wisely avoiding Victoria who was not impressed by his lack of vigour. On 26 May, he came down for breakfast but could only manage tea before retiring again. On 29 May, he attended another party but once more left early.

Victoria felt sorry for Albert. She admired much about him, but in these social moments, so important to her high spirits, he was more child than youth. Yet she drew closer to him in private and away from the frenetic, mindless social whirl. Victoria, again showing a certain maturity, could project how Albert would develop. He was the first person, apart from Elphinstone, whom she considered with potential prince consort–like qualities. In the last week, 3 to 10 June, of the Coburg boys' stay, she and Albert went to the opera and a play, where his calm and alertness restored his image to a degree.

The other suitors, whether favoured or fobbed off, would soon fade from Victoria's thoughts as serious options for marriage. But Albert would stay in her mind. If there had to be an alternative to her beloved Lord John, he was at least one in consideration.

4

KING WILLIAM'S
FRUSTRATION

King William's next move was to engineer the appointment (via Prime Minister Lord Melbourne) of Elphinstone as a Privy Councillor, a significant honour for someone not yet 29. The Privy Council had been modified with the growth of parliamentary democracy but was still an institution of power. It was the monarch's most important advisory body. The king relied on it for rulings, administrative duties and advice on matters such as the royal prerogative: what powers he had or did not have. Even if he had technical power, for example, over issues of foreign policy, the council might advise him not to exercise it.

This elevation for the thirteenth Lord Elphinstone further enhanced his status, and positioned him well for experience that would be appreciated on the remote chance he were ever to marry the princess. The duties of a prince consort were fluid and flexible and the future queen's husband could exercise them the way he wished. If he were lazy, he could sit back and let all the arms of government and the monarchy operate without his input or influence. He could always shelter from the winds of change that promised to make the monarchy largely ceremonial and irrelevant to running the country. If he were ambitious and a man of ideas, he could move to have them realised. An intimate knowledge of the various functions of state would help.

There were other ongoing scrapes between the king and the Kents. He refused to receive the duchess's daughter-in-law (married to her son from her first marriage) on the grounds that she was not of royal blood, a condition that banned her from the 'closet' at St James's Palace. Then he prevented Conroy from attending a palace throne-room reception, saying that no men but ladies only, from other royal households, were allowed to attend. These instances were traditional technicalities that would be overlooked normally, but King William enforced them in the war of the households. Matters came to a head during August 1836 when he had invited the duchess and Victoria to come to Windsor for the queen's birthday party on 13 August, and then to stay on for his own 72nd birthday celebration eight days later. The duchess ignored the invitation to the queen's celebration, saying she had her own birthday event on 17 August at Claremont Park, the royal estate in Surrey. Neither the king nor queen was invited. The duchess condescended to attend the king's celebration. King William was furious about the snub to his wife. The duchess and Victoria would arrive on 20 August.

The king made a point of arriving at Windsor at the end of dinner. He was ill. He had not slept well of late and asthma attacks were taking a toll, yet his miserable health did not prevent him from walking straight to Victoria. Taking both of her hands, he told her how good it was to see her, and that he regretted not being able to make her acquaintance more often. The king then bowed to the duchess, low enough to be seen as cynicism, and then proceeded to complain loudly about the 'most unwarranted liberty' taken in the overuse of Kensington apartments, to which he had not consented, yet he was bothered more by what was going on *inside* those rooms: the abuse of his beloved niece.

The next night the birthday banquet was held in his honour. There were 100 guests, including Elphinstone. At one point at the pre-dinner drinks, Victoria was standing with the duchess and he was near. He wheeled over to them and went to take the duchess's hand but she withdrew it and turned away. As she did, Elphinstone moved close to Victoria, took her hand and kissed it, his lips lingering. Victoria's heart skipped a beat and not even the vicious look from her mother could erase the feeling as Elphinstone moved off to his seat at the long dining table. He was four places away from the king, who was directly opposite Victoria with the duchess on one side of him and one of his sisters on the other. The tension from the intrigues of the rival royal households swirled around the dinner table.

After the meal, the queen toasted the king. He rose to his feet to begin a long and rambling speech, some of it reaching a crescendo of angry indignation. A few minutes into it, he stiffened, paused and said: 'I trust in God that my life may be spared for nine months longer'—when Victoria would turn eighteen—'after which period, in the event of my death, no regency would take place. I should then have the satisfaction of leaving the royal authority to the personal exercise of that young lady—' the king gestured to Victoria, 'the heiress presumptive of the crown, and not in the hands of a person now near me.' He paused. The room was dead silent. He was referring to the duchess, who stared straight ahead, in shock. 'She is surrounded by evil advisers and is herself incompetent to act with propriety in the station in which she would be placed.'

At this point, the king was losing his temper. His shallow breath made his words shrill. 'I have no hesitation in saying that I have been insulted—grossly and continually—by that person, but I am determined to endure no longer a course of behaviour so disrespectful to me.'

There was no movement along the dining table. He paused. Victoria looked close to tears.

'I have particularly to complain of the manner in which that young lady—' King William nodded to Victoria, 'has been kept away from my court; she has repeatedly been kept from my drawing rooms, at which she ought to have been present...I shall insist and command that the princess do upon all occasions appear at my court as it is her duty to do.'

This reference electrified the atmosphere further for those aware of, or who had heard rumours of, her affection for Elphinstone, who spent much time in King William's court when not with the Horse Guards or in the House of Lords. The king was attempting to give her the chance to see her lover when her mother and Conroy had forbidden her to see him.

King William calmed himself after this airing of long-held frustration. He glanced with a kindly expression again in Victoria's direction and ended his speech with affectionate remarks about her and hopes for her reign. He sat down and turned to the queen. She was distressed. Victoria was in tears. The duchess's shock became anger. She announced she was leaving right away and called for her carriage. But other guests, including the queen, first mollified the duchess then persuaded her to stay the night as planned. The tension between the two royal households had peaked.

Lord Melbourne, the aristocratic Whig, in his second stint as prime minister, was a shrewd manipulator of power who used diplomacy instinctively where he could. He was now aware of the royal crisis, which centred on the princess's determination to marry Elphinstone. The king's birthday speech outburst had brought the problem close to the surface. King Leopold complained to Melbourne that he should do something about Elphinstone. He had more than a vested interest in having him removed from the court. Apart from the main issue of Elphinstone interfering in Leopold's efforts to marry off his nephew Albert to Victoria, Leopold did not like the Scot's close friendship with his main rival and 'enemy', William, the Prince of Orange. Leopold and William had been rivals for the hand of Princess Charlotte of Wales, who once had been the heir-presumptive for the British throne. Leopold had won that competition. But a more intense battle between them took place over Holland and Belgium after the allied powers that had defeated Napoleon had united these two provinces into the Kingdom of the Netherlands in 1815. The Prince of Orange's father (also William) became the Netherlands' first king. The Belgians were never overjoyed with the arrangement. The second French revolution, in July 1830, sparked a reaction among the disgruntled Belgians. They broke away from Holland. Leopold became the Belgian king, and the ill-feeling between him and the Dutch, particularly William, Prince of Orange, was exacerbated.

By the early 1830s, Prince William regarded Elphinstone as his closest friend. He suggested they travel to St Petersburg together, with Elphinstone as his aide–de–camp, to curry favour with the Russians in their struggles with Belgium. The trip fell through but the friendship was cemented. It was noted by Leopold, who took a dislike to Elphinstone, and the affair with Victoria created another reason for Leopold urging Melbourne to act against the Scot. Removing him from the English court was not enough. Leopold suggested he be exiled.

With the king ailing and close to death, Lord Melbourne called Elphinstone to a special meeting at his office. The prime minister had to resolve the problem of Victoria and her fixation about her true love. Melbourne was as diplomatic as possible when pointing out the issue over the princess.

'It is so serious,' Melbourne told him, 'this rift in the royal household. If something isn't done to ease the situation it will make her early reign intolerable and perhaps even inoperable. It will be hard enough for someone so young to be monarch in any case. If she is unsettled by relationships, it will make her miserable. She could never concentrate.'

Might it not be better, Melbourne suggested, that Elphinstone take an official posting outside the country for a time until Victoria settled into her coming role.

'Where?' Elphinstone asked.

'We were thinking of Madras. We want to offer you the presidency.'

This sudden 'offer' was somewhere between a shock and a surprise for the thirteenth lord. It was a clever proposition. Elphinstone's uncle, Mountstuart Elphinstone, had been the first British envoy to the court of Kabul, Afghanistan, in 1808, and later was Governor of Bombay in 1819. He had held this post with distinction for eight years, founding a state education system and making the family name very much appreciated in India.

'How long would this appointment be?' he asked.

'Oh, that would depend...'

'Depend on what?'

'How you enjoyed the challenge.'

'A year...?'

'Well, my lord, it takes some four months to get to Madras, so it would practicable for it to be a little longer.'

'Two years?'

'It would depend on how you adapted.'

Elphinstone was given time to consider the offer, but he realised his options were limited. If he did not make himself scarce, he would be doing his beloved damage, or so the prime minister more than hinted. At a further meeting a week later, Melbourne reminded him that he would be succeeding another Elphinstone relative, Lieutenant-General Sir Frederick Adam, as governor in Madras. Adam would help him ease into the new role over several months.

Elphinstone took more time to think over the offer, which he understood would be at least a year or, as Melbourne put it to him again: 'Just until things settled down in the feud inside the Royal Household.'

It was an important move and decision. Elphinstone agreed that if he were away it would give Victoria a chance to ease into her role as queen without the internal problems that would debilitate her and perhaps render her monarchy farcical. He knew Victoria would oppose him going to Madras but may have understood that he was doing it for her. She needed all the support she could acquire at this vital time, but he was sure also that she would receive that support at court and from the government. Melbourne had demonstrated his sincere concern for her. That was one reason he was interceding with the idea of the Indian posting. Elphinstone finally put his acceptance of the job offer in writing.

The down period for Victoria before her accession to the throne continued through the second half of 1836, with the only bright moment being a visit by Leopold to Claremont in Surrey, where the Kent household stayed for five weeks. He continued his urging of a future for her with Albert. She spoke favourably of him, but demurred about a relationship. She hinted that she wished to mature before committing herself. Leopold took that to mean that Albert was a chance to win her hand. But Victoria had thoughts only for

Elphinstone. Then Melbourne informed her that he would be in India for 'about a year'.

Victoria was furious. This would have seemed to be an eternity to a teenage girl in love. A letter from Elphinstone confirmed his appointment, and kept a positive attitude, as if it was a grand opportunity for him. But he had never before mentioned any ambition to be a governor abroad. Victoria cried for a day over the letter and the thought of Elphinstone's departure. She flew into a rage at her mother, whom she blamed above all for taking her lover from her. She tried several times to write to Elphinstone but at first found the exercise too painful and gave up, which only worsened her frustration and sadness. After a few days, she finally wrote a letter in which she implored him not to take the job. She needed all the support from those closest to her for coming events, especially when she became queen. But Elphinstone's mind was made up. Victoria remained distressed. She went into a deep state of depression. His leaving had the same chilling feeling to her of the sense of abandonment she had when ill in late 1835. There was more bitterness now. She was nearer to being a monarch, a position that she believed would bring her the power to rescind such moves engineered by her prime minister. But for the moment, she was powerless to stop her lover fading away to a point on the map to which she had no access.

5

TRANSITION TO MONARCHY

Elphinstone had no real option apart from taking his banishment. At first being sent to India would have seemed to him as if he were receiving a kind of nobleman's transportation.

Looking past the demise of King William, Elphinstone would face the key figures in a fresh royal court and hostile government, with Melbourne, Conroy, the duchess and King Leopold opposed to him. His situation was untenable. He would leave court by August, board a ship in October 1836 and take up his new role in India early in March 1837. The experience saddened him. Elphinstone knew he had been exiled to fulfil the ambitions of Leopold in his 'plot' to marry off Victoria to young Albert. With further regret, he would part with his horses, which he could not take with him. His favourite, Black Prince, would go to a most grateful and touched William, Prince of Orange. William wrote a letter to Elphinstone from The Hague on 15 October 1836 and sent it via his son Harry, who after visiting Java (controlled by the Dutch) would visit India.

'How are you going on at Madras?' the Prince of Orange wrote in October 1836, aware that his letter would not be delivered until well into 1837.

> Can you reconcile to your present grandeur? I would above all like to pay you a visit, if such a thing was possible for a person situated as I am. [The prince was 'trapped' in his home country for political reasons, fearing he too might be exiled if he left.]...I hereby enclose to you, not a ringlet of hair of one of your forsaken and broken-hearted London beautys [sic], but of the raven main [sic] of your charger. He is in good health and spirits, a great deal admired by the Dutch, and carries me to my full satisfaction. When I see the good dear animal, I fancy I still see you on his back in Windsor Park, and I like him for your sake.

Elphinstone made cautious notes of his thoughts in his diary of the voyage. 'I did not leave [King William's court] without emotion after four years in which I experienced protection and kinship...Nor could I fail to reflect upon the change that may take place in its [Windsor] inmates before I see its towers again.'

Early in 1837, the king's health was failing. Doctors were counting his life in weeks rather than months. He was hanging on, mainly because of the chess game to decide Victoria's future. He felt he was losing the battles to prevent the duchess and Conroy from grabbing the power of regency, and also to direct who should be Victoria's future husband. King William resorted to attempting a clever form of financial inducement. In April 1837, a month before Victoria's critical eighteenth birthday, he sent her a letter in which he proposed applying to parliament for a grant of £10,000 a year. It would be hers with which to do as she pleased. He wanted her also to have the right to appoint her own Keeper of the Privy Purse, suggesting Sir Benjamin Stephenson for the post. If she accepted, it would go some way to keeping an important royal administrative position from Conroy. The letter stipulated further that the princess was to have the right to form her own household.

The lord chamberlain took the communication to Kensington but was intercepted by Conroy, who insisted that it be delivered to Victoria in her mother's presence. The duchess was dismayed. Victoria liked the letter's suggestion, but preferred to have her tutor, the Reverend George Davys, the Dean of Chester, as her Keeper of the Privy Purse. She also wished to have a *private* conversation with Melbourne about the issues raised. The duchess and Conroy would have none of it. She and Conroy penned a letter to Melbourne, intending it to be copied and signed by Victoria.

'I wish to remain in every respect as I am now in the care of my Mother,' it said. 'Upon the subject of money I should wish that whatever may be necessary to add, may be given to my dear Mother for my use, who always does everything I want in pecuniary matters.'

The Duchess and Conroy were tightening the grip on her with blackmail over her affair with Elphinstone. They repeated the accusations of late 1835. She was not fit to be queen; they had to be her guardians and regent. They would decide her future, even after she became queen. Another furious row ensued, with Lehzen once more siding with the princess. Victoria locked herself away for a day, but in the end relented, copied out the coerced letter and signed it.

With her birthday in sight, and the king near death, her relationship with the duchess and Conroy had reached its lowest ebb. Victoria's sensibilities on every level had been offended. She was angry and despondent. Not only had they slighted her, they had written a false letter in her name to the king. Her young soul was not vengeful by nature, but she was developing a hatred for her mother and more particularly Conroy, whom she would never forgive for this and all the other offences against her. She did not wish her uncle to die yet she now could not wait to be queen. She wondered if she would have anyone to defend her against this family tyranny. She had met Melbourne and liked him but, because of his involvement in Elphinstone's departure, Victoria wondered if he had the character and strength to stand up to Conroy.

King William discarded the letter, aware that it did not reflect Victoria's true wishes. He wrote to her again, making another offer—this time £4000 for her and £6000 for the duchess. This was clumsier than the first offer. It was clear he was still trying to cut Conroy out, this time with an inducement to the duchess. She tried to consult her daughter about the matter, but the princess would not speak to her. The duchess replied bluntly to the king, rejecting the offer out of hand.

Victoria continued to be melancholic over Elphinstone's posting. No explanation could console her. She felt more alone than ever, with Lehzen the only one left on her side. The king's condition meant he was out of the struggle, which was effectively over. The eviction of her lover from the court and the country meant that Conroy had won a major battle. He now sought to win the war by returning to the major points of contention and applying more pressure than ever: he wanted to be made Victoria's private secretary, and the duchess to be created regent.

The king could not attend Victoria's eighteenth birthday cele-brations on 24 May 1837, but he did throw a ball at Kensington Palace for her and sent a gift of a stunningly carved dressing-case.

Intrigue still swirled around the party ballroom. Lehzen noted that Conroy kept an eye on her for the entire night. He was manoeuvring for his goals while Melbourne attempted to engineer a compromise. This was put to Victoria by Baron Stockmar, King Leopold's personal physician who had been sent by an out-of-touch Leopold, and her half-brother (Charles Leiningen from the duchess's first marriage). Stockmar, nicknamed 'Merlin' for his wizard-like looks and hold on the Kensington household, was looking after the interests of Leopold, who was having a two-way bet. If his sister, the duchess, became regent, he would have some link and influence, although he was most uncomfortable with the thought of Conroy having any power and control over Victoria. Leopold viewed Conroy as mephistophelian, yet the King of the Belgians was himself not above dealing with the devil if it enhanced his own situation. Stockmar was his proxy in the intrigues at Kensington, whatever the outcome of negotiations.

There was a stalemate. No deal was acceptable to the stubborn Victoria. She would not have Conroy close to her in *any* role. She resisted the entreaties for three weeks after her birthday, and did not even respond to her half-brother, who offended her by butting in, at their mother's behest. She was receptive to 50-year-old Stockmar, Leopold's closest confidant, whom she respected. He had been an intimate of the royal family, notably at the death of Leopold's first wife, Princess Charlotte. Stockmar had overseen the will of Victoria's father, the Duke of Kent. Leopold had given Stockmar high praise for creating the Belgium Constitution, a tough assignment that needed intelligence, experience and a rare expertise. But Stockmar needed all these traits and more to handle Victoria. He was surprised to find that the just-turned eighteen-year-old had a strong mind and will of her own, contrary to what Leopold had told him. Stockmar believed he had a supreme sixth sense in understanding his medical patients' psychology. It was found wanting in this case. No matter what verbal trick he tried, he could not manipulate Victoria. He may have wondered if she had been too shrewd in dealing with Leopold, himself the most cunning of political operators.

News from King William's court in early June 1837 suggested he had just days to live. This increased the tensions at Kensington. The warring factions became more and more conscious of the diminishing time line. The duchess wrote to her daughter: 'You are still very young, and all your success so far has been due to your *Mother's* reputation. Do not be *too sanguine* in *your* own *talents* and *understanding*.'

This was less vehement than the abuse hurled at Victoria previously, yet it still was patronising and sardonic: a put-down. The princess was consoled by messages from Elphinstone, now in India, and fortified by knowing she was closer to being queen. She imagined that all would change on that day; she would have the power over her tormentors.

On 15 June, Lord Liverpool arrived at Kensington Palace to try a final mediation on behalf of Melbourne. He was not without connections in the Kent household; his eldest daughter, Lady Catherine Jenkinson, was one of the princess's ladies in waiting. He spoke to

Conroy, who reached the depths of his subterfuge by arguing that Victoria was unstable. She had been deeply depressed. Liverpool had no way of knowing that this had been brought on more than anything else by the mental battering she had been subjected to for the past three years. No-one so young and unformed, especially in the rarefied atmosphere of the most important royal court in the world, could have withstood the pressures she endured without incurring scars.

'She is younger in intellect than in years,' Conroy told Liverpool. 'She has frivolous tastes and is obsessed with dress and fashion.' He argued that Lehzen should be dismissed. Conroy wanted his own daughter, Victoire, to take her place. This was all part of the net that the duchess and he wished to draw tighter around the princess. Victoria detested Victoire and would never accept such a cruel and cynical swap. Liverpool responded by telling him that Victoria would have no private secretary. Conroy would be offered the job of keeper of the privy purse with no political power and only minor duties. Conroy would have been inwardly thrilled with this offer. He and the duchess wanted to get their hands on the Civil List money. They would sort out their intrinsic power and the size of their duties as they progressed.

Liverpool thought he was doing well. He then visited Victoria in her study on the first floor of her Kensington Palace quarters. She remained at her desk. Liverpool sat on a chair in front of it. She had insisted they meet without anyone else present and further surprised him by pulling out a paper with discussion headings. Victoria listened to Liverpool's proposal.

'We think it advisable that you not have a private secretary,' he said.

'Yes, that is acceptable,' she said.

'We do believe, however, that you should have Sir John Conroy as keeper of the privy purse.'

'Not him. Not him under any circumstances.'

'But why, your highness?'

'Do you know of the number of slights and incivilities that I have endured from him?'

'No, your highness.'

'Then I suggest that you ask Lady Catherine. She knows how your much-favoured Sir John acts.'

'I had no idea...'

'I know of certain things involving him that give me no confidence in him. None at all. They are personal. They are to do with my family and some of them concern finances. I suggest that a person of his background should never, ever touch the finances of the crown.'

Liverpool was astonished yet impressed with Victoria. Like Stockmar before him, he left Kensington Palace convinced of her position and intransigence. Liverpool informed his good friend the Duke of Wellington of Victoria's comments and he interpreted them to infer that there had been 'familiarities between the duchess and Conroy'. He further supposed this to mean that they had been lovers. This rendition of events again fuelled the rumours about Victoria being Conroy's daughter. Once more, without any proof, the rumours died away.

Whatever their relationship, Conroy and the duchess were desperate. They expected to hear of King William's death any day. Then their positions would be in doubt. A state of siege developed at Kensington. Victoria, fearing the next moves by her 'enemies', locked herself in her room, only letting in Lehzen, who brought her meals. Conroy tried one more tack in a meeting with a confidant, the speaker of the House, James Abercromby. Conroy put forward his stock argument: Victoria was too unstable and immature to be queen. Abercromby sided with him and suggested she should be *forced* to sign over everything Conroy wanted. Conroy reflected on the advice. He had already tried coercion. He did not think the duchess had the fortitude for attempting more of it.

On the morning of 19 June 1837, Conroy was informed by his spy inside Windsor Castle that King William had just hours to live. The game was over. Conroy feared that Victoria may have won. The king died at 2.12 a.m. on 20 June 1837. In a tradition stretching back to the Normans in the eleventh century, a high-powered delegation—the lord chamberlain and the king's physician—took a coach from Windsor to Kensington, arriving as dawn was breaking. The duchess received them. The lord chamberlain asked to see her daughter.

'You cannot,' the duchess replied. 'She is sleeping.'

The lord chamberlain glanced at the physician and then said to the duchess: 'I demand to see the queen!'

The stunned duchess fetched her daughter, Lehzen joining them. Victoria insisted on going alone to the anteroom where the delegation waited. As she entered, the two men fell to their knees. She motioned that they stand. The physician confirmed the death of King William IV. The lord chamberlain rambled a bit about his duty and protocol, and ended by informing her officially that she was now 'Queen of England'.

Victoria reached out her hand. Both men kissed it. She now had the power she craved. A new, more profound game was about to commence.

6

ELPHINSTONE IN EXILE; VICTORIA VICTORIOUS

The first thing Elphinstone noticed on his day of arrival in Madras, on 6 March 1837, was the smell. Even before landing at Madras, an alien fragrance was borne out on the breeze, which had its own 'mustiness' as he described it in a letter to a courtier, Ernst of Hess, who passed it on to Victoria.

> We were greeted by catamarans, made of logs bound
> together, each with a steerman and ten rowers, and
> were escorted on them for several miles to the shore
> through high breakers. I was glad of their expertise,
> for we were told that many sharks lingered hoping
> for a capsize! As we drew closer, we were enveloped
> by the oppressive heat and the smells. Some were
> recognizable and took their turn to dominate or
> mingle, noticeably burning cow dung here, pungent

> tobaccos there and as we moved through the
> crowded, dusty town, garlic, cooking oil, chillis. There
> were also Turmeric, ginger, cloves and anything you
> could think off in extremis. Closer to the governor's
> residence, I picked up jasmine and sandalwood.

Elphinstone added that Ernst would have been 'amused by the boatmen, whose attire was wondrous in its simplicity; sometimes just a turban and an excuse for a loin-covering handkerchief, which often floated off with the wind'. He was struck by the contrast of 'Black Town [the native quarter] and the spacious, elegant European quarters. The smooth, gravel roads are wide leading to the governor's spacious mansion, with its lime-coloured walls that have a gloss like marble.'

He missed the drama surrounding the king's demise as he settled into his new life. He was kept well informed by Ernst, who wrote him a hefty 44-page letter. 'Your departure greatly affected the king,' he said.

> I notice each time that people speak of you, for
> they often speak of you since your departure from
> Windsor Castle. And all the inmates of the castle
> regretted very sincerely that you were no longer
> amongst them...I was one of those who felt your
> absence the most...I expressed to his majesty your
> respectful homages and your last adieus. 'God bless
> him,' said the noble old monarch.

The British history of Madras began with Francis Day of the British East India Company buying a strip of coastal land in the Bay of Bengal on 22 August 1639. The new owners were allowed by the local Indian rulers to build Fort St George, which was the first substantial building of what would become a colonial town. Life was sedate and uneventful in the area for more than the next century until 1746 when the French, led by General La Bourdonnais, the Governor of Mauritius, took the town. The British regained control three years later through the Treaty of Aix-la-Chapelle. They fortified the town in case the marauding French decided they would like to plunder the place again. The strengthened town wall also would help keep at bay any possible threat from the Sultan of Mysore, Hyder Ali, who hated foreigners, especially *infidels*. By the time Elphinstone arrived the British had conquered most of the region. One by one, hostile princes of west and south India had been brought under the control of the East India Company. Only the Sikhs in the north were holding out; once they were defeated, the British would be left alone as the paramount power in the country.

Elphinstone's ascendency to the Madras residency coincided with a period when threats seemed negligible from other empires or from within. He did not expect to encounter the problems his uncle had done when he was the 'resident' of Puna and ran into a war with the Marathas. Elphinstone, who had been an army man since leaving school at eighteen, envied his uncle Mountstuart, who assumed command of the military during the Battle of Khadki and won, despite his civilian background. Elphinstone would have preferred a military challenge, such as a small war or even a large one. It seemed unlikely. He would have to seek distinction in other areas.

The new governor would be expected to grow Madras further into an urban centre, and to develop its naval base. Anything else would be up to his initiative. Elphinstone was not enamoured with what he experienced at first, especially after the hustle and bustle of a monarch's court in London at the heart of the empire. He struggled with the heat, flies and food, for which he did not at first have the constitution. He was ill in the first two months with stomach complaints and dysentery. After nine weeks of feeling miserable, Elphinstone ventured down to the governor's stables at dawn one morning, when the coolest part of the day was almost over. He was surprised to see the tall, angular frame of a dark-haired woman riding a white stallion around a well-manicured paddock. She wore a white shirt and wide-brimmed hat.

Elphinstone asked his aide-de-camp, Captain Lennox: 'Who is that woman? She doesn't ride side-saddle.'

'Oh, she is quite special, my lord. Her name is Husna Ahmed de Crepeney. The most beautiful young creature in Madras.'

They watched as she galloped closer.

'Tell me about her.'

'Bit of a mystery, but she is the most accomplished horsewoman. She trains and breeds them. Every Arabian stallion here has been trained by her.'

'She's a Muslim?'

'Mother is. Father is an enigma, really. He is said to be a French aristocrat, albeit a commercially enterprising one.'

'Family missed the guillotine, did it?'

'Apparently so,' Lennox smiled. 'There is a bit of scandal about her background. Her father is a landowner, merchant. He did deals with our East India Company. He visited here several times and fell in love with a stunning high-class courtesan, with whom he had a child—Husna.'

'She's in our employ?'

'Most assuredly. She studied medicine in Sweden but, of course, being a woman, was not allowed to qualify there or in France. So she decided to do medical work with animals instead. She said she likes horses more than people!'

'How old?'

'Early twenties.'

They watched as she lifted the horse's tempo to a fast gallop and came close without acknowledging them. Elphinstone could see her face more clearly than before. She had jet-black eyebrows, dark eyes, high cheekbones and full, sensual lips.

'What a dark beauty,' he said softly.

'Want to meet her, my lord?'

'I meant the horse.'

Lennox looked around and realised the governor was joking.

'Should I invite her over?' Lennox asked

Elphinstone shook his head. 'She's at work,' he said. 'Send her an invitation to the presidency ball next month.'

'Hmm. . .'

'What, Lennox?'

'That would be breaking tradition and convention, my lord.'

'What convention?' Elphinstone asked and then, by studying his aide-de-camp's expression, added, 'Ah, half-caste. . .?'

'And her religious background, my lord.'

'And she gets dirty training horses?'

'Well, my lord, you've met all our people here. They are more, shall we say, "conventional". . .'

'Strait-laced?'

'That as well. They would object, especially the wives.'

'I would have thought *only* the wives.'

'Yes my lord. The other thing bothering the memsahibs is that Miss Husna is not married. She is a real threat to the European women away from their culture. She would have to be chaperoned.'

They began to walk back to the governor's residence.

'I'll chaperone her,' Elphinstone said. 'Stay and invite her for drinks on the balcony this evening.'

Lennox looked stunned.

'Tell her several members of the staff are invited to meet the new governor,' Elphinstone said, strolling away.

'Are they really?'

'No, they're not. Tell her it's informal attire this evening.'

Lennox wandered to the stables and signalled for de Crepeney to come in from her ride. She ignored his hand movement and he was forced to wait another ten minutes before she trotted over, dismounted and passed her horse to an Indian groom. Lennox put the invitation to her.

'Was that the governor?'

'Yes, it was, Miss de Crepeney.'

'Then tell him if he wishes to invite me to anything, he introduces himself first.'

'But that is the reason you're invited this evening.'

'Bloody English,' she mumbled.

'Wouldn't say that to him. He's a Scot.'

'Even worse.'

'Are you coming tonight?'

'No.'

Husna signalled to a groom to saddle up another horse and strode off.

Lennox returned to the governor's mansion and told Elphinstone of her rejection.

'Still send her an invitation to the ball,' he said, 'and please say I'll be at the stables to ride tomorrow morning.'

'She gets there at 4 a.m., my lord, to beat the weather on long rides.'

Elphinstone arrived before dawn the next day, this time in a light mist that reminded him of early mornings in Scotland. It had settled like an apparition over the low hills beyond the mansion and fields. He found de Crepeney helping the staff to feed and water the twenty or so mounts in the stables. A mix of aromas of feed, manure and horse-blanket sweat hung in the cool morning air.

They shook hands. He was surprised by her height and taken again by her dark beauty, which he described to the Prince of Orange as 'the most outstandingly handsome woman I've ever laid eyes on. Her bone structure is unmatched; her eyes are like the night and most sensual.' Her black leather boots tipped her over 6 ft (183 cm). She did not smile and remained aloof as she gave him a quick tour.

'I've decided on the horse for you,' she said. 'It's being saddled up now.'

Elphinstone was delighted by her odd, yet seductive French lilt that still managed an Indian resonance.

They wandered to the paddock. An Indian groom was placing a saddle on a large black charger.

'Do you like him?' de Crepeney asked, smiling for the first time.

'Most impressive,' Elphinstone said, circling the animal. 'Magnificent condition. Reminds me of my own charger at home.'

'Which is now a Netherlander, no?'

'How did you know that?'

'It is the talk of the Orange court,' she smiled widely, displaying beautiful teeth, 'and I have a friend there.'

Elphinstone glided onto the horse.

'You are a born horseman,' she commented. 'Captain of the Royal Horse Guards, no?'

'You are well informed,' he said.

'And a certain princess's lover, no?'

'Too well-informed,' Elphinstone said frostily, 'or misinformed. Who is your contact?'

'The horse's name is Victor,' de Crepeney said, ignoring him and grinning slyly. 'He should suit you.'

Elphinstone dug his heels in and trotted off. He urged the big mount on and reached a gallop but then the animal became cantankerous. It jerked and reared and bucked. Elphinstone fought the reins, but the more he tried to restrain Victor, the more the horse reacted. He used all his experience and skill to steady him, but Victor behaved recklessly as it tried to throw him. Elphinstone careered around the paddock and could see de Crepeney mounting up near the stables. Distracted, he found himself sliding off Victor and hard onto the ground on his rear. De Crepeney trotted up, smiling.

'You are not injured, I hope, my lord.'

'Only my pride,' he said, trying to regain his dignity as he dusted himself off. De Crepeney offered him her hand, and he climbed on behind her.

'What about Victor?' he said, squinting off into the hills beyond where the horse had bolted.

'I'll send some hands out to retrieve him.' She called instructions in Urdu to a stable hand and then looked around and grinned, her face close to Elphinstone. 'Hold on tight, my lord. We wouldn't want any more dents in you or your pride.'

He did as instructed, wrapping his arms around her slight midriff.

Lennox appeared shocked to hear that de Crepeney had broken out Victor for Elphinstone. 'He is the most fractious horse we have! Do you still want me to invite her to the ball?'

'Yes, of course. I like her spirit. She clearly tested my riding capacity. I didn't do well.'

'But you've been ill until now, my lord.'

'No excuse. One should never lose the skills.'

'That bloody Victor is impossible to ride! De Crepeney is the only one who can handle him and even then she picks his moods before she ever saddles him.'

'Just make sure she comes to the ball, captain.'

For the first time since taking up his Madras appointment, Elphinstone felt good. There was a sense now that his unwanted governorship may have some attractions and even meaning after all.

The ball at the mansion was a glittering affair with fireworks and a traditional bonfire on the front lawn. Elphinstone's appearance with Husna caused a mixture of shock, pleasure, titillation and not a little jealousy. She wore a red traditional Indian sari, daringly bare at the back and split to the thigh to reveal glimpses of tight black breeches that showed off her long, shapely legs. Elphinstone, as was tradition, began the dancing to a waltz played a fraction stodgily by an army band. He and de Crepeney were both superb movers on the floor. When they had finished the first bracket together there was spontaneous applause from the hundreds of onlookers.

A banquet created by both Indian and English staff was followed by an acrobatic display and some traditional Indian dancing. To the whispers and shock of some onlookers, de Crepeney spoke to the members of the band and invited two of the female Indian dancers to join her on the floor for a special performance. The other guests whispered that it was an Indian variant of the Dance of the Seven Veils. Two plump, middle-aged wives of East India Company directors approached Elphinstone.

'It's shameful!' one said. 'How can you stand for something so brazen to be enacted in front of senior members of the Raj?'

'I think the music is wonderful,' he replied, poker-faced. 'Seemed like an Indian version of something German, don't you think?'

'We meant that—that *Indian woman*!' the other complainant said indignantly.

'The harp and the zither gave it away as a brilliant composition,' Elphinstone said, ignoring their comments. 'Great theatre!'

After her exotic show, de Crepeney joined him.

'That was extraordinary!' he said, clapping her in full view of the other guests.

'I think I have *shamed* the governor,' she whispered.

'Not at all,' he said. 'I loved it! Where did you learn such wonderful movements?'

'Do you know the young and beautiful Mrs James, the wife of a lieutenant in the Indian Army?'

'Yes, I do. Met them in the first month I arrived here. She is a wilful lass, if ever I saw one!'

'She taught me that dance, among many. She called it the "Spider Dance".' De Crepeney looked around at a group of Raj wives, who were giving her unfavourable looks. 'I am an embarrassment to the governor. I will take my leave in a minute.'

'No, no,' Elphinstone said, 'I shall see you home.'

'No,' she said smiling, 'we don't want any more wagging of tongues.'

Husna slipped away, much to the disappointment of Elphinstone, but her parting remark of 'I trust I shall see you before dawn at the stables, my lord,' had him smiling.

The governor's love of the high life, and the daring public company of such an unusual and exotic woman, was noted by the rather stiff officials used to a more conservative and perhaps business-like approach to running an Indian presidency. A British civil servant noted, 'We want a governor; we want a statesman, and they send us a dancer'.

Elphinstone lifted his spirits, when well enough, by riding every day with Husna, exploring the surrounding area with her. They rode, often in silence, for miles across the countryside through paddy, mustard and bean fields, the latter providing a unique and appealing scent. As the light heralded yet another humid day of searing heat, peacocks strutted across their path. In awakening villages, people greeted them warmly and offered them food and other items. They trotted by, observing meals being cooked and women beginning their day's washing. Dogs, chickens and even cows occasionally blocked their way. Beggar children ran beside them, reaching up and touching the horses and them. Some pointed to their mouths, indicating hunger. At a station—one of the many towns acting as halfway houses on the lonely dirt tracks between the major cities—there were stalls selling hot, spicy snacks, piles of sweets, sherbets, oranges, bananas, figs and dates. Hawkers balanced on their heads trays of everything from coconuts and mangoes to soda water and lemonade.

Elphinstone made an effort to make his acquaintance with the locals and the British civil servants there to look after him. After a few months, he sought inspiration from his uncle's efforts. Mountstuart had compiled what became known as the 'Elphinstone Code' for the state education of India. New Governor Lord Elphinstone soon began exploring the possibility of adding another layer of education at least in his region. Madras did not have a university. He began talking up the idea of creating one.

'I wish you luck, my lord,' Husna said on a morning ride. 'Education for the masses here has drifted since your uncle was in charge, or so my mother tells me.'

'I'll do my best.'

'*Encore, bon chance,*' she said with a wistful look. 'I was forced to study in Sweden. There was nothing in the medical profession, not even nursing, that was attractive in India. You English, *pardon*, 'British', resist educating the natives.'

'Then it is a challenge. I will start with a preparatory school, then a high school, and then a university.'

'Education by stealth?'

'You could call it that, yes.'

Victoria asserted her right to independence from her mother and Conroy a second time just a few hours into her reign when she granted Melbourne an audience in her room at 9 a.m. He was impressed by her calm and readiness. When he departed at 9.30 a.m., Victoria ordered her bed removed from her mother's room. She intended to sleep apart from the duchess from the very first night of her reign. Victoria yearned for Elphinstone to share her bed, but that would remain a dream for the moment at least. She regretted that he was not among the Privy Councillors (although he would remain one for life) but far away in mystical India when the council assembled for her for the first time in the Red Saloon at Kensington Palace. It was 11 a.m. on the morning King William had died and yet a record number of councillors were in attendance.

Dressed in black, Victoria hid her nerves. She felt 'quite alone' as she entered the Saloon. There was not a good friend in sight let alone a lover who could inspire and give her confidence. She was led to the throne for this 'audience'. The men were all taken by her elegance and grace as she composed herself and began her declaration. It was a further moment of revelation for all present. Despite inner tensions, her voice sounded nerveless and clear. Her precise language lifted their spirits. If this were the way she presented herself on the first day, they thought, how magnificent would she be with experience?

The swearing in of all the councillors and ministers followed: all bent their knee to her. Though not close to any, she knew many of them. But as they kissed her hand, she showed no preference or familiarity. Men such as Wellington, Palmerston, Melbourne and Robert Peel, leaders who would stand with any company in British history, were smitten with her charisma. Still an adolescent, she was eloquent, modest yet strong, and with that very English self-possession based on a confidence that seemed unshakeable. Few of them knew of her recent ordeals that had made rather than broken her. Cynical, sardonic, humorous and stern men of achievement, all were buoyed. Even when she looked to Melbourne for advice on proceedings, she did it with style without being deferential, and grace without an apparent amateurism. After a year of an old man in decline on the throne, Victoria was as fresh as the summer mornings of that 1837. It generated new hope in middle-aged men. The moment was romantic for all of them. She drew out paternal instincts. Even, or perhaps particularly, the middle-aged gay blades among them wanted to help and serve her. Victoria's charm was palpable. Instead of degeneration in the royal family, there was regeneration that touched each one of their eminences.

There were parallels in those early months for Victoria and Elphinstone in their new jobs. Both were guided by distinguished, experienced uncles who remained at a distance. Mountstuart never visited Madras while his nephew was governor, but wrote to him. Leopold stayed out of London for the first fifteen months of Victoria's reign, but dispensed guidelines for her behaviour in letters. Mountstuart suggested his nephew should err on the side of caution in political, military and other matters, and only after reflecting long and hard on any issue. Leopold, using circumlocution, said more or less the same thing. Victoria was told she 'could not cultivate too much discretion'. This was natural to her anyway but having Leopold articulate it reaffirmed her own instincts.

She was advised never to give ready responses to ministers, even her prime minister, whom she surprised when she told him she would 'think things over'. This often meant her garnering advice from others before delivering an answer.

Mountstuart told Elphinstone never to be slothful or a dilettante. He should have strict daily routines except on weekends. This suited his nephew. He rode most mornings with Husna before arriving at the governor's residence, and walked, swam or played polo (he started his own team) in the evening. He was in his office at 10 a.m. after a leisurely breakfast reading the papers, primarily *The Times,* which were four months old coming from London by steamer. He spent two hours on issues of importance, including his initiatives concerning education, construction and defences. In the afternoon he gave audience in equal proportions to his staff, advisers and locals with grievances, with a one-hour lunch break. He drifted from the office by 5 p.m. Mountstuart advised Elphinstone to be benevolent wherever possible in dealing with native issues.

One morning Elphinstone and Husna were trotting back into Madras when they spotted smoke billowing near the city centre. Elphinstone spurred Victor to a gallop and arrived to see a three-level building enveloped in flames. Hundreds of people were scurrying and yelling, with some trying to douse the flames. In the pandemonium, no-one at first recognised the mounted European, who began bellowing orders.

'Form a line to the well!' he called, and then repeated, 'from the fire to the well!' He dismounted and handed the horse's reins to Husna. He bellowed more orders. She translated. Soon a long line had formed and buckets of water were passed to several Indians near the flames. Police and firemen arrived. Elphinstone and Husna joined the bucket line. After an hour, the fire was under control and locals realised that their new governor had been among them managing the response to a fire that could have developed into an inferno.

Leopold suggested a disciplined daily routine for Victoria. Dr Clark had cultivated in her the habit of exercises, first thing in the morning, *always* with windows open for that most important commodity and cure-all from his perspective: fresh air. There was much of it on her riding, depending on her mood and the weather. She received ministers to discuss affairs of state between 11 a.m. and 1.30 p.m. After lunch, Victoria attended to duties and functions to which she had been invited. These were endless and had to be sorted on advice and personal inclination. A civic reception might be left to her discretion, but an invitation to an embassy affair might be accepted or vetoed depending on the moment. The queen appearing anywhere from a business to a consulate would be viewed as a royal—and, by association, a government—endorsement.

Both she and Elphinstone were encouraged to fill journals and write as many letters as possible. Victoria had been keeping an almost daily written account of her life for several years. Now, as queen, she had much more to say in her diary even if it were trite and mundane. Elphinstone made time for diary-type notes and letters. He compared Madras to Elba, the island where Napoleon had been exiled in 1814. The Indian isolation precipitated copious writing, a pastime and occupation he had disdained in the past. He preferred horse-riding and social activities. Yet there was time for all things, if managed well. One growing, new attraction for him was the 'magnificent' Husna, with whom he was building a strong friendship in the third, then the fourth month of his Madras appointment.

Elphinstone was soon irritated by his ideas for change in the colony being frustrated by the bureaucracy, the inertia of which seemed resistant to progress in India. Early on, Elphinstone was disturbed by the poverty he witnessed. He realised that his life of privilege, wealth and status in the top strata of British society had been sheltered. He believed that the main way out of the slums that he encountered would be via education. There could never be enough riches to spread around to make everyone 'comfortably off' but learning could give millions a chance to enhance their lives. He became determined to use his 'weight', power and influence to this end, no matter how long it took.

7

THE GOVERNOR'S DISTRACTION

Two months into Victoria's reign she began to express her will, although without a real sense of authority. Melbourne had encouraged her to believe this authority would come with time. Leopold had urged her to avoid talking about personal matters such as on her feelings about marriage. The temptation to do so could come after a probe, however indirect, about whether or not the rumours about Elphinstone were true. Charlotte Canning (a lady-in-waiting to the queen, and later wife of the first viceroy of India) wrote to a friend in mid-summer 1837: 'All the people here [in the town of Spa, Belgium] ask us every day if the stories about the Queen and Lord Elphinstone are true, and if he is to come back to England to marry her.'

Canning was mixing with members of Leopold's court, where the tale circulated and it was rife in Britain. Lord Falkland wrote to Elphinstone from his Curzon Street Mayfair home: 'The Queen always speaks most highly of you and asked Lady Falkland the other day if I corresponded with you or had written to you...some country folks believed you were coming home to be King Consort.'

When Elphinstone did not respond to this gossip, Falkland became indignant: 'You did not answer my first long question [in a previous letter in which Elphinstone was asked if he were coming back to marry Victoria]. I presume you will not pay this [second allusion to the same issue] much more attention. If you do not [reply], I will not write again. Whether I do or not, however, you will always have my very best trust.'

Elphinstone received daily probes about Victoria. His aunt, Carlotte E. Fleming, the wife of his uncle Charles, wrote in the same week: 'I hear a new story about you every day and I cannot help telling you of what honourable mention is made of you in all papers on both sides of the question. [The papers] are full of rumours and inventions and anecdotes and surmises and calculations about you and the little queen. I wonder how it all arose at first.'

The stories spread to Madras. When Elphinstone and Husna strolled away from the stables after a ride, he invited her to dine with him alone at the mansion. They had ridden together almost every day for six weeks, but after the reaction to her at the governor's ball, she refused to attend any more functions or parties with him.

'Why won't you come?' he asked, perplexed by her attitude.

'I have heard the many stories about you and your dear little queen,' she replied.

'She is in England. I am here.'

'But where is your heart, my lord?'

'Here, with me,' he said, tapping his chest.

'With great respect, my lord, you are still in love and you know it.'

When he did not deny it, she added: 'Do not expect me to give my heart or any other part of me to you, when yours is with another, who happens to be so important in the scheme of things.'

'So these rumours have kept you aloof from me?'

'I am French in affairs of the heart, and Indian in matters of the mind. And I will be frank with you, my lord. At first I was not impressed with your imperial airs. But I realise that you are an honest, warm and compassionate man. You are a rider, rather than a breaker, of horses. You love them as I do.' She smiled. 'And you are the best dancer I have ever met. But until you match me in a third area, well, then we remain just friends.' She stopped, grinned sexily, tapped his nose and added, 'Albeit good friends.'

'And what is that third thing?'

'True, unencumbered and honest singleness.'

Elphinstone looked despondent. She locked her arm in his.

'You would make my life that much nicer here if we were closer,' he said.

'I don't know why you want me,' she said. 'All the women here are swooning over you. And the Indian princesses!' Her eyes widened to match her smile. Then she looked serious again. 'Pardon me, my lord. That was indiscreet. You already have the most beautiful, desirable *little* princess turned queen of them all.' They strolled on to the sloping lawn that ran up to the mansion. As they came into view of the governor's staff, she unlocked their arms and folded hers.

'I am serious about the grand opportunities for you, my lord. Half the Raj males frequent bordellos. If you don't know this, you should.'

All the speculations and murmurings about Victoria and Elphinstone fuelled more than caution in Prince Leopold. He was aware of the affair and was worried that his niece might rekindle the relationship because she *could*. He was concerned about advice from the remnants of King William's court. Leopold was further vexed by the possibility that Victoria might do something on her own volition now she was beginning to see that, within bounds, her wishes were others' commands. By telling her to shut down all talk of a personal nature to those not close to her, he hoped to avoid her doing something precipitate regarding her lover in exile. Leopold used Stockmar to monitor the situation. Stockmar's suggestions were subtle. Many were geared towards isolating her, at least mentally, from any move she might consider concerning a marriage partner. Leopold was banking on young Albert developing to a point where he would be an attractive, more practicable husband than Elphinstone.

Victoria needed little prompting on how to handle inquisitors regarding her private affairs. Within months she had perfected a most disapproving look, which seared itself into the nerves of others. Her big eyes narrowed; her small mouth tightened, pursed and pulled down. Victoria's gaze held and pierced for extra seconds that froze and intimidated the most ferocious of women, or the most arrogant and bullying of men. She had had more than enough practice in her final years as princess in dealing with the intimidating Conroy and her mother. She also invoked the stinging phrase 'we are not amused', which ended conversations and peppered her diaries.

Victoria's first problem as queen was the decade-old one for her as princess: John Conroy. Aware that he would be frozen out of the new monarch's court, he made a bold early blackmail move soon after the first Privy Council meeting by sending Lord Melbourne a paper via Stockmar. It listed the sacrifices he had allegedly made on the duchess's behalf. Conroy claimed he could not depart unless three demands were met. First, he wanted a pension of £3000 a year. Second, he wanted the decoration of the Grand Cross of the Order of the Bath. And third, he desired an Irish peerage, preferably 'Viscount of Elphin, Co Roscommon' (County Roscommon, in the heart of Connaught, in the West of Ireland). Melbourne was stunned at the propositions.

'This is really too bad!' he exclaimed to Stockmar. 'Have you ever heard such impudence?'

He knew that Victoria would be against giving Conroy anything except, as Robert Browning noted, 'the Royal Order of the Boot'. Yet he had an ace in the Elphinstone affair and, although Conroy did not mention it to Melbourne, the prime minister feared he was reckless enough to make it all public and he had to be appeased. Melbourne conceded that an Irish peerage would be granted 'as soon as one became available'. The other demands would be given serious consideration. In the meantime, Melbourne said Conroy would have to leave Kensington Palace. Conroy responded that he was not yet ready to leave, at least until the other two matters were settled. But it could not end there. Conroy controlled the Kent household and, while Victoria was single, he and the duchess would be close to her. It was untenable for Victoria to live alone, despite having her own household. The duchess would accompany her everywhere, although the queen had made sure from the first day of her reign that they did not share the same bedroom. They were estranged, but for the sake of appearances, and to avoid gossip and rumour, they were presented as having a normal mother–daughter relationship. Conroy had no intention of leaving the Kent household, even when he received his demands, which he knew he would. The duchess had no-one else and was not about to cut him loose. When Victoria moved to Buckingham Palace, Conroy would take up residence there. She could not get rid of him, short of murder. He held the card of her secret relationship with Elphinstone: it was his job security.

Victoria was keen to ride again, eighteen months after the illnesses she endured at Ramsgate. It was her second-favourite pastime. She had ridden for miles with Elphinstone, sometimes in the company of 30 other riders; other times, with Lehzen's tacit consent, just the two of them together. Victoria loved the experience. The rush on the hard galloping and rebellious Barbara or the serene, long-striding Leopold, especially with her lover pacing with her, was a passion ranked close to her lovemaking. Since Elphinstone had been banished to India, and Clark had forbidden riding until she had recovered from her illness, her two biggest passions had been taken from her. It made her miserable. While she could only be in contact with Elphinstone through correspondence, she attended the stables every day, longing to jump on a horse and stride across the fields. Like many a small-statured person who could ride well, she grew in the saddle. Victoria felt it; she *knew* she was taller. She loved the fluidity of movement, the sensuality of controlling a beautiful, powerful steed beneath her. Observers viewed her at the peak of her beauty in a black velvet riding habit, top hat and veil, which contrasted nicely with cheeks of rouge and fair hair.

Victoria believed she was fit enough in June 1837 to review her troops in Hyde Park on horseback. Her mother wrote her a note, saying she thought this would be unwise. Melbourne agreed.

'Your mother is right,' he said at their daily meeting. 'You can do it from a carriage.'

Victoria's face clouded.

'I am strong enough to hold any horse in the stables,' she said with indignation. 'I wish to ride between Wellington and Lord Hill.'

'Too dangerous, majesty.'

'I refuse to sit in a carriage like a creaking old dowager with an attendant!'

'Your mother thinks—'

'I care not what my mother thinks,' Victoria interrupted. 'We are not speaking.'

There was a pregnant pause.

'Your majesty, there is just too much risk—' Melbourne began.

'Very well, my lord, very well,' she told him haughtily, with the first expression of defiance he had experienced from her. 'Remember: no horse, no review.'

But the prime minister held firm. There would be no horse for her, and would be no review. Victoria was so incensed that she ignored Clark's directives and ordered Leopold be prepared for a ride. She demanded that young Lord Paget, one of her gentlemen riders, who had ridden with her and Elphinstone in the heady days of 1835, come with her. With all the admonitions and warnings about how she could 'kill herself' on a ride, it took courage for this slip of a girl to mount even docile Leopold. Like a race jockey who had been thrown, she steeled herself to get back on, refusing any assistance from hand-wringing household ladies-in-waiting and a nervous Paget. There were no problems on her first canter. Each day she rode out until there could be no argument that she had the strength to handle any mount in the royal stables.

Victoria moved into Buckingham Palace on 13 July 1837 and began to ostracise her mother, who took apartments some distance from her daughter. Victoria had her own household of 'merry' maids of honour, which remained Whig in nature. There were no Tory wives. She was warned such an imbalance might cause problems in the future, especially if a Tory government took power. But Victoria paid no heed to such issues and Melbourne was never going to disabuse her of her political leanings, which mirrored his. Victoria further isolated her mother by either sending notes to say she was too busy to see her, or by having Melbourne respond to the duchess formally. Her mother was hurt but Victoria did not care.

Melbourne was spending sometimes six hours a day with Victoria. He endorsed her approach, especially in isolating Conroy. Meanwhile Lehzen seemed to be taking over the role of 'mother'. She slept in a room next to Victoria's bedchamber. Victoria's fear of the night caused her to have a hole knocked in the wall so that Lehzen had access. The young queen had been frightened by Melbourne's claim to have seen ghosts and his certainty that they inhabited Buckingham Palace. Victoria never saw one, but having Lehzen nearby was comforting in the huge building. It was draughty and eerie at night with the creaking of water pipes and the howl of wind through the corridors.

8

MELBOURNE
MUNIFICENT

There was no chance of Victoria being stopped from reviewing her troops at Windsor in August 1837, two months after her disagreement with the Duchess and the prime minister. She looked proud in a variation of the Windsor uniform and wearing the striking green Garter ribbon, in a two-and-a-half-hour review sitting on Leopold. She demonstrated her fitness by going for an even longer ride on Barbara, but sensibly at a canter, for even Victoria was not yet prepared to risk a full gallop with the feisty mare.

In September 1837 Melbourne told Victoria it was better to pay off Conroy with the requested £3000-a-year 'pension', and to make him a baron. The peerage was promised too, as long as Melbourne was still prime minister and in a position to confer it. Conroy was not budging without his three demands being met but the intervention of Melbourne on Victoria's behalf did relieve the pressure on her in handling the problem. She resigned herself to the fact that Conroy would be lurking nearby while her mother was close to her, and that situation would remain until Victoria was married. Only then could she separate her new household from her mother's. The internecine war drew Victoria to Melbourne, whom she soon viewed as her saviour. For a start, he had taken over the role of her private secretary, which Conroy had coveted so much.

What Victoria lacked in natural intelligence was usurped by a desire to learn and a strong motivation to be a successful, loved monarch. She intended to replace indolence with industry in the role. The young Victoria was aware that the monarchy was under scrutiny and her performance would dictate if it survived. Melbourne seemed to meet her needs. They built a remarkable bond for two people with a 40-year age difference. He began to fill the gap in her life left by Elphinstone's exile. While Elphinstone was her dashing knight on a black charger, Melbourne was a truer father figure, who would not attempt to bed her. There would be no conflict of passions between the girl desiring a lover and the child wanting a father. Her needs made her vulnerable, yet the prime minister became the important mentor whom she required until she matured into a monarch with a true mind of her own. She fed off his political acumen, philosophy and scholarly style. Melbourne's opinions influenced his attentive student. Politically he had moved from being a radical in his more formative years at Eton and Cambridge to the centre once he entered parliament in 1806 at 27. In middle age, Melbourne became a rather fatigued conservative keen on the status quo. He was from an aristocratic family who backed the Whigs, the political party that supported a constitutional monarchy but which was opposed to absolute rule (by the monarch). Melbourne had associated at university with romantic radicals, including Percy Shelley and Lord Byron. He found himself imparting his views and observations to Victoria and not always with impartiality. He was not above gossip and character analysis or assassination, which, along with all his other stories of experience, the young queen absorbed, often with raw fascination.

She wrote in her diary: 'Such stories of knowledge; such a wonderful memory; he knows about everybody and everything; who they were and what they did. He has such a kind and agreeable manner; he does me the world of good.' Another entry said: 'He is such an honest, good, kind-hearted man and is my friend, and I know it.'

They had a kind of romance, albeit a sexless one. Melbourne was a widower. His wife had gone mad and died. His son had died of epilepsy. Melbourne was gun-shy from scandal after being co-respondent in two divorce suits and he was unlikely to philander with the young Victoria, however tempting. In other circumstances with other women, Melbourne had been less circumspect. He had sadomasochistic sexual fetishes, including everything from mild spanking sessions with aristocratic ladies to whippings administered to orphan girls he had taken into his household in acts of charity. This may well have been precipitated by his experiences at Eton, where disciplinary lashings of the rod by masters and prefects were de rigueur and an unhealthy tradition.

Melbourne was aware of Victoria's juvenile lust. There would have been moments when he experienced her coquettish side, but he checked any temptations. He swapped his seductive arts to training her in the political arts and recent history. Melbourne poured on the charm and kept her amused with his sometimes dry, sardonic and 'tired' wit, which he injected into observations about people, events, society, class, foreigners and Victoria herself.

'I have a concern about my height,' she told him at a daily meeting, 'I am not even five foot [1.52 m].'

'Oh, my dear majesty,' Melbourne said with a benevolent smile, 'great things come in small packages. Think of Napoleon.'

Victoria beamed, and from the cheeky glint in Melbourne's eye knew that this was an ambivalent remark. The British elite had always ridiculed the French emperor.

'Your lack of vertical elevation is already a forgotten thing,' he said with a wave of his hand. 'Your character has seen to that. Already your dignity bolsters a favourable image with everyone.'

Victoria blushed. This was a reason for loving her prime minister. He always boosted her feelings about herself. In a moment of vanity she touched her nose.

'I don't like this,' she said with a frown. 'It is too big and it has a slight hook.'

'Oh, it is fine, majesty. I have never heard this mentioned anywhere. In any case, people with small features never achieve anything.'

Victoria's expression turned to satisfaction. She knew Melbourne to be a keen phrenologist. He had often spoken of people's characters in conjunction with their facial and other features. It was the fashion of the time and he was a leader.

'I must confess that I am often frightened,' she said, eyes well down, 'very, very shy, prime minister.'

'I must confess to you, majesty, that I have also suffered from this. But Wellington and I agree that it is a sign of high and right feelings.'

'That is comforting, prime minister, but allied to this, this nervousness are my...my moods. Sometimes I feel I cannot face my subjects or even my own court. I wax and wane between a very real sense of helplessness and—dare I confess it—extreme anger.' Before he could respond, she added: 'What perplexes me most is that I don't comprehend the source, the initiation of such extreme feelings.'

'You lose control?'

Victoria nodded, eyeing the floor once more.

'You have temper tantrums?'

She nodded almost imperceptibly. A tear trickled down her cheek.

'Hmm,' Melbourne uttered thoughtfully, 'you know these moods, as you call them, are held by most people. They are often a strong sign of a sensitive and susceptible temperament.'

A look of relief swept Victoria's face. She wiped the tear away and sniffed.

'It's simply choleric,' he said. 'Most people experience an unreasonable and frequent frustration, which leads to anger. Nothing with which to concern yourself, majesty. The condition is often linked to those with extreme passion.'

Victoria liked that. It was how she saw herself. She believed it was closely tied to a sense of the erotic. Victoria wanted to ask him about her jealous rages, which perplexed and worried her. She hated, for instance, every moment Melbourne spent with the celebrated Whig hostess, Lady Holland. But she thought better of mentioning this and 'consulted' her diary instead. Later, when she was alone, she experienced a further sense of helplessness. She was depressed again. It was a feeling maintained and exacerbated by the pressures she experienced daily in her position of queen.

Melbourne's commentaries about most things would have seemed either new or outrageous to the impressionable young woman. He did not seem to care about any reaction. He hardly ever said that she should keep his thoughts about others, or anything, to herself. There was a carelessness, a born-to-rule superiority in his utterances that vacillated between arrogance and insouciance. It all went to an attitude that in the past had led him into trouble. But this did not bother Victoria. She loved Melbourne's trite remarks. His dramatising of situations fitted with her view of life, which in her cosseted world came in large part from the opera and theatre, which she loved.

Melbourne attempted to drown any bubbling conscience in the queen by stating that any social protest or dissidence was caused by 'a few agitators'. Victoria did not quite accept this explanation. She and Lehzen had been tutored in Irish history in the previous year and they believed Ireland's people had been ill-treated. Melbourne himself had been responsible for martial law to suppress Irish activists.

One night at a dinner the next year with a dozen others present, including Lehzen, Victoria asked him: 'What happened to the poor Irish: those evicted by their landlords?'

'Oh,' he said with a dismissive wave, 'they have been absorbed somehow or other.' He eyed Victoria's full plate. 'Besides, they eat too much.' This brought a few sniggers from the others. Then he added: 'There isn't enough food for them and you!'

The other guests now laughed long and hard. Victoria went red.

Melbourne continued to berate rebels, and attempted to blunt any thoughts she may have had about the Irish cause. Those who rebelled were to be despised. When she and Lehzen seemed unconvinced, he said: 'If you are so concerned, why don't you visit Ireland and Scotland for yourself?'

Victoria blinked. He had called her bluff and she was not yet confident enough to challenge his assessments fully or make the trips suggested.

'I have no time for dissidents,' he opined. 'There is only one thing for them: either execution or transportation to Australia.'

'I have just finished reading *Oliver Twist*,' Victoria said defiantly, trying to recover lost ground.

'Didn't I advise you not to read Charles Dickens, majesty?' he said, signalling for a valet to bring him more wine.

'I was touched by his accounts of starvation in the workhouses.'

'Oh, it's all popular rubbish!' he said irritably. 'It's all among workhouses, and coffin makers, and pick-pockets. It's all slang; just like *The Beggar's Opera*...I don't like these things; I wish to avoid them; I don't like them in reality and therefore I don't wish to see them represented.'

He was again scathing about the Irish who 'mind neither lord nor laws'. This kind of reaction went against Victoria's lingering instincts. She wished to know about the underbelly of British society. She had been exposed to it superficially on her trips with the duchess and Conroy across the country in 1835. Victoria had been shaken by the poverty; the pathetic working conditions in the iron and steel towns and coal industry. She did not challenge Melbourne but noted in her diary his comments about reading Dickens, which in itself showed that she was surprised by his sentiments. Victoria was, early on at least, conscious about being queen for *all* her subjects, not just the rich and privileged classes.

Melbourne was a traditionalist despite his early 'radical' days as a student, whether or not the tradition was arcane, inappropriate for the changing times or just plain bad. Flogging, for instance, of men, women and children was acceptable to him, perhaps because it was an extrapolation of his own predilections for perverse sexual thrills from spanking and whipping. He exempted dogs and cats since they would not understand why they had been punished this way. Victoria queried him about his attitude to 'wife-beating'. He was for it.

'Why, it is almost worthwhile for a woman to be beat,' he exclaimed, 'considering the exceeding pity she excites.'

If that shocked Victoria, she was surprised by his attitude to handling children, which was different from hers. She reflected her own experience when she expressed a belief in solitary confinement and enforcing periods of silence as forms of punishment. Melbourne thought such disciplines were 'stupefying'. Victoria would continue to be influenced by the experienced, learned prime minister. She was vulnerable to those who flattered her, fanned her vanities and eased her fears about any shortcomings, mental or physical, that she perceived in herself. Melbourne's charm overrode his own imperfections in her eyes. He could do or say very little wrong. He was her lifeline in her new job: her mentor, confidant and key adviser. His humour and goodwill made her trials more bearable. Melbourne gave Victoria the strength to stand her ground against Conroy and her mother, and to face her life as a young monarch.

Early in Victoria's reign, Melbourne met with her to explain her finances. She insisted on having Lehzen present. The baroness had been in charge of handling her accounts for seven years. The prime minister was uncomfortable with the presence of the sometimes prickly baroness, but in this instance had to bow to the young queen's wishes.

'The parliament has granted £385,000 to you annually from the Civil List, majesty,' Melbourne told her, 'for the dignity and state of the crown and your personal comfort. This has been a satisfactory outcome for you as it was for your predecessor.'

'Since 1830, prime minister,' Lehzen added.

Seeing Melbourne's face darken at the baroness's comment, Victoria said: 'I am grateful, my lord.'

'You do not have to finance any government expenditure, majesty,' Melbourne remarked. 'This relieved the king [William IV] and now you of this burden.'

'With respect, prime minister,' Lehzen interrupted again, 'perhaps you should add that this also greatly diminishes the monarch's position.'

'In what way, baroness?'

'Come, come, prime minister, let's not be disingenuous. No minister of the crown now needs to require the queen's support or grant for expenditure. Her majesty will be removed from the decision-making process.'

Melbourne's face reddened. He could barely contain his anger. Victoria sat silently. Her presence prevented Melbourne venting his fury on the baroness.

'Majesty,' he said, trying to stay calm, 'you must be aware that the considerable expansion of empire placed the monarchy in jeopardy and debt because of the need to provide the funds for that expansion. It was an unmanageable and intolerable situation.'

Victoria glanced down. Melbourne glared at the baroness but she would not back down.

'My lord,' Lehzen said with a look of defiance, 'let us be frank. The situation has reversed. The crown must now go to the government for funding, whereas before 1830, arms of government had to come to the monarch. Can you assure the queen that the dignity of her position will be maintained in these circumstances?'

'I can assure your majesty,' Melbourne replied without looking at Lehzen, 'that no "begging bowl" situation will occur on my watch. I, as prime minister, will always strive to ensure that your majesty is kept in the comfort which she deserves.'

'Thank you, prime minister,' Victoria said with sweet smile, 'I do appreciate that so much.' Aware of the heightened tension, she changed the subject, asking: 'Prime minister, can you tell me how my Civil List payment will be distributed? My uncle did not really explain this to me, primarily because I was prevented from being in his presence.'

'Certainly, your majesty. It will vary, but I expect, going on precedent, roughly £300,000 of your payment will be set aside for your household's salaries and running expenses. That will leave £85,000 to be spent at your discretion. You should expect another £20,000 or so to come to you from rents from the duchies of Lancaster and Cornwall. This will lift your personal income to in excess of £100,000.'

Victoria tried not to react to the amount. It was a dizzying moment, given that she was the daughter of a bankrupt. The family had relied much on the largesse of their bankers, Coutts, who arranged financing on generous terms to keep her mother's household afloat. Now, a few months into Victoria's reign, she was one of the richest women in the world.

'How much will the duchess receive?' she asked.

'I believe we can influence the parliament to lift her Civil List income to £30,000,' Melbourne replied.

Victoria took a deep breath. 'One of my first acts will be to pay off my father's debts.'

'I am afraid the parliament cannot assist you there, majesty.'

'I would not expect that. It is a personal family matter.'

'May I ask the amount of his debt, majesty?'

'£50,000.'

'I had no idea...'

'It has to be settled quickly. I will be able to do it.'

'That is commendable, majesty.'

Melbourne left. Victoria said to Lehzen: 'He seemed most unhappy with you.'

'Of course,' Lehzen said. 'It is in his interests to not explain the full story. Putting it simply, ma'am, he wants power as prime minister at the expense of the crown. I believe he has your interests at heart but not for his loss.'

'But he is a man of his word. He said he would strive for my—the crown's—interest.'

'Hmm,' the baroness sounded unconvinced, 'but he cannot vouch-safe for the attitude of future governments and parliaments.'

Victoria sighed. The thought concerned her. She could not bear to think of Melbourne not being there for her as prime minister.

'Perish the thought of Tories!' she said with an anguished look.

'It would be far better if you could revert to being funded the old way—from rents and taxes of crown lands.'

'Hereditary revenues?'

'Yes.'

'Could we go back to that?'

'It is possible. But with the thrust of err... *democracy,*' Lehzen began, pausing as if she was swallowing something unpalatable, 'it will be difficult, perhaps for some time. But I really don't know.'

'He did not really explain the history...'

'No, my dear queen. That would be awkward. Since Charles I was executed, governments have tried to limit the power of the monarch mainly through reducing the size of the royal purse.'

9

CROWNED BUT LOVELESS

Victoria made it clear to the prime minister, her courtiers and others in mid-1837 that she wanted Elphinstone in her court. Headstrong and gaining confidence every day, she wished to assert some sort of authority and her lover was a good test of how hard she could push. Victoria did not wish to face her coronation without Elphinstone. She missed his warmth, strength, wise council, inspiration and love. Melbourne contributed some of these things but not all. Elphinstone in turn let her know that he would seek employment in the government, sensibly assessing that there would be too much opposition to him rejoining the royal court.

Victoria's determination and passion gave him hope that his exile in Madras would soon end. The word spread through England and elsewhere that Victoria would force his return. Husna heard the rumour and for the first time accepted an invitation from Elphinstone to breakfast with him after their morning ride. The heat was exceptional. Despite all windows thrown open in the dining room to catch any breeze, it was already stifling at 8 a.m. as they ate.

'You are sweating, my lord,' Husna remarked as tea was served.

Elphinstone wiped his brow with his napkin. 'After a ride, I am dripping. This awful heat makes it worse. I am going to move the seat of government to the hills. I can't stand it! My staff can't carry on.'

'I won't be going with you,' Husna said. 'I can cope and it is easier to look after the stables here, especially if we have emergencies with foaling and so on.' Observing his perspiring forehead, she added, 'You English are not built for the conditions.'

Servants scurried in and out, doing their best to maintain privacy. Grilled fish was served. Elphinstone's presence had already been felt, even with his breakfast. His predecessor had hanged his Indian butler for buying produce for himself before the governor. Elphinstone had stopped the practice of the governor having first choice on everything.

A servant interrupted them and brought tea and orange juice. Mangoes were placed on the table.

'Why are you running for the hills, my lord?' she asked. 'You aren't going to remain long in Madras anyway, are you?'

'What do you mean?'

Husna glanced at a valet, who brought toast. When he had left the room, she replied in a half-whisper: 'I hear your little queen is pining for you; wants you by her side.'

Elphinstone's face flushed but he did not respond.

'How long is your term here?'

'I am not sure. I expected a year, maybe two.'

Husna slid her food aside and stood up.

'I have work to do,' she said. Elphinstone pushed back his chair and hastened around the table to stop her. He held her by the arm.

'What's wrong?' he asked.

'You should know.' She brushed him aside and strode out, leaving him alone and brooding.

A few weeks later newspapers in Britain and India announced that Victoria had 'recalled' Elphinstone and Sir Robert Grant (the latter as a smokescreen), the governors of Madras and Bombay. No reasons were given for them giving up their positions but their successors were named. (Stuart Mackenzie, the governor of Ceylon, was expected to replace Elphinstone.) The news fuelled the rumours that had circulated in the royal court, newspapers, books and the public for over two years: Victoria was bringing back her lover, whom she missed greatly. One report said she wanted him 'to perform in the Royal household'. Whether or not this comment had a double meaning, it was typical of those that set tongues wagging. Another report said: 'An attachment between the two is alleged to have been the cause of the Lord's prior removal from London.'

The story was so strong that Melbourne was forced to intervene. He spoke with *The Times* editor. The newspaper then observed in an item: 'Whatever may be the cause of Lord Elphinstone being withdrawn from the Government of Madras, the queen's liking or disliking of that nobleman has nothing to do with it.' The mouthpiece statement then went on to protest too much with a disclaimer that few believed and many knew was untrue: 'Her majesty never spoke to him in his life; never saw him in her life except in public.'

This did not shut down the rumour mill. Melbourne had to step in again and disabuse Victoria of her 'command' concerning this issue. It was an early test of the power of the crown in her reign and that of the prime minister beyond the trivia, such as whether or not she could review her troops on horseback.

'You lied to me, prime minister!' a red-faced Victoria said, when they met at Buckingham Palace. 'You said Lord John would be away just a year. That time is long past. I want him here!'

'With respect, your majesty, I did not misinform you. At the time of his departure for Madras it seemed he would be away a year. But circumstances, as you are well aware, have not improved concerning his return.'

'But that period is now a long way behind us! I want him back. I am your queen. I order it!'

'Your emotional needs, your majesty, do not override affairs of state.'

'You are defying me, prime minister.'

'The publicity is bad enough now. If Lord John were to return, there would be a commotion leading to a calamity! A bank of information would burst. The past would torrent through the newspapers and sheets of tittle-tattle. The truth would almost certainly emerge. Your reign would be in jeopardy.'

Victoria was flustered and upset. Melbourne added: 'You know the people who would *talk*. Could we stop Conroy? No! Could we expect the duchess to let her dreams and manipulations die? No.'

Victoria began crying.

'May I ask, your majesty,' the prime minister began, his tone softening, 'if you have been in correspondence with Lord John?'

'That is my private business!'

'You will know then that Lord John has asked me for a position in government in London. I have told him that this is impossible at this time. I have, however, extended his tour as president.'

'How long has it been extended?'

'He will return after five years, in 1842.'

Victoria's face drained.

'Get out!' she yelled. 'Get out of my sight!'

'Your majesty—'

'You are dismissed, prime minister!'

Melbourne departed, concerned and in a quandary. He felt he was doing the right thing politically. Common sense told him he was doing the best by Victoria, if she wished to maintain her image, her goodwill with the public and her reign. Melbourne wondered if reality would now finally dawn on her. He received more pressure from Stockmar and Leopold to prevent Elphinstone's return, which would ruin their efforts to induce Victoria to reconsider Albert. The problem for them was timing. Victoria's passion for the former captain of the Horse Guards seemed to have increased, not diminished, probably, they guessed, due to secret correspondence. Absence was surely making her heart grow fonder. Stockmar and Leopold could not afford to present Albert so soon since he had not yet matured into the man they thought would attract Victoria. There was at least two years' development and training for him before she might be interested. They were gambling that the Elphinstone affair would have blown over by then.

Melbourne moved behind the scenes to rescind the order for the Madras and Bombay governors to return. Excuses were made. Grant was said to be too ill to travel. (He died in office in Bombay on 9 July 1838.) Elphinstone was said to be required for the implementation of certain policies and that he would stay at his Madras post for the moment.

Melbourne had to use all his considerable powers of persuasion with Victoria, who remained aggrieved and more than a little miffed with her impotency as monarch. She wondered what good was it being queen if she had no power to do as she wished, especially concerning the man she loved. But her deep concerns were pushed aside as her coronation approached.

Victoria, now nineteen, was woken at 4 a.m. on Thursday, 28 June 1838, to the sounds of gun salutes heralding the day she was to be crowned queen at Westminster Abbey. She'd had fitful sleep and had trouble slumbering again. She was too alert and nervous. She rose at 7 a.m. and it helped that the sun was shining. While she dressed, washed and had breakfast, London became a seething mass of excited humanity as people arrived from every point in the country for the huge event. Workmen began setting up wooden stands at various points that the procession would take up Constitution Hill to Hyde Park Corner, then Piccadilly, St James's and Pall Mall to Trafalgar Square and Whitehall, and finally to Westminster Abbey where thousands would watch her enter attended by eight train-bearers.

Hours later, Victoria was cheered all the way by the onlookers who choked the packed streets of the route. She looked her best, wearing a diamond circlet and the parliament robes. They were of crimson velvet, furred with ermine, bordered with gold lace and fastened with a tasselled golden cord.

During the ceremony, the crown and orb she carried were too heavy; the throne was too low; bishops lost their reading places and the archbishop crushed the ruby ring onto her fourth finger, when it had been wrongly made for the fifth. Most of the mistakes were created by the officiating clergy, who literally had no clue, on many occasions, what they were doing. But Victoria rose to the occasion, which she judged to be the proudest of her life. If others missed a beat, she went with the error with such style that no-one other than the key players on show would have known a blunder had been made. She was sufficiently in control to help 90-year-old Lord Rolle, who, when paying homage, caught his foot in his robes on the steps of the throne and tumbled to the bottom. When he tried again, Victoria stepped forward to greet him so that he might not fall a second time. It was a touching moment where Victoria's compassion was evident, despite a newspaper commenting on 'Lord Rolle's role in the pre-arranged roll'. (Gullible foreigners were told that his fall was all part of tradition.)

The coronation was full of mistakes but Victoria had no regrets, except for one: she would have given much for her lover to have been present to experience her crowning moment.

1 0

THE FADING ELPH

After the coronation, the fantasy and dream of being a sovereign diminished. The same nagging problems were with her concerning her mother and Conroy. The latter had met with a railway accident but it was not serious. Melbourne said it was a pity he had not died. Victoria and Lehzen agreed, such was the bitterness Conroy had engendered over the decade in which the duchess and her daughter had become estranged. Their relationship had become damaged for so long that it was perhaps beyond repair. The duchess managed to slip her accounts £70,000 into the red, despite her increased Civil List payment. She claimed she had been paying off her husband's debts but this had been done without fanfare by Victoria. This assertion caused more friction between them, especially as Conroy compounded the lie by telling parliament that the late Duke of Kent had *no* debts, which was meant to give the Kent household and himself an appearance of economic responsibility. The squabbles between the two royal households increased, and the duchess added pressure on her daughter by encouraging the duchess's ladies to argue with Victoria. Lady Flora Hastings was the most menacing of the duchess's household in her efforts to upset Victoria, and Lehzen, whom some admired, others loathed but all respected.

More than two years of no contact, apart from on paper, with Lord Elphinstone led Victoria into a down period. She had poured affection onto Lehzen, and Melbourne, on whom she had a girl's crush. But having had a vibrant, intimate and exciting relationship, these were no real substitutes. Victoria longed for her dashing Scot. Her feelings had spilled into speculative press articles in 1837. By now the reports were appearing even in cartoon commentary. A drawing in 1838's *Comic Almanack* by the nation's leading caricaturist and satirist, George Cruikshank, depicted Victoria as the 'Queen of Hearts'. The picture was accompanied by an explicit enough poem:

> The Queen of Hearts, VIRGO, a bright constellation,'
> (That she will turn up a trump is the hope of the nation.)
> By a whole pack of outlandish knaves, who are suing,
> Is sorely beset, for she shrinks from their wooing.
> Each holds out a circle in which to entrap her,
> And everyone hopes that he shall entrap her.
> But occult operations behind the state curtain
> Shew an Elph, that makes their success very uncertain . . .

Cruickshank was respected for his impartiality in covering court and political events. He had few peers in his comprehension of matters concentrating the minds of parliament and the monarchy. His drawing expressed something troubling those in the court and cabinet: head-strong Victoria was more determined than ever that she would end the exile of her lover and transport him back to the palace. Others were now picking up on the rumours. One satirical piece in a London paper, which was syndicated worldwide and even appeared as far away as the convict colony of Van Diemen's Land (later Tasmania). The article in *The Hobart Town Courier* was by-lined 'The Satirist'. The opening read: 'We have derived from high sources, the following interesting documents, the authenticity of which it is impossible to doubt.' The first alleged letter from Victoria, addressed 'Windsor Castle,' began: 'Dear Elphinstone—you cannot think how I long for your return from that filthy hot place in which I am sure you must be melted. Indeed, indeed, I am very anxious to see you. Why can you not return . . .?'

This article was wrong on several counts, but it demonstrated how far and wide the knowledge of the relationship, and their desire to be reunited, was known. But Elphinstone's tour had now been extended by Melbourne to five years in the hope that this issue would not be revived and therefore add to the divide between the households. The young queen felt her feelings for Elphinstone would never die, although time, distance and realities could modify her thoughts about how the future would be 'managed.'

Victoria's relationship with King Leopold had deteriorated through 1838. She had not appreciated his pushing further for Prince Albert to be her future consort. Victoria's memory of Albert was of a beautiful, effete *boy*. She had but a mild interest in a future with him. Leopold, the once-favourite uncle, had been too much influenced by the duchess and Conroy. In Victoria's eyes now, Leopold was exposed as a user, a permanent opportunist. He asked Victoria to help out financially her sister-sovereigns in Spain and Portugal. He went too far in demanding that she use her influence with Melbourne to aid the Belgians in their territorial disputes with the Dutch after the Treaty of 1831. Victoria was older now and a monarch, not sixteen and a beleaguered, vulnerable princess. She would never be above championing a cause she felt *right*, no matter what her constitutional position. But in this case, she would play the compliant monarch doing the correct thing. Victoria turned the matter over to her prime minister. Melbourne drafted her response to Leopold. Victoria touched it up, making it a more severe reply that created a rift with her uncle. She thought she might avoid political discussion with him in the future, but as politics and royalty were conjoined, there was little hope of that. Yet Victoria did resolve to avoid political influence from abroad. Baron Stockmar, who had been placed with Victoria by Leopold to enhance his position and future bargaining power in everything, became a casualty of Victoria's more mature approach. He remained in the court but on the outer in terms of his influence.

Melbourne was spending up to six hours a day with Victoria towards the end of 1838. In effect, he became her part-time and main 'carer'.

Rumours even developed about *their* relationship. When they were out at night, calls of 'Mrs Melbourne' greeted them. The prime minister laughed off the comments, which he may have accepted as complimentary, given the age gap between them. He was determined to bolster and steady the young monarch. Her mood could be vindictive. Conroy always, the duchess most of the time, and her mother's lady-in-waiting Flora Hastings often were the subject of acute prejudices. The young queen did not yet realise how seemingly trivial gossip could have ramifications far beyond her household, and that what began as personal incidents could become matters affecting the government.

A rumour among the household ladies mounted early in 1839 about Conroy concerning the unmarried, 32-year-old Lady Flora. He was seen many times in her room, even by Victoria when she wandered the palace. She and Lehzen wondered if Conroy, well known for his womanising, was having a secret affair with her. Flora was just his type, they decided: elegant without being ravishing, graceful without being alluring. She was the eldest daughter of the first Marquess of Hastings and attractive enough to capture any man's attention.

On 10 January 1839, she saw the duchess's physician, James Clark, who had been knighted by Victoria. Lady Flora had been ill with intermittent swelling of the stomach for about a month. Clark, not for the first time, was troubled in his diagnosis, or lack of it. He had recently caused concern with everyone, even the duchess and Victoria, when he disclosed an ambition to allow an esteemed medical colleague, Dr Arnott, to make an enquiry into hygiene at the palace. Victoria had indulged Clark to learn more about his friend. Arnott, she was told in earnest tones, believed that 'bad' air was the cause of all illnesses, even death. Clark concurred (or conspired) with Arnott in the obsession that proper ventilation would allow people to live for *300 years*. Without blinking, Victoria had expressed interest, but then told Melbourne she did not want the survey carried out. Unsaid but understood was that Clark's obsession had led him down the path of quackery, yet still Victoria kept him on.

Unmindful of all this, Lady Flora took his advice concerning the illness. He did not carry out an examination other than the odd mild prod in her midriff. Instead he prescribed 'very simple remedies', which he made up himself. It consisted of twelve rhubarb and ipecacuanha pills, and a liniment compound of camphor, soap and opium. Lady Flora was advised to take a pill at bedtime and to rub the liniment on her stomach, or any affected part of her body. This she did dutifully but the pain did not subside. Clark said he wanted to see her twice a week for the next five weeks.

On 12 January 1839, Victoria and Lehzen noted a 'change' in Lady Flora's figure. They thought she was pregnant. Given their disregard for the cool, partisan lady-in-waiting, their amateur assumption was wishful thinking. Their imaginations ran wild. Conroy continued to be seen with her. She had spent the recent Christmas holidays with her mother at Loudoun Castle in Scotland and had travelled back to London with him. Could they be having an affair? Could she be pregnant to him? The thought titillated them. If this were true then it could be the answer for driving their two antagonists out of the palace and their lives. Victoria then discussed the rumour with Melbourne, as she did almost all things on her mind. He thought it likely that Conroy was having an affair with Lady Flora. Part of his conclusion came from noticing the duchess's jealousy of her for the time spent with Conroy.

'What an amazing scape of a man he is,' Melbourne remarked, 'to have kept three ladies [Conroy's wife, Lady Flora and King George III's daughter Princess Sophia] in good humour.'

Victoria was not amused. She observed with vehemence: 'He is capable of every villainy.'

Soon after this, Clark told one of the palace ladies that he thought Lady Flora appeared to be pregnant. His comments were indiscreet, but he was trying to reassert his claims to being a diagnostician. He had blundered in not understanding Victoria's illnesses in late 1835; now he was jumping in quickly to assess Lady Flora, just in case he was seen to be tardy in his medical analysis once more.

The assessment circulated the court and reached one of the 'delicate' senior ladies of the bedchamber, the 'monkey-faced, mischievous' Lady Tavistock, who took most seriously her role as moral guardian of the women at court. She spoke to Lehzen about the 'shocking' development. Lehzen suggested she should bypass the duchess and speak to Melbourne about it, knowing that the prime minister already believed that Lady Flora might be in 'the family way'. Lady Tavistock met Melbourne.

He suggested that she keep the story to herself and 'observe'. Doctors often made mistakes. The prime minister was generalising but he had the inimitable Clark in mind. Many at court and outside it knew of his less-than-convincing medical judgements and theories.

Melbourne then asked to speak with Clark. What was his opinion? The doctor explained his rhubarb treatment. Melbourne had always enjoyed his rhubarb with cream rather than camphor and had no idea of its efficacy. He wanted to know if Lady Flora were pregnant. Clark hedged his bets. He could not be certain, unless he examined her, and Lady Flora had refused his offer. This increased his suspicion that pregnancy was a strong possibility. Lady Flora continued to do her duties with little apparent inconvenience, which Clark believed indicated that she did not have a disease. This left the other option. But he was making his call less on medical analysis and more on *moral* indignation. The consensus at court was that she was having an affair with Conroy. Her shape and responses to Clark's *expert* verbal probes suggested that her relationship with Conroy had *probably* created her condition. This was not quite enough evidence for Melbourne, who was aware of Clark's eccentricities and extreme 'fresh air' theories. He agreed to a wait-and-see policy—which meant watching Lady Flora to see if her middle region expanded.

The whispering became louder at court. the prime minister's two interviews with Lady Tavistock and Clark fuelled, then confirmed, the salacious, outrageous and *delicious* story. Victoria feigned shock but could not disguise her delight. 'We have no doubt she is—to use plain words—*with child*!' she wrote with relish. 'Clark cannot deny the suspicion; the horrid cause of this is the Monster and demon incarnate...JC.'

This diary entry for 2 February 1839 gave Victoria a sweet sense of revenge. Lady Flora and Conroy had been horrible during her medical crisis three-and-a-half years earlier. Now the two of them were receiving godly justice and punishment. It seemed to Victoria that the Lord could be so wickedly symmetrical yet apt in dispensing justice.

Court atmospherics were electrified. Victoria made sure her mother was informed of Lady Flora's condition and was pleased to hear (they were still not talking) that she was stunned. The ladies decided, for Victoria's sake, that Lady Flora could not appear at court again until her situation had been cleared up, one way or the other. This led to her submitting to an examination from Sir Charles Clarke, a specialist in women's diseases, with Clark in attendance. Lady Flora was humiliated but emerged triumphantly with a 'certificate', signed by the two doctors, that said in as many words that she was a *virgin*. She claimed that the doctors did not believe she was or had been pregnant.

But despite the lack of evidence of vaginal penetration, the doctors were still unconvinced. Lady Flora appeared to have an enlarged womb. They saw Melbourne and told him of their doubts, which they had not expressed in the certificate. Victoria let her mother know of the uncertainty in a note. The duchess was outraged. She supported Lady Flora, dismissed Clark from her service, and advised Victoria to do the same. She refused. Clark would stay in her employ. She could not afford to fire him, because he, like Lehzen, knew of the Elphinstone affair, which was ongoing, if only on paper and from a great distance. Clark's royal job was saved, but his prestige was in danger. Melbourne urged Victoria to see him a lot and to humour him. The Scot was furious about the dent in his reputation. He had a sudden loss of patients.

11

VICTORIA FACES
THE 'M' WORD

The scandal broke out of the stifling confines of Buckingham Palace. Indignant relatives, including Lady Flora's powerful, though ailing, father, Lord Hastings, demanded to see Melbourne. He wanted to know who had sullied the good name of the family and his daughter. The story broadened and was seen as a Whig plot against the Tories, given the Hastings' conservative politics. Melbourne assured him that this was not the case, and blamed it all, with some truth, on the tittle-tattle among the ladies in waiting. Meanwhile, Victoria sent for Lady Flora, not to apologise but to offer much sympathy. The queen had to be seen to be hovering above the fray. Otherwise it may have caused the hurt lady to tell everyone the story from those heady days of October 1835 when she had been in the middle of the troubles over Victoria's medical problems. Lady Flora was not appeased. Her influential relatives kept pushing for the truth about who had begun the poisonous commentary that had besmirched their innocent daughter's reputation. No-one at the palace would say. Lehzen and Clark were singled out as probable culprits. There were calls for their dismissal but Melbourne brushed them aside with some diplomacy. He knew Victoria would not dismiss these two from the court. As far as she was concerned they appeared to have tenure while she was queen. Given good health and propitious circumstances, that could be decades.

Conroy could not be kept out of the controversy and was determined to undermine the palace. Behind the scenes—his favourite territory—he used newspapers to goad Hastings into public disclosure over the scandal-mongering. A useful facility for publicity was to have damaging, accusatory letters published, for they always stirred London's chattering classes. One such communication was published in *The Examiner* by Lady Flora herself. She claimed Clark had been talked into believing she was in the family way. The 'talker' she was convinced was 'a certain foreign lady', whom everyone knew had to be Lehzen. The 'scandal' became a political issue. Melbourne and the palace, with Victoria targeted too, were attacked in the press. By 22 March 1839, Melbourne's government was defeated by five votes in parliament's upper chamber. If he went down in any count in the Commons, his government would fall. Victoria was in despair. She felt partly responsible and feared losing Melbourne. He was not just a solicitous prime minister; he was her best and most powerful friend. She was worried about a Tory government coming to power.

'But *I* am but a poor helpless girl who clings to him for support & protection,' Victoria wailed into her journal, '& the thought of ALL, ALL my happiness being possibly at stake, so completely overcame me that I burst into tears and remained crying for some time.'

The Commons did not go against Melbourne and he clung to power. Still the feuds raged. Victoria froze out Lady Flora again, and enraged her supporters in the press. Deeper down, Victoria would have loved to have removed her mother from the palace, which would mean Conroy would be gone too. The old Duke of Wellington intervened, trying to persuade Conroy to leave. Melbourne said Conroy would not listen and he was correct. Victoria's popularity dipped mainly because the press—the main vehicle for informing the public—was turning against her. Clark's head was called for again, but he let it be known that he would write to the papers if Victoria sacked him. Most presumed that he would tell his side of the current Lady Flora story, but there was a real threat to Victoria that he would go back to October 1835 to demonstrate what a rotten cad Conroy had been all along.

The sordid accusations raged on. Melbourne could see his government falling. He was not desperate but did wish to hold his position, if only to guide the young monarch through trying times. He decided to sow the seed of a solution in Victoria's mind. It revolved around one idea: marriage. She would have her own household if she had a consort, who would have his own entourage. 'The duchess' (as the queen still referred to her mother with scorn and hatred), 'the Devil' (Conroy) and that 'wretched woman' (Lady Flora) would be superfluous and vanish with all the problem baggage they carried. Victoria disliked the marriage concept put to her. She called it the 'schocking [sic] alternative'.

Melbourne had to understand, Victoria told him, that she only wished to *discuss* it, not to *do* it. She could hardly utter the 'm' word. In fact, the prime minister was not allowed to talk about it now, only later, when she was ready. There were several blocks in her mind. First and foremost, she still had strong feelings only for Lord Elphinstone, even though their affair had been four years earlier and he had been in India for 26 months. He had mentioned in his letters to her a desire to visit London in the middle of his five-year tour of Madras. Victoria did not disclose this to Melbourne, whom, she had learned, had engineered Elphinstone's banishment in the first place. Melbourne's 'answer' was again to interfere in her private life, this time in an even more important manner. Victoria acknowledged marriage could, just *could*, have merit. She would have realised more than before that she could not consider her first love as a partner and prince consort. His lack of royal credentials would be a problem, although that had not hindered her thinking when she was a princess. But now she was queen, she had a different perspective. He could be placed as a courtier. Perhaps she could then resume a secret relationship with him. Elphinstone had been a lord of the bedchamber for her predecessor, which made him a close companion of the king. He could be appointed to a similar, suitable position close to her. For one thing, Elphinstone was a Privy Councillor. For another, he was in the Lords. In the latter role, he could become a lord-in-waiting and a member of the royal household, officially informing her of goings-on in the upper chamber. That would give her 'access'. Victoria wondered if she could have an 'arranged' marriage with a suitable partner, while keeping up the relationship with a lover. Many monarchs had done this over the centuries. Why couldn't she?

The issue of a suitable partner would have to be raised again. Melbourne pressed her carefully, gently. She responded by telling him how her uncles (Leopold and Ernst) were pushing her to marry Albert. She again made it clear that she was against any official union at this point in her life. She did not see it as necessary for 'three or four years'. Victoria's at times low self-esteem caused her to worry that she would be too much for any husband to handle. 'I dreaded the thought of marrying,' she told Melbourne. 'I was [so much] accustomed to having my own way, that I thought I was ten to one that I shouldn't agree with anybody.'

Melbourne assured Victoria she should get her way yet she was unconvinced. She worried that she would 'win' arguments but only after calamitous scenes with that future husband. Victoria was as ever worried about her depression and ugly temper. She had been working on both but did not feel confident enough to take on a spouse. For this reason, she harboured thoughts of continuing her love affair with Elphinstone. It had been previously all fun with no responsibility for either of them. Their set-up in 1835 was ideal. He hardly ever experienced her temper or depression. When they had their assignations it was all romance and poetry. The debonair Scot was a dominant type, though without a temper like hers. *He* commanded *her*. She loved it, while still realising that he would not ever bow to her other than ceremonially. It would annoy her that the kind of man she really desired—an Elphinstone, a Melbourne, a Wellington, even a Napoleon—would never do. It was perhaps the worst contradiction in forming a relationship when queen. She might have to compromise. This would be hard to accept for a royal young woman who had become used to receiving what she wanted. Also, by the middle of 1839 she was enjoying her role without sharing the limelight. Having created the thought of marriage, which she disdained, Melbourne then manipulated her into thinking through all the issues she might encounter. The mention of Albert's name became almost an incantation.

'How would your mother react to Albert?' he asked Victoria over lunch at Buckingham Palace.

'She has urged me to marry him more than any other.'

'Might she and Prince Albert side together against you?'

'The duchess would join almost anyone against me. But Albert? He is not a dominant type. I fear him not.'

'Could she not bring the prince to her thinking?'

'Perhaps. But if he is that weak, he will not be my husband anyway.'

'You think you could organise Albert the way you wish?'

'Yes.'

'You have his measure then.'

'Remember, I have met him but once, albeit over three weeks. We have exchanged letters. His writing shows he has matured but not to the point of standing in my way. . .'

'Of course, the prince is a Coburg, like your mother. How do you feel about marrying one?'

'That's not a problem,' she said and then laughed. 'In any case, the men are better!'

Melbourne chortled and then looked pensive.

'How do you feel about marrying a foreigner?'

'No worse than marrying an Englishman. At least not from my observations and, as you know, I have been forced into quite a bit of observing! Sometimes I feel I am at the zoo.'

They both laughed again.

Victoria was wistful for a moment. She was thinking, as ever, of Elphinstone. Melbourne guessed the reason for her sudden silence.

'Have you heard from the lord, majesty?'

'Only in my prayers, prime minister.'

Melbourne's expression lightened. 'I think you know of whom I speak, majesty.'

'As I have told you on another occasion, my private correspondence is no business of yours, prime minister!' she snapped, delivering her signature cold stare.

'You are correct, your majesty. Pardon me.'

'You are pardoned. But again, *please* refrain from questions of that nature.'

Melbourne left the lunch a fraction chastened, a condition he would accept from no-one else. He'd had a little victory in the marriage wars. His method of turning her head towards accepting the previously detested concept of matrimony had worked. Victoria was contemplating it for the first time. Melbourne continued to put mild objections to Albert in a classic use of reverse psychology but Victoria seemed (in her correspondence) to be aware of Melbourne's ploy. She dismissed further speculation by saying she could not make up her mind about considering Albert until she saw him again. He would be making a visit in September 1839. She had not seen him for more than three years. He had been a boy then. She was curious to assess his development.

12

CRISIS OF THE BEDCHAMBER

Victoria's dread about losing Melbourne looked like happening in May 1839 when his government lost a vote in the Commons over the implementation of Reform Laws on behalf of sugar workers in Jamaica. On 7 May, the Whig politician Lord Russell, 47, informed her that the government must resign. She cried. Victoria had long listed Tories among the things that gave her the 'horrors' along with insects, turtle soup and going blind. Now the conservatives looked likely to take power. Melbourne suggested that she retain her female household, which meant her collection of women married to Whig parliamentarians would stay. She accepted that Whig gentlemen at court, who were also in parliament, would have to go. Wellington declined her offer to form a government. At 70 years of age, he was old and deaf and not up to it, he felt. The conservative statesman Sir Robert Peel, 51, was the next potential Tory prime minister to see her. Victoria was unimpressed with him, mainly because he was a Tory and not physically to her adolescent liking. She did not find his aquiline features appealing. Nevertheless, discussions went smoothly until it came to the question of her female household. She was steadfast. There would be no change to her Whig team. She would not remove any Whig lords either if they did not have seats in parliament. Peel was stunned. The pliant, nineteen-year-old monarch could be a tough old queen. She believed Peel was behind a plot to oust the ladies closest to her with the ultimate aim of removing Lehzen, whom the Tories believed was behind the Lady Flora debacle. And that is where the politics of the Bedchamber Plot, as it became known, lay: Whigs versus Tories brawling in and around the queen's boudoir, and who should be the inner members of her household, with close and intimate contact to her.

Victoria had been too quick to dismiss Peel because she didn't like his unpolished demeanour after dealing with the urbane Melbourne. Peel had erred in pushing Victoria when she was angry instead of giving her time to settle her thoughts. He decided he could not form a government under the circumstances, which left Melbourne in power but in a precarious position. The Bedchamber 'crisis' was intertwined with the Lady Flora issue and led to a further fall in public support for Victoria. She ignored this and socialised hard with balls, her twentieth birthday and late nights. High-spirited dances lifted her from the mental malaise brought on by political anxieties, yet even this reverie could not match the excitement generated by the news early in June that John Conroy would leave the Duchess of Kent's household. It had all been due to the subtle old Duke of Wellington using flattery. First, he invited Conroy, a supreme social climber, to an exclusive party as if he were treating him as an important friend. The duke followed it up with the ultimate letter of manufactured congratulations telling him he was right to depart: 'considering the sacrifices that you make [in leaving the Kent household],' Wellington wrote, 'and that it is liable to misrepresentation [meaning he will be seen to have been bought off or bribed to leave] it is an Honourable and a Manly course.'

Coming from the most famous *honourable and manly* Englishman of the era, this was a communication to be framed and placed above a study desk. The crafty old duke remarked in private that the letter was a *Pont d'Or*—a golden bridge—over which Conroy could retire to the Continent. The gold was his £3000 annuity with a baronetcy and the promise of a peerage offered by Melbourne two years previously.

Conroy was not to know that Victoria would never allow the peerage while she reigned. The title would give him access to the court. She had also a growing documented excuse for blocking him from this honour that Conroy coveted most and this was his financial dealings on behalf of others, including the duchess, which were dubious at best and often fraudulent.

Conroy's departure should have thawed relations between the duchess and Victoria, but a chill remained. Neither would speak to the other nor compromise. Not even Wellington's intervention helped. The divide was increased with the worsening 'illness' of Lady Flora. Melbourne, Victoria and others at court still believed she was pregnant. The public was only given brief glimpses into the household battles, and they were unfavourable to Victoria. She was hissed at at Ascot, where she received some verbal abuse from Tory wives, who called out the now familiar refrain, 'Mrs Melbourne! Mrs Melbourne!' By 26 June 1839 Victoria felt obliged to visit the ailing Lady Flora, and received a shock. She was wasted, Victoria told her diary, 'literally like a skeleton, but the body very much swollen like a person who is with child...she was very grateful for all I had done for her.' Victoria was holding to the view that she was pregnant while still being relieved that Lady Flora was unlikely now to disclose her (Victoria's) own secret concerning Elphinstone.

The duchess persuaded Victoria to postpone a ball. On 4 July 1839, dinner guests were told not to attend the palace. Lady Flora died early the next morning. She and her family requested a post-mortem, as long as Clark did not carry it out. Doctors discovered that she had suffered all year from a tumour on the liver. She had not been pregnant. The furore heightened. Victoria was now seen as the main culprit for not supporting Lady Flora. Melbourne was challenged to a duel by a Tory. He wisely declined. A Tory insulted Victoria and was challenged to a duel by a Whig. They were both poor shots and missed each other. People stopped toasting the queen here and there and she received more abuse when in public. Lord Hastings, still defending his daughter after she died, sent the press Clark's original prescription for rhubarb and camphor. Clark's Scottish blood was up. He defended himself in the press and this took some of the heat away from Victoria. He was attacked in the esteemed medical journal *The Lancet*. Clark's diagnosis and prescriptions were ridiculed. It implied he was incompetent. The article asked why he had jumped to the conclusion that an increased waistline meant decreased morals. Victoria's own guilt for the way the affair was handled caused her to snap at Melbourne and her diary revealed a self-loathing over the incident. Victoria had felt the thrill of revenge for the way Lady Flora had treated her in siding with Conroy and her mother in the events of late 1935 at Ramsgate. But this feeling had evaporated.

The Bedchamber Crisis meant that Victoria was in no mood for romance. She wrote to Leopold on 15 July 1839 dismissing his urgings about marrying young Albert, telling him what she had told Melbourne: she was content with the status quo. It was still too early and the issue could wait two or three years. Victoria now did not want Albert to visit in October. She claimed it was possible she might like him enough to marry him but added: 'Then again, I might like him as a friend, and as a *cousin,* and as a *brother,* but not *more* . . .' Victoria knew much about the *more,* which she had had with Elphinstone and she still longed for it. Leopold spoke with Albert, who had been dreaming about marrying the Queen of England. He was not too happy about being kept dangling. He didn't mind waiting for three years as long as he knew she would marry him in the end. Being a royal consort for permanent hire was a trying business. If he could not receive guarantees while he waited years, he might miss out on the worthy princesses available. It was a vexing time for the young Coburg prince, whose vision of life—marrying very well as a springboard for achievement—left him a small window of opportunity. Leopold sagely wrote back to Victoria agreeing with everything yet still suggested that Albert be allowed to come to London. Victoria agreed without enthusiasm. Yet as the weeks slipped by the thought of Albert's coming took her mind off the sordid business surrounding the sad death of Lady Flora.

13

VICTORIA'S PROPOSAL;
ELPHINSTONE'S
COMPENSATION

Albert's visit was critical to the twenty years of planning by Leopold and Stockmar, who had groomed him from birth for this chance to control, or at least have profound influence over, the British throne, and therefore an empire that had yet to see its zenith. They believed they were supreme psychologists, who knew how to 'play' the young, still impressionable Victoria, despite her resistance to the arranged marriage they had been angling for. They had assessed her in person; they had dissected every thought in her writing; they had noted every utterance and facial expression with regard to Albert and her reactions when he had been pushed in front of her in 1836. They had seen her response to his looks and knew that the young woman would be vulnerable to his physical appeal. They had assessed her reaction to other young suitors. Victoria was easily smitten. Her diaries were replete with descriptions of people's looks. If a prime minister, such as Melbourne, were handsome with a confident bearing, he was admired. If he were ordinary-looking, like Peel, she would be initially repulsed. She would not settle for someone who was not attractive or her physical ideal. Second was her need to be impressed by a future partner's mind and strength. The dull and the weak; the pompous and the snobbish; the humourless and the overly earnest; the unambitious and those lacking in drive need not apply for her hand in marriage or anything else. Leopold and Stockmar were uncertain about her sexual precocity, but put it down to her innate Hanoverian nature. Leopold warned Albert that she would not be an easy conquest in terms of her character. She was headstrong and irrational, where he was calm, cogitating *and* rational. Victoria was given to extreme mood swings; he would have to learn how to walk away or intercede; be solicitous or stand his ground. She was not used to, or comfortable with, 'ruling' on her own. Victoria leaned on Melbourne all the time but she was enjoying the attention and focus on *her*. If she were left for a few years more, she might not be manageable or malleable for Albert.

Stockmar and Leopold felt that Victoria was not as bright as Albert but he would never dominate her, especially if she was passionate about an issue or subject. She would have to be persuaded, not led. They warned Albert not to let her think that he would usurp her role, even though that was their aim. He had to concentrate on playing the part of her true love and potential consort. Albert had to amuse her, respond to her whims and desires. He had to be close and beside her, not to lead. He would have to bury his distaste for late nights. Victoria loved revelling. He had hated that part of his last visit and still loathed the idea. Albert was an early-to-bed, early-to-rise, *disciplined* type. Victoria had two outstanding passions apart from those carnal: music and horse-riding. His accomplishment at both would be vital to her appreciation of him. Albert was good at playing the organ; he loved his music. He was just as passionate about horses. He was an outstanding horseman, who rode to the hounds, and enjoyed the outdoors. Albert could more than keep pace with her, which would be important to Victoria.

Leopold and Stockmar were ready to roll the dice. They believed that the timing was perfect but there was just one chance. If Victoria rejected him, that would be it.

The removal of Conroy took the pressure off Victoria in how she regarded Albert. She did not have to rush or feel obliged to marry him. She could assess things with her usual cool, or so she thought. Leopold kept in contact, writing about his nephew. As the weeks slipped by, Victoria became intrigued at the prospect of seeing Albert again. She became more excited about a visitor than ever before in the days of the last fortnight before his arrival. Albert, for his part, was less thrilled. He had been distressed about not being given assurances by anyone, least of all Victoria herself, that she would promise marriage. Albert told a friend that he would not be kept 'vaguely waiting'. He would break the 'engagement-that-wasn't' at once. But when he arrived at Windsor his reception changed his thinking. Victoria was in a different frame of mind, due to Melbourne's influence. She consulted him at every turn in the courting dance with Albert. Melbourne was pushing her into it; giving her the confidence to make the move to marriage.

When Albert drove into the upper quadrangle of Windsor Castle, Victoria's heart leapt. She thought him 'beautiful'. The next day they rode together through the glades of Windsor Forest. Victoria wrote: 'Albert is, in fact, fascinating and looks so handsome; he has such beautiful blue eyes...His figure is fine, broad at the shoulder and slender at the waist...I have to keep a tight hold on my heart.'

The now twenty-year-old Victoria was smitten again. Gone were the worries and nightmares about politics, the duchess, Lady Flora and her perceived low public support. Not even Elphinstone far away could intrude into her thoughts. The boy who fell asleep at dinner with his face nearly in the soup a few years earlier was now a twenty-year-old man.

'This is the moment to seal it,' Melbourne told her. 'If he leaves without you asking him ...'

'I know, I know,' Victoria said.

'How do you feel?'

'Oh, he is enchanting, beautiful!' she said, and then paused.

'Elphinstone is still in your thoughts?'

Victoria did not reply. She simply stared at Melbourne.

'The rumour from India,' he said with a sigh, 'is that he is involved with someone. I am told reliably that they ride every morning together.'

Victoria was upset by the remark but kept her peace. After a long silence, Melbourne said: 'Most importantly, majesty, you must think more of Prince Albert's suitability for the monarchy over a long marriage.'

'You think he is right for that, don't you?'

'I can't think of anyone more suitable at this time, majesty.'

Five days after Albert arrived, Victoria sent for him. Royal protocol called for *her* to propose to *him*. She was extremely nervous with her emotions running ahead of rational thought. But she had Melbourne's full support and urging. She had been led to believe that she would never do better than Albert for the role she would propose for him. After the experiences she had been through and the lack of real love since Elphinstone departed, she was ready to be precipitate and take the gamble herself. Although it was protocol for the queen to do the asking, it took courage to put her proposal to him, but she steeled herself. Taking his hands in hers, she said:

'Dear Albert, I do love you so, and would be honoured if you would share your life with me in marriage.'

'My darling Victoria, nothing would give me greater pleasure. Yes, I want this too!'

Albert saw the proposal of love more as an offer to fulfil his dream to 'do good' on the world stage than anything else.

'He was not in love with her,' according to biographer Lytton Strachey. 'Affection, gratitude, the natural reactions to the unqualified devotion of a lively young cousin who was also a queen—such feeling possessed him, but the ardours of reciprocal passion were not his.'

Melbourne saw Victoria straight after Albert departed the room. At first she 'beat about the bush' and talked about the weather and everything except what had just transpired. According to diarist Henry Greville she felt a little nervous with her old friend Melbourne. At last she summoned the courage.

'I have got well through this with Albert,' she said.

'Oh!' Melbourne responded, 'you *have!*'

Victoria and Albert both burst in a lather of writing to relatives and friends expressing their love for each other. Leopold was triumphant. After such lengthy planning with Stockmar, he had achieved his aim. And Albert knew his place.

'While I shall be untiring in my efforts and labours for the country to which I shall in future belong,' he wrote, 'I shall never cease to be a true German; a true Coburg and Gotha man.'

Victoria wrote to Elphinstone, trying to explain that while she had strong feelings for him, Albert was the only choice she was left with under the circumstances, which included her desire to be independent of her mother. But she held out hope to Elphinstone by saying she would endeavour to install him back into court at the first opportunity.

News of the royal romance swept the realm. Elphinstone's uncle, Admiral Charles Fleming, aged 65, heard about it just as he was rejected by the government for the prestigious, highly paid position as master of her majesty's hospital at Greenwich. He was a most unpopular figure. Victoria and Melbourne had no hesitation in turning him down. He decided to make veiled threats about exposing the (Elphinstone-Victoria) relationship if he did not get the job. Elphinstone was in Madras. Had he been in London Charles Fleming would not have pressured Victoria and the government. Melbourne heard that Charles was ill and probably would not live long. The royal 'good news' marriage story was dominating the papers and taking the public mind off weightier issues. Any ugly rumours in the press about the queen would spoil the romantic atmosphere and perhaps her image. A decision was made to grant Fleming the Greenwich hospital position, which, in effect, was giving in to a blackmail threat. Other potential distinguished appointees were aggrieved, given Fleming's reputation. The hospital's trustees were unhappy. Journalists and editors were informed and became suspicious of the appointment. Articles and press comment were hostile but thin on specific grievances. None had any idea why Fleming had been given the job. *The Newcastle Courier*, in summarising the leading London papers, noted that when the appointment was announced there was 'much animadversion' or adverse scrutiny 'in the newspapers for some time since' (the appointment had been announced on 18 October 1838). There was some comment about the esteem of the previous holder of the job, Sir Thomas Hardy, the flag captain to Admiral Lord Nelson and commander of HMS *Victory* at the Battle of Trafalgar. References were made to Charles' being an Admiral of the Blue, the lowest ranking (in order, red, white and blue) of three. Readers were reminded that he was 40 when he married a 14-year-old, and that he had been disliked in the navy for his harshness in handling his crew. But the negative publicity soon died. Melbourne had once more avoided a major, perhaps disastrous development for Victoria.

Victoria was happy with the public reaction to the betrothal. It allowed her and Albert to learn about each other with little interference. She was pleased to note that Albert was interested in her dresses and would comment on them favourably. She wished to show him off when she reviewed the troops on a very cold November day. They both shivered, particularly Albert, who wore white cashmere pantaloons. Victoria was impressed enough to note in her diary that he had nothing on underneath them. Whether he wished to impress her or the troops or both was a moot point.

Soon the practicalities of what those *labours,* to which Albert would dedicate himself, would begin to reveal themselves. He was appalled that he had to explain, for the Tories' benefit, that he was not a Catholic but a Protestant. He was annoyed, even insulted, by being offered £30,000 a year from the Civil List and not the £50,000 he expected. The Tories, with Wellington to the fore, had opposed the higher payment and this increased Victoria's antipathy towards conservatives. They endeared themselves to her even less by dithering over whether Albert should become a Privy Councillor. He, in turn, was further irritated by having to accept being given Melbourne's secretary, George Anson, a devoted Whig. Albert wanted his own German choice. He complained to Victoria, but was ignored. She did not want his countrymen monopolising him. It was the first moment she asserted her independence and was quickly followed by the second. Albert wanted a honeymoon at Windsor Castle. Victoria wrote to him, reminding him of his place. 'I am the sovereign,' she began and then explained that she was too busy and had to be 'on the spot' at Buckingham Palace and close to the political action. Albert was further disappointed to read that Melbourne would dine with them three or four times a week, and always on Sunday. There were already three people in the matrimonial partnership and it had yet to begin officially. All these issues, particularly the lower-than-expected annual pay, made him disgruntled. Leopold was concerned about Albert when he stopped in Brussels on his way to his wedding early in 1840. He informed Victoria that her future husband was not the sulky type, but could be somewhat melancholy if he thought he had not been treated well.

The initial rebuffs to Albert's 'position' that exasperated him were to be expected. His 'success' in the foreign land of England would depend on how he reacted. His character was being tested, and it was this that would decide how he progressed. In the meantime the pragmatic, business-like and serious young man, dressed immodestly as a British field marshal, would slip back into the fairytale for the wedding on the morning of 10 February 1840.

The British Empire was embarking on a second era of expansion after the setback over the rebellion of the American colonies. French settlers in Canada had been influenced by French and American revolutions, and had revolted; Australia, still regarded as the 'criminal colony', was attracting free settlers and had to be managed; New Zealand had yet to be colonised; the Cape Colony (South Africa) had been won from the Dutch but needed attention; India was governed by the East India Company, which, as Elphinstone reminded Victoria often, was proving inadequate for controlling it. The young queen was yet to show any serious interest in political matters abroad. Leopold, Stockmar and Melbourne hoped that Albert—with his ambition, drive and fastidious care for comprehension of all things to do with the monarchy and government—would influence her. This was part of the promise that all the senior British figures, such as Wellington and Peel, saw in him and caused them to voice their approval of his role after contacts in his first months at court. Victoria had so many royal relatives in Europe that she was just beginning to absorb something of the politics in those countries, especially if it affected the relatives' lives. But the only part of the world outside Britain and Europe that she was taking a keen early interest in was India. Letters from Elphinstone in Madras, either direct to her or passed to her from others, had built a romantic image of what had become known as the jewel in the crown of the empire.

Elphinstone had heard all sorts of unconfirmed reports about Victoria and Albert, but without official information travelling overland or by sea to India he was left in the dark and unaware of Victoria's engagement. He had preoccupied himself with his education 'reform' and had managed to create preparatory and high schools. He engineered that he be presented with a demand for higher education signed by 70,000 residents of Madras, who wanted 'some effective and liberal measures for the establishment of an improved system of national education'. Elphinstone had written the petition himself and it pressed the need for an English college. In response to his own 'democratic' demands, he created a plan to establish a university and then applied for extra funds from the British Treasury. Drawing on his own experience in Edinburgh's Royal High School and at Eton, he envisaged twin departments. The first would be a high school for the cultivation of English literature, regional language, philosophy and science. The second department would provide instruction in the higher branches of literature and philosophy (British and Indian), and science. The university board was constituted in January 1840. (This was the precursor to the present Presidency College, Chennai.) It was a hard-fought beginning, yet Elphinstone envisaged much more, including a systematic education system for all India. He knew he could not deliver this in his relatively short tenure, but he was determined to be an early force in its development.

By coincidence he did not read Victoria's letter telling of her engagement until the morning of 10 February 1840, her wedding day. The mail had arrived the night before and he had taken a few minutes in the morning to open the more important correspondence, which included the letter with Victoria's personal seal. The news shocked him even though he had heard rumours about the betrothal. All Elphinstone's vague, nagging sanguineness about a future relationship with her evaporated as he read and reread the letter. He looked at his calendar and realised it was the wedding day. It was a surreal moment. His first thought was to cancel his morning ride with Husna, but on reflection he was determined not to feel sorry for himself. After all, he rationalised later in a letter to Prince William of Orange, it was expected and he could do nothing to intervene. But it was still a shock and it left him reeling.

Elphinstone went on the morning ride with Husna but said nothing. She noticed his sullen mood when she did not receive an invitation for breakfast. In the afternoon, she heard the news from a close mutual friend of Victoria's, Lady Edwina Barrington, the wife of a relative of a member of the board of the East India Company, who was on a sabbatical in Madras.

'That explains the very sad figure this morning,' Husna said to Lady Barrington.

Elphinstone had a business lunch on 10 February in Madras with Scottish merchants in which all participants agreed to wear kilts. He was distracted and mentioned to Prince William in the same letter that it was like a blur. He believed he addressed them, but did not think he spoke well. His mind was still in disarray at the news. Later in the day, still kilted, he wandered back to the mansion to confront writing a reply to Victoria. But first he sat in the shade on the front lawn and tried scribbling some verse. Elphinstone had been a contemporary of outstanding poets Tennyson and Shelley, who inspired him. He wrote a poem expressing his feelings about his relationship with Victoria. It was four verses. The first read:

> I'll hang up my harp in the willow tree,
> And will off to the wars again;
> My peaceful home has no charms for me;
> The battlefield no pain.
> The lady I love will soon be a bride,

With a diadem on her brow;
Oh why did she flatter my boyish pride?
She's going to leave me now.

Then he returned to his office and his large, oak-panelled desk and wrote to Victoria. He stared at a blank page for many minutes before his quill rippled across it. He was consoled, he said, by her joy and he wished her and Albert a happy and productive marriage. A brief missive was all he could manage. He sent his apologies to the organisers of a mayor's dinner, citing illness, and decided to dine alone at the residence. He would normally have one strong double malt Scotch whisky before his meal but this time he said to an Indian servant: 'Leave the bottle.'

He was on his second glass when the servant entered the dining room. 'My Lord, I am sorry to interrupt you,' he said bowing, 'but you have a visitor—'

'Not tonight, Ravi, please.'

'Lord, it is Miss Husna. She will not leave.'

'What?'

'She is very insistent about seeing you.'

Before he could say anything else, Husna was at the door wearing a striking blue sari. Her hair was piled high. Elphinstone stood up, surprised.

'Is that invitation for dinner still open?' she asked.

Elphinstone pulled out a chair opposite him. Husna sat down.

'I thought you should have company tonight,' she said.

'You can read moods?' he asked.

'I have ridden with you almost every day for half a year. It would be odd not to, seeing someone first thing in the morning so often.'

This caused a genuine smile to crease his lips.

'You have inspired me already,' he said, 'such a splendid oriental vision!'

'Thank you, my lord.'

He poured her a strong Scotch. Husna nodded her approval.

Elphinstone studied her. So far, she had 'managed' their platonic relationship. He told Prince William that he had let her do it, saying that her defiant, independent manner was a sweet antidote to all the grovelling and sycophancy from others that accompanied his position as governor. Elphinstone demanded respect for the office but detested subservience. De Crepeney, he said often, was the most exotic woman he had ever met, yet he bemoaned his luck that, for reasons he claimed she never fully explained, she was unattainable to him. Elphinstone however, was aware that she would have nothing to do with him intimately while he was linked in some way to Victoria. He confided to Prince William, whom he regarded as his wisest counsel, that he wanted to be with her as much as possible regardless of a romantic attachment. Elphinstone valued her presence, her opinions and most of all her friendship. That was his mindset on the night she came to dinner.

Husna did not let on that she knew of Victoria's marriage. Instead, she kept the conversation light and warm. After the meal, Husna stood, wandered around the table and beckoned to him. Elphinstone held her hand and led her up the winding staircase without a word being said between them.

It rained in London on Victoria's wedding day, but did not dampen the spirits of the crowds. Their numbers and demeanour, and the positive press reporting, demonstrated that Victoria was again in favour with the public after the lingering impact on her unpopularity of the Lady Flora affair. Only the Duke of Wellington received a bigger cheer than either the queen or Albert as the main players converged on St James's Palace for the ceremony. After the event, they travelled by an old coach to Windsor Castle, for a short stay and not, as Victoria decreed, a honeymoon. She was very much on top at the beginning of their marriage. In a rare reversal of roles and even personalities, Victoria, still the fun-loving young party girl, was intent on getting back to her work and Albert, the industrious, ambitious youth, wanted more time to relax in the country.

Lady-in-waiting Lady Bedford told another of the ladies she thought the queen was 'excessively in love'. Albert was 'not being happy...He is not a bit [in love] with her.' Lady Bedford may have noted more their characters than their feelings. Victoria was overjoyed to be in love again. Albert's mind was already boxing with coming challenges.

In Madras, Elphinstone and Husna stirred as a cock crowed and was answered by another just before dawn. They nestled close. He kissed her cheek.

'Are you riding this morning?' she asked.

'Not sure. I have a hangover. Even magnificent Scotch leaves you with something if you have too much.'

Husna stretched and swung out of bed.

'I think you should come,' she said, her voice croaky. 'You need the air every day because of your illness. And besides, I want your company.'

Elphinstone yawned and sat up. She leaned across and kissed him.

'In that case,' he said with a smile, 'I will come.'

They began dressing. Elphinstone pulled on white trousers and brown riding boots.

'Thank you for last night,' he said. 'What made you change your mind?'

'I learned about your little queen's ceremony yesterday,' she said.

'Oh? But I only received the letter the night before last.'

'Your little queen has other friends here. One of them received the news from her and informed me.'

'Who was that?'

'Not really any of your business.'

'So you . . .?'

'I came here with the express intention of taking your mind off things.'

14

VICKY'S BIRTH; ELPHINSTONE'S FEVER

Victoria learned she was pregnant a few weeks into her marriage. Everyone expected her to be thrilled but the court was dismayed at her reaction. She was furious and moody. The news set off a period of depression that confused her young husband, who was made to feel he was to blame for something, rather than being praised for doing what the nation expected him to do. The conception led to a fusillade of tempestuous letters and diary scribbling in which she vented her feelings. She wrote that it was 'the ONLY thing' she dreaded. It was 'too dreadful,' she told Leopold. She 'could not be more unhappy,' she informed another relative in Coburg. Victoria 'hated the idea' and had prayed that she be spared her condition for at least the first half year of her marriage.

'I cannot understand how anyone can wish for such a thing,' she wailed, 'especially at the beginning of a marriage.'

The pregnancy triggered a depression similar to that which she experienced in late 1835 and memories of what she considered to be the worst months of her life until that point. Then she had been made to feel so sordid, irresponsible and alone as her mother, Conroy and Lady Flora had badgered, harassed and pilloried her to a state of anxiety that was unbearable. She had wanted to die, and nearly did. Only the support from Lehzen and the fallible Clark squeezed her through that period. These two recognised her severe depression a second time around and were in full support again. The much-maligned doctor had done his homework on pregnancy since being lectured so humiliatingly in the *Lancet* after the fiasco with Lady Flora. He knew all the signs short of being a mother himself, yet still he called in an obstetrician (Charles Locock) for an examination, just to be sure. When her condition was confirmed she exclaimed to Leopold: 'If my plagues are to be rewarded by a nasty girl, I will drown it.'

Victoria's first thought after the shock was that she *had* to produce a male, but not to satisfy the nation's desire for a future king. She simply wanted a boy. The whole business erupted into a confusion of emotions as those close tried to mollify her.

The public knew nothing of her sensitivities. They had only had the newspaper accounts, mostly favourable now, about the new royal couple, which kept her public (newspaper-led) support reasonable. But regard for the queen took a leap on 12 June 1840 when a would-be assassin, carrying two pistols, leapt from Green Park as the royal carriage moved down Constitution Hill. He fired at them. Albert instinctively put his arms around his pregnant wife to protect her. The shooter missed and was set upon by onlookers, and later arrested.

A short time later, when the couple were out driving, Albert noticed another man pointing a gun at them a metre away from the carriage window. The gun seemed to misfire. He reported the incident to Prime Minister Peel that night: 'I saw a man of the age 26 to 30, with a shabby hat and dirty appearance. He stretched out his hand and snapped a small pistol.'

Peel advised him and Victoria to stay at the palace for a while.

When this was conveyed to Victoria she revealed her courage, saying: 'Never! Alert the police. We shall ride out again tomorrow and see if he returns.'

The same man did appear again on the edge of Green Park. He pulled out his pistol and aimed at them again. But it misfired once more. The would-be assassin was John Francis, a stage carpenter from Covent Garden. The police thought the man might be 'mad'. When told this, Victoria commented: 'He is not in the least mad, but very cunning.'

Francis was condemned to death, but his sentence was commuted and he was sent to prison for life.

Only two days after this attempted assassination, a hunchbacked dwarf, John Bean, aimed and fired a pistol at Victoria as she rode to the Chapel Royal. It was a third shock, and not of great comfort that Bean's pistol was loaded with tobacco and paper, giving rise to a tabloid spate of drawings of 'smoking guns'.

Shaken but unbowed, the royal couple was applauded the day after this incident when their carriage bumped out through the palace gates. The following night, they were cheered at the opera. Their popularity rose. The pistol threats had another important impact on Albert. It precipitated the passing of the Regency Bill in parliament.

'In case of Victoria's death, and her successor being under 18 years of age,' Albert wrote to his brother, 'I am to be Regent—alone—Regent [!] Without a Council [!] You will understand the importance of this matter and that it gives my position here in the country a fresh significance.'

Victoria was happy about this breakthrough; Melbourne too. He put it all down to the prince's character. 'Three months ago,' he remarked, 'they [the parliamentarians] would never have done it for him.'

Albert was not sure how to handle his wife during her pregnancy. He stayed well clear during the day in the initial months, unless called to be with her. He was attentive during the trying time, easing her misgivings. The child was born three weeks premature on 21 November 1840. Victoria had a tough twelve-hour labour.

'Oh, madam,' Dr Locock said at the birth, 'it is a princess.'

Victoria was disappointed. She replied snappily: 'Never mind. The next will be a prince!'

Albert dashed off to represent the queen in council for the first time. He was just as excited about this meeting as the arrival of his first child. Both were the initial signposts for two much hoped for parallel paths: producing a royal lineage, and being a highly functional, administrative *regent* in all but name.

Victoria's mental reaction to her experience of pregnancy, birth and babies in general had caused her to be disgusted by bodily functions, which was contrary to her hearty Hanoverian nature. She pushed the little princess royal (Victoria—'Vicky' to distinguish her) away with no inclination to nurse her. She spoke of the whole experience in German to distance it further; it was *die Schattenseite,* the shadow or dark side of marriage. She wrote that babies were 'frog-like' and 'ugly' until they were about six months and taking shape.

In mid-1840, Elphinstone learned that the Duke of Sussex had appointed him as the Grandmaster of the Masonic Lodge in Madras. There were eight masonic chapters in the region, and while taking this honour with good grace, he was not an enthusiastic supporter of masonic activity, which was limited during his tenure. After nearly four years of banishment, the exiled Scot seemed not too keen on being overworked in many activities in steamy, somnolent Madras. Sir Alexander Arbuthnol passed through the town and enjoyed the company of the governor with Husna whom he thought was 'quite the most outstanding dark beauty I have ever seen'. Arbuthnol added in a letter to his wife: 'Lord Elphinstone had a reputation for being a man of pleasure and by no means diverted by his official work. He was a man of very good ability and he discharged his duties very well.'

Elphinstone was tempted to return to London when struck down with an unspecified illness, the ubiquitous and all-encompassing 'fever', in late March 1840. Husna gave up part of her veterinary activities to look after him, much to the chagrin of the presidency's resident surgeon. Reports went back to Britain that Elphinstone had chosen the aloof French-Indian and unqualified *female* instead of a professional English doctor of twenty years standing in the colony.

Husna nursed Elphinstone back from a condition that had no known cure. She monitored his temperature and diet. She made sure he did Indian yogic exercises every day, to the ridicule of British observers. Gradually he returned from what Husna told him frankly was 'the brink'.

'Time' would be the healer, she told him, and it took three months before she pronounced him off the 'seriously-ill' list. When an English reporter asked her how she saved him, Husna replied provocatively: 'I treated him like a prize stallion, which he is,' knowing that her remarks would be picked up everywhere, including Buckingham Palace.

A press report in *The Times* noted: 'We are happy in being able to state that Lord Elphinstone's health is greatly improved. His lordship is unable to walk, but will be able to mount a horse in a few days, it is expected.'

He did not return to full fitness for some months more when he recommenced his morning rides with Husna. In October they ventured into the hills for an exploratory look with the view to his presidency being moved there.

'I won't join you,' Husna told him. 'It's either Madras or Stockholm; not Madras or the hills.'

'Let's cross that river when we come to it,' he said.

'No,' she said, with a fierce stare, 'no rivers or hills.'

On the ride home he spoke of his desire to return to Britain.

'Well, that is interesting,' she said as they trotted along a dusty track to the outskirts of Madras. 'Next year I may well be returning to Sweden to do more study. There is some talk of allowing females to qualify as doctors.'

'That means if you don't come to the hills with the move, we won't see each other for some time.'

'I've told you; I won't be coming to the hills.'

Elphinstone became preoccupied by building a summer residence at Kaiti at nearly 3000 metres altitude in the Nilgiri Hills, or 'Blue Mountains', outside Madras and moved the seat of government there to beat the incessant heat.

'Elphinstone's excuse [for moving the government into the hills] was that his doctors had found him and several members of his Council, as well as secretaries of Government, exhausted by the heat,' the Indian newspaper *The Hindu* noted. 'He advised them that a change of climate was necessary if they were to get about their work.'

If Elphinstone were going to be governor, he wanted to do it in some comfort. He was determined to make the move. Elphinstone especially liked this region inhabited by the ancient Toda tribe. The area reminded him more of the rolling hills and downs of Southern England than the craggy heights of his beloved Scotland. Elphinstone encouraged other Europeans to build summer residences in the hills with the aim of creating a community in the region. But his experiment brought controversy. Not every East India Company employee wanted to live so remotely. There were protests and appeals to the company's directors, who were scandalised, according to *The Hindu*. They remonstrated with the governor and referred the matter to their 'court'. This decreed that Elphinstone's move inland was illegal. The company censured him. He ignored the ruling, pitting himself against the directors. Pressure was put on him to return to Madras, which he did, with some bitterness and much reluctance. By 8 December 1840 the region was being governed from Madras once more. He replied to the East India Company directors' letter of censure saying that 'if he had not acted as he had, there would have been a general breakdown of the administrative machinery'.

Elphinstone was incensed. He let Victoria know his feelings in a letter, which sowed the first real seeds of the East India Company's demise. It was suggested that the company be dissolved and that the Crown itself take over the running of India. Victoria was still a novice in such matters and she had little idea how her empire was run. But she would learn through self-interest and Elphinstone's advice influenced her attitude to the future running of the 'jewel'.

Elphinstone's forced return to Madras allowed him to resume his guarded relationship with Husna. Over dinner at the mansion in late December 1840, when all the presidency staff had departed, he complained to her about the East India Company.

'They have an informant in my office,' he said with a frown. 'My every move was known.'

'I am not surprised. Not all your people wanted to go into the hills.'

'What do you mean?'

'I didn't want you to go. I was the only medical adviser to say it was not necessary.'

'You wouldn't be that devious to inform on me, would you?'

Husna got up from the table.

'Perhaps I would,' she said.

'You've been spying on me?' he asked, shocked.

'And you have not been honest with me!' she said, tossing her napkin on the table and upsetting a wine glass. A pool of red liquid formed on the table cloth.

'I think you are still in love with your little queen,' she said, dropping her voice. 'Why else would you return to England when I am still here?'

She strode towards the dining-room door. He tried to stop her.

'No my lord,' she said, brushing past him, 'you are still in love with her!'

Husna did not appear at the stables the next morning and two days later, on New Year's Eve, Elphinstone was told that she had left by boat for Stockholm.

He was upset to lose his best friend and lover.

Victoria was shocked and angry to learn in March 1841 that she was pregnant again, which indicated she may have become careless when in the grip of her passions. She has been diagnosed in retrospect by psychiatrists and psychologists as having a form of depression and an abnormal sex drive. She may, as diarist Greville claimed, have had a sexual crush on Melbourne, and other men she viewed as 'beautiful'. But only once outside marriage had she done anything about it. Her fishbowl life and position limited her chances to almost nil for spontaneous romances. Albert was avoiding her sexual demands and hoped that by continuing his attentiveness to her—with gifts, warmth, expressions of love and devotion to their family life—he could satiate her desires. It wasn't enough, and neither was his excuse that the Church forbade sex during pregnancy. The lack of servicing and her hormonal changes caused Victoria's mood to spill over into anger, spite and other emotions.

Victoria's 1841 pregnancy prefaced a period of flux and change. Again, Melbourne lost in parliament and had to concede government. This time, due to the shrewd young Prince Albert, the bedchamber crisis was averted by Victoria being persuaded by Melbourne and him to give up three of her Whig ladies. Peel could govern in his own right. Victoria, in a fragile state and often depressed, was tearful about losing Melbourne, yet there was a compensation or two. Melbourne continued, unconstitutionally, to advise her as Albert began to fill the breach as her key confidant. Melbourne endorsed Albert's stepping up. Victoria acquiesced. She was preoccupied with her condition and mental state, and less concerned about Albert usurping her role. Melbourne's final 'shot' as prime minister was to suggest to Albert that the last block to Albert's advance—Lehzen—should go. It was time to tell Victoria. But Albert knew his wife's moods. Her pregnant state did not provide the moment. She would be too 'excited' by any effort to remove the woman who had been her governess since she was five. Victoria was now a woman of 22 and Queen of England. Lehzen and Albert were vying for Victoria's heart and to have most influence over her. Albert was winning. He detested Lehzen, often calling her the 'dragon'. Events in the palace nursery aided the prince consort's determination and Lehzen was blamed for little Vicky's problems. She was sickly. Victoria thought it might be the child's diet of ass's milk and chicken broth, another eccentric remedy prescribed by Clark. Others put it down to the way Lehzen handled her. Dramas continued.

15

BERTIE'S ARRIVAL;
LEHZEN'S
DEPARTURE

Early in November 1841, Melbourne gave Victoria some advice that presaged a main theme in her career: the struggle for power and influence between the monarchy and the government's executive arm. He informed her that the ministerial part of the constitution, the workings of the government, rested mainly on 'practice, usage and understanding'. There was no set official publication that explained or described it. Confusing her at a higher level he added: 'It [the unwritten British constitution] is to be sought in debates, in letters, in memoirs, and wherever it can be picked up.'

She and Albert understood well enough that since 1830 the executive power had resided in the hands of the government and its ministers. Her power had been limited. They realised that the personal power and influence of the monarchy depended on the drive, personality, character and popularity of the individual monarch. She and Albert had to gain the confidence of ministers if they were to wield influence and any power over events. The monarchy could become an unofficial department of state, to help compensate for lost powers. Albert believed this would help it remain afloat in the rising tide of democracy. Their approach would create a pattern to be followed by the heir to the throne, the Prince of Wales, who was born on 9 November 1841. Victoria liked the bigger-than-average-sized baby, who had big, dark blue eyes, a largish, refined nose and a girlish mouth.

After adoring the new addition she slipped into a deep mental malaise for the second time after giving birth. It coincided with Lehzen going down with jaundice and turning yellow, much to Albert's quiet but cruel merriment. Victoria's state and the weight loss of the little Vicky caused the worst row between husband and wife in their nearly two years of marriage. Albert retreated but wrote her a blistering letter. 'Doctor Clark has mismanaged the child and poisoned her with calomel,' he seethed, 'and you have starved her. I shall have nothing more to do with it; take the child away and do as you like and if she dies you will have it on your conscience.'

Husband and wife wrote to Stockmar, looking for support from a neutral umpire. Victoria, at least on paper, was being conciliatory. She felt compelled to support Lehzen and to tread carefully around her sensitivities, even though she was unaware of the fight going on in the palace's inter-apartment mail. Victoria did not want Albert ever to learn of her affair with Elphinstone. She felt sure that his pious, pristine and delicate nature would not cope with what he would perceive as betrayal. Even though the Elphinstone relationship had begun before her even meeting Albert, he would be sure to see it as a form of retrospective infidelity.

'Lehzen is a crazy, common, stupid intriguer, obsessed with lust for power,' Albert wrote in a fusillade of abuse for his rival. '[She] . . .regards herself as a demi-god, and anyone who refuses to acknowledge her as such, as a criminal.' Albert thought Victoria had been taught to see Lehzen as an 'oracle', yet some observers suggested Victoria's best qualities had been developed by her. His frustration at not realising his full influence over his wife had boiled over and Lehzen's connection to her offended his sense of logic and rationale. Victoria's apparent clinging to Lehzen did not fit with his appreciation of his wife. What hold could this wretched woman possibly have over his dear spouse, he wondered on paper to many correspondents. Instead of Melbourne being the third party in their marriage, Albert now saw the lean, sharp-nosed and unprepossessing figure of the 'fire-breathing' German baroness. He understood Melbourne. He was a 'brilliant', polished man of finesse. Of course he would impress a young, politically naive girl, *any* girl. But Lehzen? It just did not add up. An older, more mature Albert may well have asked relevant questions about what it could mean. Something in the past, perhaps? But the young consort, for all his intelligence, could not make sense of it. The Lehzen–Victoria relationship was beyond him. It made him react childishly.

The experiences of Victoria and Lehzen at Kensington had bonded them. Albert had no idea that Lehzen had stood up against everyone in defence of her charge at the most critical hour. Lehzen had also been the go-between and even the facilitator of Victoria's relationship with Elphinstone. She had always angled for him and detested both the contrived match with Albert and Albert himself. She did not like his fussy ways at court. She was at one with the women courtiers, who were affronted by his lack of warmth and charm, and total disregard for them. In short, she did not believe Albert was man enough for Victoria. She suspected, like many at court, that he was homosexual and only carried out his procreational duty once a year, and then under sufferance. Lehzen knew her beloved queen better than anyone. She knew how difficult Victoria could be. Handling her would test the most compassionate and understanding of men. Rightly or wrongly, Lehzen never thought Albert had the 'skills' and strengths to handle her. Perhaps she had idealised Elphinstone too much in these respects. But the baroness had seen the Scot enough at close quarters to judge. She believed that his exceptional depths of feeling and kindness, coupled with his strength of mind, meant that he was better equipped than anyone for the long haul of a challenging high-powered, high-profile marriage. Lehzen also thought the bonds of spontaneous love were stronger than a contrived coupling. Her resentment towards Albert stemmed from how Victoria had been set up by the 'wizard' Stockmar and the conniving King Leopold. She objected to their *über*-piety. All that was in the past yet Lehzen could not forgive or forget. She carried her attitude to the royal court in a coldness towards the consort. Consciously or unconsciously she undermined him and his marriage.

Victoria would have to be loyal to Lehzen if her affair with Elphinstone were to remain secret. Conroy had been bought off; Elphinstone had been sent off. It might not be so easy to get rid of Lehzen, who had no-one else and had been 'wedded' to Victoria's life for most of it. The palace experience was all she knew. Lehzen was in her forties and unattractive. Marriage was probably not an option. She would fight to stay close to Victoria, whom she had done most to develop as an intelligent, well-read, well-rounded monarch. Stockmar could see that something had to give. He interceded, letting Victoria know more of Albert's grievances. The seed of Lehzen's demise was sown. A way around the problem was to 'reform' the nursery management. This left Lehzen without a major role and she was not travelling with Victoria everywhere. The loyal confidante was on the outer, yet she had enough character not to cause a scene. She knew Victoria loved her but events and people had moved on. Albert had the right to act the way he did, within reason, and he was a strictly logical, *reasonable* man. In this case, he had become obsessed, exaggerating the deficiencies of his wife and her mentor and mother figure. After years of angst and complaints, he had his way. Lehzen left quietly, on 30 September 1842, without even saying goodbye. This was not because she lacked the courage; she simply did not wish to cause a scene or upset Victoria, which was appreciated by all concerned. Her 'settlement' was good: a pension of £800 a year, which was much more than any other comparable retiring lady-in-waiting could hope for. But she had earned it, if long service and the capacity to keep confidences were a measure of worth. Lehzen planned to live with a sister in Buckeburg, Germany, and work her kind of 'magic' for moulding children—now her brothers' offspring—into what she and the standards of the time saw as worthy young adults.

Albert now felt there were no obstacles to his relationship and the way he wished the court to progress. Gossip at dinner, he expected, would be replaced by discussions on military, political, scientific and international issues. For many, including Victoria, there would be duller but better-informed gatherings especially on problems that troubled the seat of empire and needed at least comprehension by her. Harvests, never a topic for before-dinner drinks, came up in discussion. Court chatter about trade, which was taboo previously, now received 'mention', mainly because it was in the doldrums. Even the 'R' word—*revolution*—received attention, especially as there had been talk of it in many parts of Britain. The Scots were grumbling; the Irish were livid and the Welsh were uncooperative. The Duke of Wellington said that in war he had never seen a town as touched by violence as Birmingham had been in 1839. There was less or no tittle-tattle about who was having an affair with whom, although the odd bit of scuttlebutt revived some of the ladies' interest during the main course when good wines loosened mischievous tongues. No-one had previously discussed the poor conviction rate of Irish murderers (fewer than 5 per cent in recent years); nor had the ongoing revolt of French colonists in Canada been a topic digested with dessert. But all the males were riveted over port and cigars one night when Wellington mentioned the possibility of war with the United States. There was also silence when Peel brought up the uncomfortable fact that British ships were being held up by Chinese pirates in the Far East. They were looting or destroying cargo. Retaliation was promised to Victoria. It was undertaken and led to the Treaty of Nanking later in 1842.

It was the beginning of a period of greater awareness for Victoria, and more particularly Albert, as they preoccupied themselves with touring the country, and public events, such as the races at Epsom on Derby Day. At Albert's suggestion (which Lehzen would have objected to), he and Victoria mingled with the crowd between races. The monarch had more traction with the middle and lower classes than she did with the aristocracy, who refused to warm to another *German* who had gained prominence in the social structure. Its members were frigid towards Albert, who remained his reserved and distant self. He paid no attention to the 'important' ladies of the upper classes or their children at balls, parties and other events, which further distanced him from the aristocracy. He was too punctilious and clipped; too *foreign* for their parochial tastes. It did not seem to bother the royal couple. They had growing mass appeal. The aristocracy could fall in with this or please themselves.

This popularity was aided when Peel reintroduced income tax on Victoria's own income, including the bulk of her £385,000 from the Civil List. This seemed logical now that the monarch did not have to pay any expenses of government. Victoria was annoyed and held a grudge about becoming a taxpayer. She told Lord Rosebery that she felt it 'rather derogatory to her dignity'; she may not have realised that she was very much like the vast majority of her subjects in holding that sentiment.

Peel had quietly 'cornered' Victoria by taking away her ability to pay for any Government activity, which reduced her influence. The canny prime minister had gone by the principle 'he or she who has the gold, rules'. He quantified her comfort and dignity more than adequately while boosting the institution of democratic government at the expense of the monarch. Peel was shrewd too in the way he played this move politically by announcing that Victoria had 'volunteered' to pay income tax. This had a twofold effect. It lifted her image in the public mind, and also made a most unpopular tax in peacetime more palatable for her subjects to accept. The tax of just 3 per cent only affected those with more than £150 a year, which was a small percentage of the population, but this did not make it any more popular. It was said to be temporary but, without a specified time frame, this was an underhand yet effective way of foisting income tax on the public for a protracted period.

Victoria was now viewed in the public mind as a good citizen who paid her taxes just like everyone else.

16

LOVERS' REUNION

Elphinstone returned to London from Madras via the fast route overland to Cairo in 1842. He did not expect any favours or position at Victoria's new court after his six-year banishment. He had kept in touch with developments and knew he would be out of favour still, although not with Victoria. It was his duty to present himself at court as the returning representative of her majesty abroad. It was a moment of emotion and tension for both. In the rarefied atmosphere of the ornate reception room at Buckingham Palace, with courtiers standing nearby or flitting in and out, there was no opportunity to express what was in their hearts.

Elphinstone assessed that Victoria's pure and youthful beauty, unhindered by the weight of 'authority', and her odd mix of coyness and determination, had been replaced by primness and a dour expression. He was looking for glimpses of the girl he once knew, with the hint of a smile, perhaps the merest glint in her eyes, or a fleeting gesture of warmth. For her part, she was smitten again by his good looks and masculinity, which had so taken her from the age of twelve. He was tanned and even stronger looking than before. All the urges that had swirled in her for so long were stirred again. But she kept her feelings in check.

'I must thank you, my lord, for the wonderful letters and sketches you sent,' she said somewhat stiffly, accepting his hand as they sat discreetly either side of a long table. 'You sparked in me a love of India that will never die.'

'I gathered this from your letters and that pleased me greatly,' Elphinstone said.

'What plans do you have?' she asked, again with a formal expression.

'See my family and friends; visit the Lords,' he smiled warmly, 'fulfil my role as one of your councillors, ma'am.' She blinked and he caught a hint of the headstrong young woman he once knew. 'Must return to Scotland and do some riding. Lots of riding in the highlands.'

Victoria glanced at a courtier near the door.

'Privacy, please. No-one is to enter until I announce it.'

'Yes, your majesty,' the courtier said with a nod as he backed out of the room.

'I am finding it hard to control my feelings,' she whispered, eyes down. 'I have thought of you . . . every day since . . .'

'And I you.'

'It is impossible for us.'

'I accepted that some time ago.'

'No, you misunderstand. I mean for the moment. There are still too many about me with fresh memories. It is seven years, but the moment is not right.'

'For what, your majesty?'

'For you to return here, to my court.'

'You still want me—'

'In the court, yes, very, very much.'

He was surprised and pleased. It was a consolation for a lost opportunity.

'If I had been my age now when we . . .' she paused. 'It would have been different, so different. Only now I am able to see my position with clarity.'

'But you are happily married?'

'Very. Albert fulfils every role of a demanding situation,' she paused. Again for a second he caught a hint of the wild girl he had seduced when she added: 'Well, *nearly* every role.'

Sensing a sadness in him, Victoria reached a hand across the table.

'You will never know the pain I went through trying to get you back,' she said as tears emerged. He moved around the table. She stood and he held her, touching her forehead and wiping away tears. Elphinstone kissed her lightly on the forehead and moved back to his seat.

'As long as you are happy,' he said, reaching for her hand again. 'That is important for the nation.'

'I am,' she said, 'most of the time. But I have my moods.' She gave a little laugh.

'Dear Elphi,' she said softly, 'dear, dear Elphi. I always saw the wisdom of the world in your eyes. And you brought the world to me in your correspondence like no other.' She grasped both his hands in hers and added: 'For what it is worth, my darling, I cried for you a long time after you left.'

'And I for you, in my heart.'

'I want to tell you this just once,' she said, her expression serious. 'If it had been left to me, I would have waited much, much longer until you returned, but the family . . .'

'I know, I know,' Elphinstone said, putting a finger to his lips.

'I am not saying that Albert was not right for me and my destiny. He was and is. But I just wanted you to know.'

'I had my spies at court,' he said.

'And I had them too, in Madras.' She arched her back and released his hands as she sat up. 'I heard about the most beautiful woman in India. What was her name?'

Elphinstone said nothing.

'I was so jealous at the time,' Victoria added, 'It was Melbourne who first told me in order to put me off you when they were all attempting to marry me off to Albert. I reproached myself for not wanting you to have this woman.'

'She is in Sweden or France, I know not which; I am here.' He paused and added, 'I must take my leave, ma'am.'

'You cannot go until I command it,' she said, suddenly affronted, 'I am your queen!'

Elphinstone kept on his feet. Victoria stood and came close.

He bowed low, kissed her hand and backed towards the door, leaving her standing, hands on hips.

'I have not given you leave!' she called.

Elphinstone opened the door, bowed again, waved and said: 'I know your majesty, and I bid you farewell and a truly lovely day.'

Victoria's assessment about the timing for his return to court life accorded with the information he had received in letters from friends, such as the Prince of Hesse. But Elphinstone could only really assess things by being in the place of his former occupation as lord of the bedchamber and speaking with the monarch personally. His immediate sense was that events had moved on and passed him by. No matter what she felt, Victoria *had* to behave in a detached manner with him in the company of others. She was married with children; she was queen. Victoria had a duty to the public. She and Albert were already setting the impression of a model family. Not the merest hint of impropriety, whether real or imagined, could float from the court. Elphinstone had to be treated as an 'old and dear friend', nothing more. Nevertheless, regardless of her love for Albert, which was part real and part manufactured by virtue of her role and duty, Elphinstone was, and forever would be, her first love. She would tell all her daughters in later years, and other close friends that 'one's first true love was always the greatest, most stimulating and powerful love'. It was sacred. She concluded it was 'the divinest thing in the world'.

No-one ever asked her how she came to this conclusion. It would have been an awkward question for Victoria. Logic dictated that she could only know how much better a first love felt than any other if she had more than one lover.

At that telling yet poignant moment, Victoria had to hide her excitement about Elphinstone. There had been developments in her life that made resumption of anything beyond companionship and perhaps later 'monarch and courtier' again difficult although not impossible. As she informed him, it would be still too early for any formal relationship at court. But deep in Victoria's heart, given her record of emotional responses, she again experienced a huge pull towards Elphinstone.

Their affair had been cut short by others when they both wished it to continue, even to marriage. The relationship had never died. It did not end by their own volition, or become acrimonious. In that sense it was still pure. Elphinstone maintained his love for her. It had not diminished. He had no wife or permanent lover. His passionate relationship with Husna may have had a future but was now in abeyance. He had built a reputation in Madras as being a man disinclined to commit: a 'player'. Deep in his psyche was a forlorn hope that he would be reunited, somehow, with the only woman he loved. This blocked him from giving to others, apart from Husna, but because of her caution and ambivalence, theirs was a relationship in suspension. Elphinstone did not appear to women as callous, a misogynist or unreliable. His warm, manly, mannerly and courteous nature confused his admirers. He was so liked by everyone that hopeful possible partners would have wondered what was wrong with them, rather than the alluring, yet mysterious governor.

The reaction in this meeting with Victoria on his return was expected, yet Elphinstone had to experience it to really *know* it. He realised that he should not push for a resumption of anything like his former role in close proximity to the monarch. If he were upset at the reality, he did not show it. He remained cheerful (if his letters are anything to go by) and positive. He just wished to vanish from the palace system and to distance himself from reminders of his past experiences at court. Elphinstone planned there and then to *disappear* back to India but this time to its wilds; the remotest parts that had never been visited by Europeans. It was not an act of running away; it was more an escape to find himself.

17

THE PERFECT
BUTLER

Prince Albert's true nature did not take long to emerge. He became royal 'house-keeper of the Palaces', sweeping out corruption (a black market in unused candles); reducing spending at dinner; cutting down on the number of non-working governesses in the nursery; getting rid of promiscuous maids-in-waiting; increasing kitchen hygiene; making heating more efficient in the frigid apartments; and generally improving the palace economies and efficiencies. His fastidiousness knew no bounds. Biographer Lytton Strachey wondered: 'was he the wife, and she the husband? It almost seemed so.' Strachey believed that Albert was homosexual, yet it may have been wishful thinking for Strachey was of the same persuasion. The prince consort was, after all, siring the abundant royal children. The biographer and some others at court also seemed to confuse Albert's lack of engagement with the females in his immediate surrounds with his sexuality. But they were more likely to have been unconnected.

'From resembling a foreign tenor,' English author Michael Holroyd noted in the Foreword to a later illustrated edition of

Strachey's biography of the prince, 'Albert changes during the course of his marriage into an idealised butler.' Strachey's 'code' for Albert's sexuality began with him saying he was 'melancholic and isolated'. He noted also that he was 'a shy young foreigner, awkward in ladies' company, unexpansive and self-opinionated . . .it was improbable that, in any circumstances, he would have been a society success.'

Again, these observed traits did not necessarily have any bearing on his sexual inclinations. Strachey further remarked that Albert was 'utterly' severed from the 'support and solace of true companionship'. The prince excited idolatry, starting with his biggest fan, the young Victoria, who was mesmerised by his looks. The other young ladies and 'maids' at court agreed that he was handsome. But their infatuation died when he paid them no attention. Mild flirtation at least and something more intense were expected parts of court life, especially with the obsessive attention to dress and appearance in general. But Albert gave them nothing, not even a glance. The women of all ages were disenchanted yet his ignoring of them was more likely to have been because he found them trivial, uninteresting and inconsequential to his drive to expand the role of the monarchy. On top of this, he was unlikely to flirt with others because he was reverential towards his wife, who in any case, as a woman or queen or both, would not have appreciated any such dalliances, however harmless.

Those more remote from palace intrigues remained in star-struck admiration of Albert. But Strachey believed this fickle and unknowing public response did not meet Albert's emotional needs. According to the biographer, he had no friends to turn to. His German intimates and family were not allowed to join him. Looking for clues to his make-up, Strachey noted that Albert did not take after his womanising father.

'Owing either to his peculiar upbringing,' the biographer observed, 'or to a more fundamental idiosyncrasy, he had a marked distaste for the opposite sex.' Strachey was persuaded that 'though later on, he grew more successful in disguising such feelings, the feelings remained.' Once more, this was a generalisation too far. For one thing, he may well have had revulsion to his father's philandering with whores, whom a young Albert may well have despised. For another, Albert, had a good relationship with his mother-in-law, the Duchess of Kent, despite his wife's estrangement, and he would later be close to his daughters, particularly Vicky. And of course, he had an intense relationship with Victoria, regardless of their sex life, which together did not register that he found 'the opposite sex' in general as reprehensible.

When commenting on domesticity at Buckingham Palace, Strachey wrote: 'The husband was not so happy as the wife, in spite of the great improvement in his situation, in spite of a growing family and the adoration of Victoria, Albert was still a stranger in a strange land, and the serenity of spiritual satisfaction was denied him. . .Victoria idolised him, but it was understanding that he craved, not idolatry. . .He was lonely.'

Other observers noted that Albert tried all kinds of ways to avoid intimate contact. But the onslaught of Victoria's sexual needs, which appeared to him as carnal avarice, may well have had many others ducking for cover.

One night in mid-spring 1842 he ran out of excuses as Victoria knocked on his bedroom door. This was the third year of demands made intermittent by her reluctant acceptance of his explanation that Christians did not have sex with a pregnant woman. Albert's pious noises left the queen moody and begrudging because of his abstinence.

Albert this night cowered behind the door. She knew he was in his quarters and his silence was an attempt to bluff her into believing he was asleep at 10 p.m. But Victoria knew he worked with papers and books strewn on and around his bed. She knocked louder. Again there was no response.

'Albert, you can't be asleep at this hour.' She paused. 'Are you ill?' She hammered the wooden panels now.

'Open this door!' she screamed in German. 'I am the queen!'

'And I can't take it.' Albert thought. He waited, sitting on the floor until she sulked off back to her own room. The next morning he did not appear at breakfast and Victoria was genuinely concerned. Clark was sent for. On hearing that the doctor was on his way, Albert emerged looking pale and exhausted. He'd had no sleep.

'What on earth were you up to last night?' Victoria demanded. 'You must have heard my calling and knocking?'

'I had the most terrible headache.'

'But I am your wife. I can help . . .'

'I did not wish to burden you,' he said softly in German.

Clark arrived and insisted on seeing his patient alone in his bedchamber.

'I believe you have a headache,' Clark remarked with a sceptical look. There had been no love lost between them since the Lady Flora affair and Albert only used him as his physician because Victoria ordered it.

'I have a mixed powder for you,' Clark said sitting on a chair by the patient as he lay on the bed as if ill. Clark rustled in his satchel and handed him a small packet.

'What is it, Clark?'

'It is a wonderful Indian–Chinese analgesic combination. Never fails. I am my own experiment with it! Take this every day until it runs out.' He added with a sly grin, 'You will not disappoint or indeed be saddened yourself.' He winked at Albert. 'Nor will you have one of these miserable headaches.'

Albert managed to avoid Victoria's advances for a fortnight with her enquiring every night if he had recovered. When Clark pronounced him 'well', Victoria pounced. When she pressed him to fulfil her conjugal needs he relied on the 'medicine'. He wondered if it were a true aphrodisiac or a placebo. Whatever he concluded, he made sure he was never without it. And it worked in a way that answered Albert's prayers. Victoria was pregnant again. This gave him the excuse he craved and nearly a year's reprieve from her obsessive pursuit of sexual favours from him. Victoria enjoyed sex far more than its results but nevertheless produced a second daughter, Princess Alice, on 25 April 1843.

Once Elphinstone had attended to his financial affairs in Britain, he took a steamer back to the Bay of Bengal. He had written to Husna, hoping that she might return to India to be with him. She replied, saying that she had finished her para-medical course in Stockholm but this did not allow her to work as a doctor in France. She was now in Paris at Napoleon III's court looking after the horses at the hippodrome where she had become close to Céleste Vernard, a brilliant rider and courtesan of court, whom she had met through the English woman 'Lola

Mentez'—the theatrical name of the former Mrs James, who had left her Indian Army husband in search of 'adventure' as a high-class courtesan. Husna had no plans to return to India at that moment. But the last bit of her letter gave him a sliver of hope about a future with her. Husna had heard he was not attached to Victoria. She wondered how connected he was to England. Most importantly for Elphinstone, she intimated she missed him.

In May 1843 Elphinstone began touring and trekking in regions of India that had taken his interest during his tenure as Madras governor. He had built contacts with scholars, writers, journalists, orators, scientists and even religious and social reformers. All advised him where he should go and what he should see. He would start by hunting wild boar and hyenas in the jungles in Bengal. But he would concentrate on tigers, which were in abundance and often caused havoc among the local people. He had his sights on the biggest of them, after learning that some were nearly three metres in length and weighed more than 150 kilograms. After Bengal he planned to travel through the 'top' of India—Kashmir—regarded by many as the most beautiful area in the world. In the mid-nineteenth century it denoted the valley between the Great Himalayas and the Pir Panjal mountain range. Elphinstone was one of the very few Europeans, if not the first, to tackle this remote region. He also wished to see the Ganges Plain of North India (Hindustan). Elphinstone—the trekker, mountaineer and hunter—wanted to see for himself if these romantic and remote regions were indeed more enchanting than his home country.

His experience in England had not enticed him to think about returning. Elphinstone decided that if he were going to spend time away from his homeland, he would make the most of the trip both as an adventurer and investor. He believed his return was an opportunity to consolidate his wealth and he purchased sizeable estates in Ceylon (Sri Lanka) and India, which were available to members of the Raj at cheap rates. Elphinstone was unsure how long he would be away and did not care if it were a long time.

A fourth royal child, Prince Alfred ('Alfie') was born 6 August 1844. Victoria's euphemism for sex was 'fun' and she continued to demand it from her disenchanted husband. But with such rapid human production she was kept, if not barefoot and pregnant, then preoccupied by the increased population of the nursery. Albert, feigning as ever that 'fun' during the nine months gestation was a religious 'taboo', managed to continue to avoid more regular intimacy. This did not improve Victoria's moods, or modify their swings. But as long as he did the fatherly and family things with his wife and children, Victoria was mollified and essentially 'happy' while remaining unsatisfied. She believed that part of her role was to provide a good *Christian* family image and example to the nation.

While her desire for satisfaction was undiminished, she remained unimaginative in her attitude to sexual mores, which was typical of the times characterised by repression, strict morality and an indefatigable ignorance. An instance of this was a concerted move in parliament to legislate against lesbianism. She told Prime Minister Peel in her weekly meeting: 'I don't want this legislation to go through.'

An astonished Peel gaped.

'May I ask if your majesty is *for* such appalling activity?'

'Of course not,' she said with a fierce look. 'I believe the act is impossible!'

'The act?'

'Of these, you know, mythical lesbians.'

The prime minister was speechless. Victoria wriggled uncomfortably and filled the conversation's gap.

'I have consulted both the royal physician and Prince Albert on the matter,' she insisted, 'and they agree with me. And if this alleged vice is not physically possible, it would be absurd to introduce legislation to outlaw it. I and the prince do not wish to see such legislation discussed and aired and perhaps even reported on in the press. Would you not agree?'

Peel left the meeting under strict instructions. When he met with cabinet there was astonishment among its members.

'I'm afraid her majesty finds the whole business distasteful,' the prime minister reported.

'Which?' one cabinet member chimed in, 'the proposed legislation or lesbianism?'

'They say *no Sovereign was more loved* than I am,' Victoria boasted to Leopold after being cheered by big crowds in London streets when she was driven to open the Royal Exchange in late October 1844. But she was grounded in the reason. '[Our] *happy domestic home...*gives such a good example.'

Albert was also able to brag in a letter to Stockmar: 'Here, after four years, is the recognition of the position we took up from the first. You always said that if the Monarchy was to rise in popularity, it could only be by the Sovereign leading an exemplary life, and keeping quite aloof from and above party.'

This image-building with the children in public helped Victoria overcome her often manic lust. He busied himself with meetings on the arts and in acquiring a property on the Isle of Wight—Osborne—that was bought for £26,000. The money had come from Albert's economic drive and parsimony. They were also diverted by holidays in Scotland at Blair Athol, which they enjoyed, and further travels abroad, including to France on board their new yacht, the *Victoria and Albert*. Albert travelled alone for the first time since his marriage when his father, 59, the Duke of Saxe-Coburg died, leaving his older brother Ernest to rule the little duchy. Albert wept more for nostalgic reasons than over the departure of his father, whose womanising had broken the home and destroyed Albert's early childhood. The not-so-beloved Papa had used emotional blackmail and bullying in forcing Albert to ask Victoria for a big allowance. The duke was true to his character as a lecherous drunk; he had passed on hereditary syphilis to Ernest, which had left him impotent. Albert had not inherited the condition, which fuelled strong rumours that he was illegitimate. His mother had been dismissed from the Saxe-Coburg court for having an affair with the Jewish chamberlain, the cultivated Baron von Mayern. The incident and his father's behaviour had left Albert a disturbed five-year-old when his parents went their separate ways. He developed, in his looks and refined intellect, into a character very like von Mayern and at odds with that of the duke.

Albert had already moved on in his mind when he attended the duke's funeral. Steeped in the obsessive drive to create a royal dynasty, he was thinking about how his new son Prince Alfred would one day rule

Coburg. Ernest was never likely to produce a legitimate heir. Albert told him that little Alfie would be trained 'to love the dear small country to which he belongs, as does his Papa.' The Prince of Wales, Bertie, would be developed for something less modest: King of the British Empire. The bright princess royal, Vicky, aged four, was already being lined up for the heir to the King of Prussia, who was aged twelve. No likely match for little Alice had been found just yet, but both parents would keep scouring the limited pool for any potential partner.

18

TIME OUT AT OSBORNE

Elphinstone's adventures in India looked like ending in early 1845 but a flare-up in the country's north where Sikhs resisted British expansion caused him to stay. By the time he had travelled through the regions south and around the trouble-spots, the British were looking to settle the region down under as much of their imperial control as possible. Soon after the death of the one-eyed emperor, Maharajah Ranjit Singh, in 1839, the East India Company had begun building up its armed forces, mainly in the regions close to the Punjab. In 1844, the British had annexed Sindh, in the Punjab's south. They then established a military base just south of the Sutlej River at Ferozepur, 120 kilometres south of Lahore. This city marked the frontier between the British-ruled India and the Punjab. Elphinstone visited Ferozepur in February 1845. He was aware from discussions and correspondence with two associates—former Governor-General Lord Ellenborough and his successor, Sir Henry Hardinge—that they were concerned with Sikh power in the Punjab. They directed their military commanders to prepare siege-gun batteries, which could be used for defence or attack.

The British attitudes were influenced by Major George Broadfoot, who sent intelligence reports from the Punjab. His informants recorded the corruption in the Punjab court and the general mayhem in this last independent kingdom, which happened to be the richest with its store of grand diamonds. Many British officials wanted to annex the Punjab, which would give them complete control of India. They were held back by not having the manpower or resources to maintain the territories if they did move on them. But then diplomatic relations broke down between the Sikhs and the East India Company. The latter's army, commanded by Sir Hugh Gough, began marching towards Ferozepur. The force consisted of Bengal Army formations; one British unit to every three or four Bengal infantry or cavalry units.

At this point in September 1845, Elphinstone marched with the 14th Light Dragoons, which was commanded by Colonel William Havelock. He had been Elphinstone's military secretary in Madras. They moved from Bombay through central India to Ferozepur.

The Sikh army began crossing the Sutlej River on 11 December 1845 in response to the British activity and threat. A Sikh force clashed with the British, including the 14th Light Dragoons and Elphinstone, at the Battle of Mudki on 18 December. The British won. They continued to win until the main Sikh bridgehead at Sobraon on 10 February 1846. The Sikh forces fought stubbornly but were eventually surrounded and trapped. They would not surrender. The British showed no mercy in the final attack that broke the Sikh army.

The Treaty of Lahore on 9 March 1846 forced the Sikhs to surrender the valuable region between the Beas and Sutlej rivers. The Lahore Durbar (the court administrating the affairs of state) had to pay an indemnity of 15 million rupees, for which it could not find the funds. This in turn forced it to cede specific areas to the East India Company: Kashmir, Hazarah and all the forts, territories, rights and interests in the hill countries between the rivers Beas and Indus. This allowed Elphinstone to join a British trekking party, which explored the valley of Kashmir. He stayed three months, then set out for Ladakh via the Husora Valley. Elphinstone's aim was to move onto the Giljit Valley, which had never been explored by foreigners. The British governor-general objected, fearing the expedition would be lost. Elphinstone defied the authorities and crossed the Hurpo Pass to Rondu on the Indus River, 500 kilometres north-east of Lahore. He became the first Britisher to make the journey.

Elphinstone slipped back into London in October 1846 with hardly a notice in the papers. The life he had been leading in his 'conquering' of mountains and in countless villages and regions both explored and unexplored by his countrymen had etched itself into his countenance and physique. He was more tanned than ever and it accentuated his handsome features, which were now tinged with lines and ruggedness from his life outdoors. Elphinstone felt stronger, especially in the legs, after constant trekking, than even in his vigorous youth. The fever that had nearly killed him had been kept in check by his improved and impressive condition. No longer did the heat bother him as it did when he had had to retreat to the hills outside Madras. He wore a hat, but had learned to hydrate more and pace himself in the humidity and stifling summer months.

Elphinstone still loved Scotland but more as an idealised memory than somewhere he would live again. He had acclimatised and would seek a warmer clime either in his work in the future or in retirement. He believed that his decade of exile, imposed and later self-imposed, had been a blessing. He had encountered and explored a new, challenging country far beyond the world of English royal courts. The more than three-year trek through remote parts of India had been an exploration of his inner self. It changed him, he felt, into a more thoughtful, caring human being. Life in India had left deep impressions. Elphinstone was more conscious than ever of his privileged existence and work experiences first in the army, then in the royal palaces, as a colonial governor, as an army commander, and finally as an explorer and adventurer. Travelling without the trappings of luxury and power taught him different values. The capacity to share, selflessness, patience and perspective had been woven into his mentality. He had taken his religion for granted but, after being exposed to various sects and belief systems from Hinduism and Islam to Buddhism and Christianity, he had broadened his outlook. Elphinstone's thinking had been deepened; he had questioned his faith. After experiencing the work of missionaries he was ambivalent about their necessity, effectiveness or impact in a land with such diverse cultures and a multiplicity of religions. In 1846, Elphinstone wrote to Victoria that he felt virtue was not necessarily synonymous with just Christianity. The ancient Hindu books also had maxims about pure and sound morality, he told her, based on the nature of man as a rational and social being.

His own position as such a human being made him uncertain of what lay ahead for him in England. He would return to politics as both a Privy Councillor and as a peer in the Lords. But he was unsure beyond that.

Elphinstone had a private audience with Victoria a week after his return. He found her plumper now yet perhaps more 'comely'. The initial blushes of pubescent beauty had now slipped away forever. In its place was a less pretty but still sensual woman. With her authority had come the allure of power, which was an aphrodisiac for the holder and the beholder. Elphinstone was devoted in the dutiful sense to her as monarch, yet he still found she had a strong physical appeal. Despite his widened experiences in India with beguiling, fine-featured Indian women, his carnal knowledge of the queen still resonated in a raw, exciting way. But his feelings were far deeper than that. He was in his fortieth year and had never been as passionate about anyone else, except for Husna, whom he had not seen for five years. Because of this, and the prospect of renewed court contact with Victoria, it was doubtful now that he would ever marry and have a family. Elphinstone's heart belonged still to Victoria. It suited her too. She preferred her male and female courtiers to remain single while they were with her. She was against widowed ladies-in-waiting (or anyone else) marrying again. Victoria desired dedication. She hated anyone leaving her, and dreaded the thought of any of her children departing. She had hung on to Lehzen, even when it harmed her marriage; she was upset when the political system forced Melbourne and later Peel to depart from their daily routines of consultation and advice. Elphinstone being taken from her had caused her prolonged grief and yearning. Even Albert's short visit to Coburg for his father's funeral caused Victoria anxiety.

But in 1846, she was buoyed by 'arrivals', first of her latest child, Helena, on 26 May and five months later the re-emergence of Elphinstone.

'I want you in the court,' she told him, hardly repressing her delight.

'I hope Albert will be comfortable with it.'

'Albert is preoccupied with his work. He would not care. In fact, he approves of my friendships with others.'

'When do you think I might join the court?'

'In the new year. I will find a good position similar to the one you held with my uncle.'

'I was his lord of the bedchamber—his close friend, dining companion and even his dresser.'

'Exactly, my lord.'

Elphinstone had gifts for her. This time a painting of the Himalayas, and a stunning pendant, a miniature dagger with a diamond embedded in its handle. She loved them both, especially the pendant.

'I love jewels!' she said, 'especially from India. This will be a wonderful addition to my collection.' She examined it and added: 'The Hanoverians had to adorn their crowns for special occasions, such as coronations, with items hired from *commercial* jewellers. Much nicer, I say, to build up one's own collection. My hunger for such adornments, my dear Lord, knows no boundaries!'

'I discovered it on my trek . . .' he began.

'I am unconcerned how it was acquired, just as long as it is presented to me. My Lord, I shall gratefully accept any gift from you! All your letters from India are enough! Those sketches of yours of those wonderful people, their faces, their cities and lands! How I love them!'

Elphinstone smiled.

'I had no idea of their true impact,' he said. 'I just thought your thank-yous were you being your polite and gracious self.'

'Oh, no! You created a fascinating realism. Because of you, India has become one's obsession.'

'You must travel there. It is the most beautiful country in the empire.'

Victoria reversed Elphinstone's banishment from the royal court. She informed the diminutive 54-year-old prime minister John Russell, who succeeded Peel, of her 'request'. It was a little over a decade since those dreaded days when she was a helpless princess and young queen, who had no power. Prime ministers and cabinets had officially to approve all such appointments, but every so often the young monarch would assert her prerogative. Elphinstone was made lord-in-waiting, a different role from the one he had occupied in the court of William IV. This time, in line with his experience and maturity, he would be the whip in the House of Lords, which would give him responsibility for organising responses to legislation passed to it from the Commons. Elphinstone would also report on the Lords' initiatives, reviews and decisions on appeals to it. He would be Victoria's official link to the upper chamber. In this era, the House of Lords was more vital to government operations than the Commons, and he paid attention to its machinations. Elphinstone would be taking up some elements of the job he had as lord of the bedchamber to William IV, such as escorting and looking after political and state leaders on British visits. Again, he would serve as a confidant, close friend and protector of the monarch.

Elphinstone began work early in January 1847. Late in June 1847, when summer was settling with warm promise on a sceptical England after a particularly cold winter and spring, Victoria decided on a last-minute visit to the Isle of Wight. She was keen to visit her house there for sentimental reasons before another of Albert's designs was implemented. He wished to create a grand Italian Renaissance palazzo, which meant tearing down the existing three-level Georgian structure. Victoria also wished to avoid the noise of builder Tommy Cubbitt, who was putting up a new facade at Buckingham Palace before he moved to the Isle of Wight to make more noise. Albert would not be there. He was visiting Cambridge. Victoria did not wish to be lonely, despite her entourage, so she invited Elphinstone.

He accepted the offer and travelled alone by train, boat and carriage to the Isle of Wight, much to the surprise of Victoria.

'What, no valet?' she said, greeting Elphinstone when he arrived at the house in the evening carrying his own bags. They did not embrace. He shook hands with her.

'Your majesty,' he said, as servants flitted in and out of the drawing room, 'I have become used to carrying at least some of my own luggage here and there on those long Indian treks.'

Victoria clapped hands. A servant appeared. He hustled away with Elphinstone's suitcases to a room set aside on the second floor of the house. Victoria had the top level to herself. Guests stayed on the first two floors and courtiers and servants in the basement and a cottage in the grounds. She offered Elphinstone a drink. He asked for a whisky and water.

'Come,' she said, 'I want to show you this beautiful place, which my husband and his wreckers are going to smash down in a few weeks.'

On the top level, which held her five-room private quarters, Victoria led him to a window in a library and asked him to look down. She pointed to a rickety outside stair.

'This place is so old there has always been a risk of fire,' she said, 'and we've had a couple of nasty episodes in the kitchen. Have to show all the guests the fire escape. It goes from the roof to the ground.'

Elphinstone nodded absentmindedly. He followed her down the sweeping inside staircase to a front portico, to watch the fine sunset. It was warm. Victoria waved a hand at the excavations that ran from in front of the portico for about 200 metres.

'Ugly, isn't it?' Victoria observed. 'I know Albert has a wonderful vision and it will all be special and impressive. But I have loved the ordinariness and seclusion of it.' She sipped her drink. 'Sometimes I hate change.'

'I am sure the prince will make it a change for the good and you'll love it.'

'It is in part my vision too,' she said, 'but I could have waited for a year or two.'

'That water is enticing,' Elphinstone said, squinting into the distance above the trees to the clear blue Solent, the strait that separated the Isle of Wight from the British mainland. 'I want to swim. Need the exercise. Is the beach good?'

'What? Now?'

'Won't be in long.'

'You Scots are all the same, utterly uninhibited.' She reflected a moment and smiled. 'That's why I adore the Highlanders. They say and do what comes naturally.'

A maid hovered, wanting to know if they needed more drink or food.

'No, Jennifer,' Victoria said, 'just a robe for the Lord. You'll find one in his room. He wants to go swimming. Silly, isn't he?'

Victoria and Elphinstone strolled to the beach. Two young ladies-in-waiting followed at a discreet distance.

The sun seemed to be drowning in a rippling dark pool as they passed a quaint stone alcove about 50 metres from the beach.

'That's where I thought you might like to sketch,' she said, pointing. 'I do it every time I visit. Love it! The view is exquisite.'

Elphinstone nodded.

'You said you had good stables on the island. . .?'

'Oh, we have!' Victoria said. 'I was hoping to ride the beach and the fields.'

They glanced at each other and smiled. They were both thinking of the past when they could escape the confines of the palaces on long, private rides. After walking about 300 metres, Elphinstone turned his back and took off his robe. He walked into the water and began to swim.

After about ten minutes, he waded back to the rough sand-pebble beach.

'You've looked after yourself,' she said, watching as he towelled down.

He shook his hair, wrapped the towel around him and sat beside her on the beach.

'Tell me Elphi, truly. Did you fall in love with anyone after that French-Indian woman?'

He considered her for a moment.

'Does it matter?' he asked.

'I just want you to be happy. After what happened to both of us we both should have rewards.'

They began to make their way back, with the ladies falling in behind them once more.

'I must say, my lord John, it is very pleasing for me in so many ways to have you in my court, where you always belonged.'

Elphinstone bowed low.

'My sentiments entirely, your majesty.'

'Seeing you this way is a sweet triumph for me. Now, I can have your company whenever I choose. Whereas before . . .'

He nodded his agreement.

'I must tell you,' she said, looking around at the ladies, who were closer, and lowering her voice, 'it gives me a modest sense of *power*. I just *told* Russell what I wanted. In politics, as you know, my influence is circumscribed by parliament, my ministers and councillors.' She paused to glance at him, 'Councillors like your good self.'

'I've observed your struggle, majesty,' Elphinstone remarked. 'It is much tougher for you than for your predecessor.'

'Quite. But it is deeper than simply my powers as opposed to that of the political system. From the beginning the duchess, Conroy and Stockmar contrived with Melbourne to thwart and steer my relationships with almost *everyone*.' Victoria glanced at him. 'Now no-one can tell me whom to see or not to see. My only boundaries are discretion, common sense and the necessity to keep up the appearance of having a strong, working marriage—which it is.'

'May I observe, your majesty, that if it had not been for you, the monarchy as an institution would have been in danger, even ended. You are so admired and respected. The monarchy is safe while you and Prince Albert present the image you have.'

Victoria beamed and after a short while said: 'The Battenbergs are coming this evening. They'll dine and stay the night. They'll be in the guest suite on the ground floor.'

'Don't think I've had the pleasure.'

'Oh, they're great fun. You'll like them: witty, well-informed and fine conversationalists—Prince Alexander of Hesse, and Julia, the sister-in-law of Grand Duke Louis. She is ravishing! You won't take your eyes of her.'

19

BERTIE
BELEAGUERED

Albert was doing everything right for the monarchy. He was elected chancellor of Cambridge University in 1847. Predictably, he did not take it as an honorary role by letting others do the thinking and planning. He was soon working on a study program that would progress the ancient institution faster than at any time since its inception in 1226. Showing exceptional perspicacity for a 27-year-old, he suggested that too much emphasis was being placed on the classics and mathematics. He urged more application to political economy, psychology, geography, chemistry and astronomy. He was opposed by a vice chancellor who did not believe that new scientific discoveries should be introduced to the university for a *century*. The thinking was that innovations had to be tested over time before they were accepted. Albert disagreed. He invited the backward-thinking vice chancellor to Windsor for a discussion in which Albert put his case with conviction. The academic went away considering the prince's suggestions seriously. Later, Albert's ideas became part of a reform at Cambridge that saw extended fields of studies and opportunities for a wide range of degrees. The vice chancellor admitted that Albert's chancellery had brought 'a new and glorious era' in academic history. Considering Cambridge was then 621 years old, this was quite an accolade. Even *The Times,* which had been stinting in its praise of Albert, was effusive. It editorialised that the nation owed him a debt of gratitude because he had been the first to suggest, and then the most determined, to carry out the changes.

Albert was becoming an outstanding facilitator and conciliator. He had been working on a rapprochement between his wife and mother-in-law. After more than seven years he had resolved many of their differences and misunderstandings. They could never be very close again but thanks to his efforts they were at ease with each other and looked forward to being in each other's company, more or less like any similar relationship that had had its periods of estrangement. He may have struggled for empathy with women, but he knew aspects of the psychology of human beings, instinctively and in his assessment of people. He put it into practice to positive effect.

Albert was not quite as successful in handling young Bertie, the Prince of Wales, and his education. The boy suffered from not being as bright as his older sister. Tutors struggled to illicit a willingness to learn, although he had an amiable character. It was tough early for Bertie, who turned six in 1847. Expectations were far too high for one so young. It did not help that Stockmar informed his parents that their position 'was a more difficult one than that [faced by] any other parents in the kingdom'. Stockmar, it seemed, was not taking into account the difficulties *for the child.* His remarks put pressure on Victoria and Albert to urge Bertie to do better. The boy had a good demeanour and he wanted to please. Tutors were arranged for Bertie. But they pushed him too much, believing that he *must* learn and perform in all subjects. At Albert's instigation, he was to be punished if he did not study hard and progress. Victoria objected to this, especially over Bertie's indifference to learning the Bible. The first tutor had the unfortunate name in the circumstances of Mr Birch. Bertie become emotionally attached to him but Birch was dismissed mysteriously, paid off with an income and sent to Lancashire. His replacement, Fred Gibbs, was more concerned with pleasing the father than the boy. Bertie was upset that the first tutor had been taken from him. He didn't like Gibbs and, if riled by him, pelted him with sticks and stones.

When things settled down, the tutor had the difficult task of explaining to the child that he would one day become king. Bertie found it hard to grasp. He had an older sibling. Why wouldn't she become the monarch? After all, his mother was queen. Bertie asked Victoria about this apparent conundrum. It was left to her to explain the intricacies and irrationality of males taking precedence over females. Bertie was confused. His elder sister Vicky dominated the little boy and he found it hard to imagine that he would one day be in a superior position to her.

Bertie might have decades to come to terms with a future he did not necessarily want. His father's approach had too much of the mechanical 'information in, information out' mentality. There was no manual for bringing up any child let alone a prince, and typically Albert was putting his mind on it *his* way. But his 'plan', as Victoria called it, did not allow for fun, a sense of independence, or any right for the child to do what his heart desired. There was no chance for a roll in the mud in the horse stables, or for running off into the fields or woods with friends to experience a sense of freedom. Albert and his tutors pummelled him with God and Christ, morality and responsibility. Life was blocked out as 'good and righteous' or 'bad and sinful'. But Bertie could never muster his father's self-righteous, god-fearing disciplines. He was more like his mother, who disliked the over-pious and was sceptical about the hierarchies of all religions. She had been bred to have a visceral hate for Catholics but disliked them being persecuted and restricted. In private she expressed a greater distaste for Protestants. If Bertie were to develop like his mother, he would be more 'of the flesh' and all its human strengths and weaknesses. If so, his overbearing father was pushing his son's carefree Hanoverian spirit in an unnatural direction. It was a recipe for eventual rebellion.

Bertie was taken to the magnificent Great Exhibition, the brainchild of his inspired father. It was a 'festival of work and peace' housed in the Crystal Palace, a domed building of glass designed by Joseph Paxton, the creator of Chatsworth conservatory. An amazing and wide-ranging number of works of art, invention, engineering and architecture were on display. Bertie was mesmerised by many things he saw. He raved about waxwork models of 'the murderous thugs of India'. He wrote with enthusiasm about them in his diary, which his father, and sometimes Stockmar, read to make sure his mind was on a pure, pristine track. The adults were shocked that, despite all their guidance, urging and reinforcement, his thoughts were deviating so 'alarmingly'. Stockmar reminded the little lad that he had been 'born in a Christian and an enlightened age in which such atrocities are not even dreamt of'. Bertie was *made* to feel guilt for the excitement he felt about the vigorous, tough-looking Indian brutes. He was left in anguish and confusion.

Bertie craved friends his own age, but had none. If he had been sent to Eton or Harrow he would have had classmates to play with every day. Albert tried to address this by inviting young Etonian sons of peers to tea on Sunday. But he always supervised the event. The young boys were intimidated by the rigid husband of the queen. It was not the environment for boys to be boys, especially when a parent with a holier-than-thou attitude was standing over them inspiring nothing but nervousness, even dread. This experiment failed too. Bertie was left disgruntled, resentful and friendless.

20

CAVIAR AND CONVERSATION

Albert needed all his developing diplomatic skills and more in 1848 to meet the tide of insurrection surging over Europe. Sensitivities to privilege, class and wealth were peaking with revolution in France where the monarchy was overthrown. King Louis Philippe and his wife had escaped from the Tuileries by the back door. They were forced into exile in England. The Austrian chancellor, Prince Metternich, 74, had lived for decades in fear of upheaval. He made a rushed exit from his country and also ended up in England. Royal families everywhere felt threatened. The ideas of a radical German economist, Karl Marx, were spreading. There was ferment and revolution in the kingdoms of Hanover, Bavaria, Naples and Prussia. Countless small duchies (including Schleswig, Holstein and Leiningen) were under pressure. Even tiny Coburg and Gotha were in danger. Ireland was in a rebellious mood. Terrible poverty had been brought on by a potato famine made worse by insensitive landlords evicting tenants. Irish activists were talking civil war as their country's population dropped alarmingly due to starvation and a mass exodus to the United States. Just three countries seemed to be holding firm against this tidal wave of change: England, King Leopold's Belgium and the tsar's Russia. But there were no guarantees of survival. In Russia, the tsar was a despot, repressing his people and any opposition. In England, Victoria and Albert were taking no chances of bitterness being incited against them. They would be seen to be doing the *right thing* at every opportunity. When wheat was in such short supply that only the rich could afford it, Victoria reduced the royal kitchen to making a half-kilogram of bread a day and decreed that only secondary flour was to be used.

Her world was being tipped upside down. So-called 'Chartists' in England were making six major demands: a vote in elections for every male aged 21; the right to a secret vote; the right for those without property to be elected to parliament; payment for members of parliament (making democratic representation semi-professional at least and attractive to all levels of society); equal electoral districts; and annual elections. These points marked a watershed in British history as six million signatures were gained in support of them and presented to parliament after a huge meeting on London's Kennington Common. The Chartists had formed due to a confluence of working-class grievances beginning with the Reform Bill crisis of 1831–32, when the middle class, but *not* the working class, could join the parliament. Chartism was a national movement. It was strong in the textile towns of Lancashire and Yorkshire. It had solid support in the East Midlands and the Black Country.

Victoria's concern about these changes slipped over into the chatter at lunches and especially at longer dinner engagements on a Friday at Buckingham Palace. One such night in February 1848, when heavily pregnant, she entertained eighteen guests, including Elphinstone and an ailing 69-year-old Lord Melbourne. Elphinstone was seated opposite her at a long dining table decorated with large, low vases of red geraniums and a vast silver candelabra. Gloved footmen served an eleven-course dinner, beginning with light *caviar de starlet*.

Discussion turned to the ungratefulness of an unsympathetic press, who seemed to the royal court to be giving too much store to the views of rebels and republicans at the expense of those of the establishment. Victoria was baffled by the lack of appreciation of her own sentiments about those less privileged than her.

'When a young girl,' she said with a fleeting glance at Elphinstone, 'I saw all those sad workers in shocking conditions in towns in the north. I've worried about them ever since.'

'You've never really overcome the substantial differences between the establishment and the lot of many of your poor subjects,' Melbourne said with a soft, wheezing voice. 'Have you, majesty?'

'At that time, you disabused me of any compassionate views about those not so well off,' Victoria said indignantly.

'I always believed,' Melbourne began with a cough, 'it was better for you to remain ignorant of the pain and suffering of others, especially if they were unworthy—rebels, troublemakers, Irish and so on.'

'But I have not, my lord,' Victoria replied, 'I feel for certain cases I have read about. I don't like gypsies being abused. I *hate* dwarfs performing at circuses.'

That remark caused the guests to fall silent. Everyone was aware of her feeling of inferiority over her height

'With respect, ma'am,' Lady Saddrington, interrupted, 'you have always sympathised with the widows of workers—men who have been killed at palace work sites.' The beautiful young widow understood this as no other guests did; her husband, a fine architect, had been killed while working at Windsor.

'Thank you, Lady Saddrington,' Victoria said with a sweet nod and smile.

These were individual cases at which Victoria would suck in her breath or be irritated over, but then she would move on. She also reacted to the suffering brought on by the Irish famine that was 'too terrible to think of'. She was upset at the prospect of the cost-cutting achieved by mass burials without clergy. In a previous era this reaction by a monarch with her sensitivities could have achieved something. But a frustrating sense of impotence drove her thoughts.

'In the midst of all this,' she told the other attentive guests, 'the landlords appropriate the people's corn! After all we have done to supply the needy with food! God alone can bring help, for no human means seem able!'

Elphinstone, with his more enlightened religious views, had layered her thinking beyond dependence on a deity's whim. He smiled slightly when she remarked about the Irish famine: 'How stupid of the Church to call for a day of fasting to help God intervene over it, when man's intervention with a day of *feeding* would have helped the Irish a fraction more.'

'Old Testament superstition,' Elphinstone said.

'Yes, out of date,' Victoria agreed. 'I am sceptical of preachers telling us that the famine is a result of collective Irish sinfulness.'

Despite these observations, which were a measure of her compassion, she refused to believe that protesting workmen had arguments of any merit. She stood fast in thinking they had been misled by professional agitators and the 'criminals and refuse of London.' Victoria had stooped to tokenism, having the odd group of wives from poor areas visit the palace for tea. This appeased on the surface any sense of guilt she may have had from not recognising an under-class and the dispossessed.

Discussion turned to the introduction into parliament of the Ten Hour Bill by Lord Ashley (later Lord Shaftsbury).

'It demonstrates Ashley has a strong sense of *noblesse oblige*,' Elphinstone remarked, 'He wants to limit the hours of workers in factories and mills, many of them children. I congratulate him.'

'Well I am against it,' Victoria said.

'Why, majesty?' Elphinstone asked.

'Because it would deprive industry of seven weeks' child-power a year.'

'Is that not trivial, compared to compassion for children being used as slave labour?'

'Trivial? No. The Bill will weaken England's competitive foreign trade position, and then more people are thrown out of work than ever.'

'But, majesty,' Elphinstone said gently, 'such lack of sensitivity over workplace iniquities from the business and industrial establishment, and the government, is clearly linked to growing unrest in the country.'

Everyone else fell silent again. No-one, with the possible exception of Albert, dared contradict Victoria this way.

'Majesty,' Albert chimed in, 'I too am surprised by your attitude. You have mentioned many times to me how appalled you were at fifteen about the shocking working conditions of iron foundry workers in the north. Surely this Bill is a step towards changing such problems?'

'I am not sure about that,' she said, 'but I am haunted by Buckingham Palace being overrun as the French royal family's home has been.' Victoria looked as if she might cry. 'I fear for you and my children. I am afraid for everyone at court. A revolution would see my family in trouble as a symbol of the establishment. The monarchy might well be obliterated.'

'That will not happen, majesty,' Elphinstone said, 'especially if the crown is seen to be ready to accept progress.'

21

ON A HIGH WITH THE HIGHLANDERS

Victoria's concerns over emerging revolutionaries did not put a brake on her fecundity. A little over a year after Helena's birth, she was pregnant again. On 18 March 1848 and when the ferment of revolt was brewing in cities across the country, Victoria gave birth to Princess Louise. She was the biggest baby yet with a very white skin, which set her apart from the other five. It was once more a physical and mental ordeal for Victoria, whose nerves were on edge as she worried over trouble outside the palace walls. She seemed to have been in a state of perpetual pregnancy or recovery from it for approaching a decade. Not quite 29 years of age, the queen was resigned to her fate of child-bearing and the pain and hormonal disruption associated with it. Yet perhaps through her stoicism at this dangerous time she was having a perverse pleasure in the experience, despite her earlier revulsion. (There was always the sex itself, which she never tired off. If anything she was hungrier now than when she had first met Elphinstone.) While the country was shaken by feverish revolutionary demands, Victoria was rocking a cradle once more, or at least directing that a governess do it.

Zealots might be at the palace gates demonstrating, but the queen was preoccupied in propagating the 'Royal Species'. Would-be republicans permitting, they would 'rule' Europe.

Those around the queen, including Albert and the prime minister, did not help her demeanour by suggesting that she decamp to Osborne House, two days before the biggest Chartists' rally ever in London. Elphinstone was consulted. He thought it wiser to stay at 'home' at Buckingham Palace. He had already mustered a praetorian guard of sorts made up of friends from his military days and in the Horse Guards. They were close to the palace and would surround it if necessary to aid the police force. Elphinstone placed artillery in strategic spots on bridges and in the royal stables. He was the most unconcerned of court members and more than once in correspondence remarked that in most instances of crises there was 'nothing to fear but fear itself'. His experiences in India had taught him this. But his advice to the royal court was ignored after it was learned that Lord Malmesbury on his country estate had armed five of his gamekeepers with double-barrelled guns. Other establishment figures were doing similar things. The queen and the palace might well become the focus for an act of insurrection. If that were the case, no amount of artillery and guns would hold a mob that could number hundreds of thousands.

The royal family retreated to the Isle of Wight. Not long afterwards the threat of revolution subsided. The Chartists were prevented from rallying. Instead their leaders walked alongside three cabs carrying the petition with its multi-million signatures to the parliament. There was no major riot. Rallies were peaceful. The 'fortressing' of parliament, government buildings and palaces in London had proved unnecessary, although some believed it had acted as a curb on any thoughts of violence.

A challenge to the monarchy of another kind emerged in the form of Victoria's foreign secretary, the inimitable Irish-born Lord Palmerston, now 65 years old. There were clashes on how to handle political problems in Europe. Victoria, with Albert increasingly more than her mouthpiece, had differing views on how the carve-ups of new and old states should be handled. They saw it through the prisms of royal connections and relatives, to whom they wished to remain loyal. Palmerston viewed everything in terms of the might and power of Great Britain and its empire. The two positions were increasingly incompatible. On 20 August 1848, Victoria protested to him that a private letter addressed to her had been opened at the Foreign Office. She wrote to Palmerston with the same reverence to herself that she expected from everyone, particularly him: 'The queen wishes Lord Palmerston to take care that this does not happen again.'

But Palmerston wasn't listening. He offered to mediate in a dispute between Austria and Sardinia. It was declined by Austria, but Victoria was annoyed that he did not tell her of his offer. She protested again in a letter: 'The queen is surprised that Lord Palmerston should have left her uninformed of so important an event.'

Albert was providing most of the thoughts in this tetchy correspondence as he and Victoria fought to hold vestiges of power for the monarchy, which would struggle to keep up with someone as autocratic (as seen from the palace) as Palmerston. He continued to act without her consent and this caused the royal couple much angst. Victoria wanted him dismissed. Prime Minister Russell resisted.

Victoria and Albert felt that disturbing events abroad and several incidents at home were causing strains that could be avoided by finding a hideaway. There had been more shocks from would-be assassins, or more correctly unstable individuals waving bulletless, home-made guns. Albert had tidied up Windsor Castle, creating a model farm and a dairy embellished like a church with stained glass windows, only to see it invaded by a gang of bold youths who stole a royal sketchbook. The Isle of Wight was not easily accessible and the climate was not always good. Brighton was rather too 'popular' for Victoria's liking. She felt 'invaded' there. Elphinstone suggested they discover Balmoral. It was isolated and beautiful. Dr Clark endorsed this, mainly because of the plentiful fresh air. The royal court decided to visit there after Victoria and Albert made their first trip to Ireland in August 1849.

A happy, drunk George IV had been the last monarch to visit that parlous country 28 years earlier. Victoria was not prepared to become inebriated on the visit to overcome her dread of the place. Despite her earlier studies with Lehzen, she seemed prejudiced against the Irish more from ignorance than reason but Albert was more understanding. He comprehended some of the reasons for Ireland's 'misery and criminality' and was proffering ideas for reform to help the country recover.

Victoria's dread was unfounded. They ended up enjoying the stay and believed they had broken down the barrier between the Irish and themselves. They left for Scotland in a good mood, Albert in particular needing a break. He had lost the energy and looks that a decade earlier had seen his wife describe him as 'beautiful'. His diligence in attending to issues, from great affairs of state to changing the awful Buckingham Palace toilet system above the royal bedchamber, had taken its toll. Albert had spent too much time hunched over his desk, planning and creating. He attended endless meetings. He worked over breakfast and three-course lunches. There was a formal dinner most nights, in which he indulged in four courses and a large daily intake of alcohol. This over-imbibing and overeating was due to a lack of discipline and was brought on by nerves and tension. Albert made no time for serious exercise. He still rode a horse, but once a month instead of every few days. His lean frame had become fat, especially around the hips and stomach. His hirsute cheeks were puffy.

At 30 the prince consort looked 40, and a plump 40 at that. In the context of the era his condition was not unusual. Paunches, especially on statesmen, were admired; potbellies were physical evidence that the individual was prosperous as opposed to the lean look of those who could not afford to eat well. Smoking was also popular and assisting in keeping life expectancy for the average middle- and upper-class male to around 53. Author Michael Holyrood observed that through the course of the royal marriage Albert had 'adapted himself body and soul to the role of the prince consort'. He sacrificed what was 'original in his character to become the caricature of a worthy man'. Victoria, more for her energy, drive and position after a hectic decade, had 'the ascendency' over her husband.

'Besides Victoria, he presented a painful contrast,' biographer Strachey observed. 'If only, by some sympathetic magic, she could have conveyed into that portly, flabby figure, that desiccated and discouraged brain, a measure of the stamina and the self-assurance which were so pre-eminently hers!'

Clark had recommended for Albert a simple, balanced diet, which next to his obsession about fresh air was paramount in his prescriptions for good health. Albert, the most disciplined of people in most walks of life, especially the moral and spiritual, ignored the medical recommendation and worked even harder on his ideas, big and small. One concept among many that he was dwelling on concerned workhouses—repositories of the poor, down-and-out and unemployed—where a great number of the inmates were old servants. He wanted men and women in domestic service to be protected from the whims of a single capricious master who might give the servant a bad reference. Albert planned a meeting of 'worthies' from business and government to aid all servants. They would guide them on gaining annuity schemes (early forms of superannuation and pensions) and other measures to improve their lives.

Lord Melbourne died on 24 November 1848. Albert showed little reaction to this after feeling that the former prime minister had stood between him and his wife early in their marriage. When Victoria mourned the man she had once had a crush on, Albert was scathing: 'His aristocratic hauteur was suited more to the old regency days.'

'Maybe,' Victoria retorted, 'but he was so helpful to me. And he was a charming dinner companion.'

'Not for me. And frankly he was a poor adviser to you on the economic conditions in the nation.'

Balmoral Castle became the royal destination. It was small compared to others, but it was adequate with its four quaint towers, granite walls, slit windows and high, pitched roof. Albert and Victoria were enchanted with the place and its people, the craggy outlooks and, most of all, the feeling that they were away from prying eyes in this remote paradise. The family went on hunting expeditions: the queen and her brood on ponies, while Albert joined the Highlanders ahead of them, stalking deer. They transformed from a German to a Scottish clan with ease and enthusiasm. Albert, true to form, attempted to conquer the language, buying a huge Gaelic dictionary and learning 30 words a day. Victoria, following her natural instincts too, tried to learn Scottish dancing.

'How am I doing?' she asked her instructor, who had come to the castle for special tuition.

'Put it this way, dearie,' he responded, 'you clearly and admirably go by the local dictum that "if it is worth doing, it is worth doing badly".'

'Oh, really?' Victoria said, 'you'll have to show me how to improve.'

'You could start by being gentle. Try, my dearie, to dance like a lady.'

Victoria did not take offence. There was no kowtowing by the Scots. To her, they were all like Elphinstone at base: 'never vulgar, never taking liberties, but so intelligent, modest and well-bred.' They showed respect and kept their distance. But when they did comment, it was always with humour.

Later, over dinner with Albert, who had his dictionary at the table, she remarked: 'The Highlanders all seem to have a cheery outlook. They never appear dreary like the English, or maudlin like the Irish. I don't find in them the stiffness and formality of the Germans, the frivolity of the French, or the dullness of the Dutch. The Scots seem to calibrate their mentality just about right, at least for me.'

'You've been conditioned to a degree to the Highland attitude by knowing Clark.'

'Not only him,' she said, knowing her husband's ambivalence and at times loathing for her physician. She would have had the chivalrous Elphinstone in mind.

'I sometimes wonder if I have Highlander blood,' she said.

Alfred nodded absent-mindedly, his face buried in the dictionary.

Balmoral became the most popular retreat for Victoria. The rustic idyll was conducive to her favourite leisure pursuits, including quality time with the children, and she recorded the happy, romantic atmosphere in her journal. She joyfully became more Scottish, stalking deer, eating bannock and attempting to comprehend everything the locals said in their delectable but often unintelligible brogue. She became fond of some of the Highlanders. One of them, a strapping young man with an insouciant manner, which she would not have put up with in someone at Buckingham Palace, attracted the 30-year-old queen. She mentioned him in her journal as 'young J [John] Brown' on 11 September 1849, just as she was informed she was pregnant again. Clark was more confident in his diagnosis, having attended to her so often in this condition.

Albert seemed to be feeling the cost of his expanding family. After William IV's widow, Queen Adelaide, died in December, Albert had his eyes on her annuity of £100,000 and wanted half of it at least to come his way. He wrote two long letters in this pregnancy period to Russell in which he begged for an increase in his annuity from £30,000 to £80,000. Russell had no desire to face the Commons over this. He advised Albert to be patient, especially as the fine print of his claim expressed a desire for 'the ordinary establishment and pursuits of an English gentleman'. These included 'a Hunting Establishment, a pack of Hounds, a breeding Stud, Shooting establishment, a Moor or Forest in the Highlands of Scotland, and a farm'. Russell's rejection of this saved Albert from himself after a decade of achievement in building up goodwill for him and Victoria. The consort had in mind taking advantage of the 1800 *Crown Private Estates Act* that allowed Victoria to behave like a private person and acquire property. But he would be doing it with public money.

Victoria was not troubled when she gave birth to Arthur on 1 May 1850. Clark noted with relief that her demeanour was the best he had ever experienced. Instead of railing against her fate, she was accepting and even tempered. Much of this may have been due to the surrounds when this familiar nine-month journey began. There was no tension, only freshness in the Scottish air outside and inside this more modest palatial abode.

Peace began to break out in most of the troubled countries of Europe. In nearly all cases, existing regimes managed to crush the rebellions and attempts to change them. Louis Napoleon, nephew to Napoleon Bonaparte, had emerged triumphant from the revolution and had been elected president of France. Victoria and Albert gave him their tacit approval once there was evidence that Napoleon was doing his best to bring stability to his country. The Pope was a temporary 'casualty' of the upheaval. He had fled Rome and was for a time a fugitive in Gaeta, central Italy. Prussia and Austria were still coming to terms with their problems as rebellion simmered. Albert showed his deeper allegiances by advocating, in a 'violent and incorrigible' manner, a German unionism. He insisted on 'a new German Empire', with the King of Prussia as its head. These views were not appreciated by prominent British leaders but Victoria did not intervene as he expressed these controversial comments.

Britain itself was tranquil. The public and government focus had turned to India where Sikhs in the Punjab were rising against colonial rule. Hundreds of officers and men had been killed since war began in 1848. Victoria, with her Elphinstone-inspired attachment to *her* exotic outpost, fretted with the families of army personnel stationed there. In January 1849 at the Battle of Chilianwala, the Sikhs were declared the unofficial winners based on the huge number of losses in the Anglo-Indian or British-controlled mixed army of Indians and British. There was more slaughter at Gujrat on 14 March. This time the Sikhs' large number of casualties saw them viewed as the losers. They were pursued for 160 kilometres to Rawalpindi where they surrendered. In an effort to prevent any future uprisings in the region, the British paid off the most compelling and determined young maharajah, Dhuleep Singh, with £50,000. He was settled in Norfolk where he was encouraged to live the life of a country gentleman. The Punjab was then annexed by the East India Company. Victoria was given the maharajah's magnificent diamond, the Koh-i-Noor, soon after Arthur's birth. She adored the 'gift' more than anything else in her possession but showed it off in private only. Elphinstone understood better than anyone else that it was a contentious acquisition. He advised her not to wear it in the presence of Indians, especially proud princes.

2 2

PEEL AND WELLINGTON: IN TRANSITION

On 27 June 1850, Victoria was leaving Cambridge House in her carriage when a man leapt forward and struck her in the face with his cane. The assailant was set upon by a crowd, but it was a shock in several ways. The individual, Robert Pate, was an experienced army officer in the 10th Hussars, and was also a dandy. These were two species of Englishman expected to show allegiance to her majesty. It was less than two months after she had given birth and she was just about fit again when the incident happened, leaving her with 'brown and green' bruises, which would become scars on her neck.

Advisors suggested that she not go to the opera that evening. But again she ignored them, saying: 'If I do not go, it will be thought that I am seriously hurt.'

The plucky Victoria was hurt more a few days later when it was learned that Sir Robert Peel had been thrown from his horse and seriously injured. He died on 2 July. Victoria was more concerned about her husband's reaction to the death of a man for whom they had such high regard. Albert saw Peel as a second father or, more pertinently, the most important senior influence on him. Peel had been a mentor and had encouraged the social consciences of Victoria and Albert with such advances as the *Mines Act 1842*, which began the regulation of an industry that had seen men treated as badly as pack-animals; the reintroduction of income tax; the *Factory Act* of 1844, which had a similar intent and impact to that of the *Mines Act*; the repeal of the Corn Laws, which had been triggered by the Irish potato famine; other tariffs to protect workers; and the Maynooth Grant, where an attempt was made to conciliate with the Irish using a sizeable grant to a Catholic seminary.

Peel had done most to help Albert to persuade the headstrong Victoria to allow the monarchy to ride with changing British politics. Peel was a Tory with a vision of one nation, undivided. He brought Albert with him in his concern for the middle class, a desire for an expanded voting franchise, and a sincere concern for the working classes. Now Peel had gone, Albert was devastated. Victoria herself was upset but resigned more to it. She asked Clark to examine Albert. The royal physician thought the problem was his 'mind...diet has been of no avail.' Clearly, Clark did not have as much time for psychology as his patient. Most medical problems, he believed, could be cured by those open windows and the correct diet; most other illnesses were 'in the head' and therefore side issues.

Early in 1852, Elphinstone found himself out of a job as Lord Russell's minority government of nearly six years fell over an issue of defence. Napoleon's France appeared to be rattling the sabre. The British public and the press wanted defences shored up by more than tokenism. Russell believed he could simply bulk up the local militia. Palmerston, ever the thorn in someone's side, had been dumped as foreign minister at the end of 1851, much to the delight of Victoria and Albert. He had his revenge by arguing in the parliament that Britain had to have a powerful *national* armed force. The parliament agreed with Palmerston. Russell's tenuous Whig government had clung to power because its opposition—the conservatives—had been split between those who kept prices high by tariffs on imported goods (Protectionists) and Peelites. Peel's more liberal stand would allow cheap imports into the country, particularly food that helped the poor.

Elphinstone was more than ever in support. He was against protectionism but very much for a strong national armed service. He had influenced Victoria on both issues to the point where she found herself supporting Palmerston, which until then had been anathema to her. Elphinstone believed Russell had been as effective as he could be with his *Education Act 1847* (which Elphinstone had worked behind the scenes to support after his experiences in India); his improvement of the Poor Laws with the development of workhouses by Poor Law unions; his handling of the Chartist demonstrations; and his pushing through of the *Australian Colonies Government Act*, which had formalised the proposal for six new administrations in that country. Russell had also supported Albert's creation of the Great Exhibition.

The first acts of the new conservative prime minister, the 52-year-old fourteenth Earl of Derby (alias Edward Smith-Stanley), were to make himself First Lord of the Treasury and leader of the House of Lords. Derby was well aware of Elphinstone's work as lord-in-waiting, which ensured Victoria's Whig sentiments were held and enhanced. The Scottish lord was his first target for dismissal from the queen's court. Sixteen years after she had stopped a government forming because it wished to get rid of Whig ladies and men at court, Victoria was a far more experienced and therefore respected and powerful figure or, more accurately, *figurehead*. She knew that if she refused a prime minister's dictates it would endanger not only the image of the monarchy, as it had in 1837, but its very existence. Victoria had no choice but to let Elphinstone and other Whig supporters go. She was embittered. It made her feel impotent, which was the intended consequence of reducing the power of the monarchy. Her hate for the Tories was never more pronounced. She hoped that Lord Derby would fail to form a government or, if he did, that he would last long enough to prove 'his incapacity to rule'.

Victoria was pregnant again in mid-1852 and this helped take her mind off what she perceived as an appalling, achieve-nothing, weak government. Derby upset the very moral Albert with his choice of courtiers, plucked from among the 'dandies and roués of London and the Turf'. The choices were the antithesis of the image Victoria and Albert wanted for the royal court. Albert lectured Derby about the damage they could do to the court's image. Future appointments must not be near-bankrupts; they must have characters that would stand moral scrutiny. Albert spoke of the scandal concerning Lady Flora that had rocked the monarchy in 1839; he reviled Melbourne and his tendency to turn clichés on their head, especially to do with Albert's pristine attitudes. He had never forgotten that Melbourne said to him: 'damned morality will undo us all!'

Despite her contempt for Tories in general, Victoria kept an open mind. She at least appreciated Derby for listening to her views. He avoided her pet hate among her prime ministers by speaking fluently and clearly when explaining policy. She was drawn also to the new Chancellor of the Exchequer, Benjamin Disraeli, a descendant of Italian Sephardic Jews. He had Portuguese ancestry, delving back to Iberia before Jews were expelled in 1492. His ancestors had been forced to emigrate to Europe, wandering down the centuries to northern Italy, the Netherlands and finally England. His father, a literary critic and historian, imbued him with a love of the English language. He began studying law but switched to novel writing and politics after some financial setbacks.

Victoria at first had a few issues to overcome in dealing with Disraeli. She had maintained her juvenile preoccupation with looks, and he fell short. She was distracted by his appearance, which she stereotyped: 'thoroughly Jewish-looking, a livid complexion, dark eyes and eyebrows and black ringlets. The expression is disagreeable.' Victoria also took umbrage at his wife, whom she found 'very vulgar, not so much for her appearance, as in her way of speaking'.

Nevertheless, she invited them to dinner because she liked conversation with him. Disraeli's novels and his 'curious notes' on parliamentary debates had first attracted her. The output in both areas was 'highly-coloured'. His language was 'very flowery' yet entertaining, and Victoria liked to be amused by the articulate, the humorous and the lateral-thinking. Disraeli's attitude to her showed unerring respect and dedication. Yet he maintained a fearless individualism. He was not afraid to speak his mind but in such syrup-diluted phrasing that Victoria found his views digestible. She thought him funny, quirky and cerebral. Disraeli was the saving grace for her in an otherwise shaky, uninspired period of government. Victoria believed that the only advance in Tory thinking was for Derby to admit to her that support for protectionism was no longer good politics. Few in parliament and even fewer outside would vote for it.

After rebuilding Osborne House in the Italian renaissance style for £200,000, Albert and Victoria had been thrifty enough to scrape together another £31,500 for the freehold on Balmoral's 7000 hectares after leasing it for four years, adding to another 2400 hectares they had already bought. The properties were bargains made cheaper by the well-practised yet unethical method of taking a leasehold, installing themselves and than making offers to buy freehold below the market rate. Landlords were hardly going to reject offers and frog-march the royal family off the property. Victoria and Albert were doing well with a nice private property nest-egg that they could leave to their children. Victoria further indulged her passion for jewellery, paying £2456 for a suite of diamonds and rubies, an emerald brooch and a set of stunning Australian opals. This was without Albert getting his demands for more money from the Treasury. These purchases were part of the couple's building up of a considerable private estate, separate from the *public* crown. They were receiving the best possible free legal and investment advice on how to do this.

The biggest distraction in the standstill year of 1852 came on 14 September when the Duke of Wellington died, aged 83. He had been the crown's wisest and most faithful grand guide in all matters. His power and influence in Britain was unsurpassed. Albert, preoccupied with the after-life and a sombre, weighty send-off for such a figure, insisted on a heraldic state funeral in November. He chose the heaviest dirges ever composed to make sure the occasion was bleak rather than a celebration of a great fighting knight of the realm, who had outlasted most of his enemies on the battlefield and in life. Albert commissioned a large bronze funeral carriage, with a coffin that was more suitable for a giant than the 1.75 metre Wellington. The coffin swayed, especially when one of the carriage's six wheels became stuck in Pall Mall mud.

Victoria was moved at the sight of Wellington's favourite horse with the duke's empty boots reversed in the stirrups. She found the most depressing aspect of all was Handel's 'Dead March' from *Saul*. She stood with Albert on the new balcony at Buckingham Palace as the procession rumbled by. He revelled in the forbidding growl of a drum roll while Victoria burst into tears at the sound. It was an overwhelming, even frightening reminder of someone dear to her departing forever. Victoria regarded Wellington as irreplaceable, alongside Melbourne and Peel. At 33, she suddenly felt isolated. There were few close confidants she respected and trusted left. Only a handful, like Elphinstone, remained from her early days and he had been removed from his parliamentary and reporting job to her.

Victoria kept up her correspondence with Elphinstone, telling him that he would be restored just as soon as this lingering 'pusillanimous' government was itself removed. But letters were never the same as the correspondent being present. For this sensitive monarch, if there were a heaven, or 'perfect' conditions like it on Earth, people such as Melbourne, Peel, Wellington, Albert, Elphinstone and all her children would always be near. Her worst nightmares still came from them leaving her and the heraldic event to see off the duke only exacerbated her emotional response. She was so distressed that she had to see Clark after the gruelling day. As ever, he prescribed brisk walks in the morning air and time to overcome this latest loss.

The suggested remedy did not quite work and Victoria was only lifted from the doldrums on 17 December 1852 by the nineteen-vote defeat of Lord Derby's government. She gave him an audience. Couldn't Derby link up with Peelites, seeing his team had abandoned protectionism? Derby countered by suggesting that Palmerston become the leader. Victoria said no. She put up the granite-faced, yet bright William Ewart Gladstone, 43, after discussions with courtiers and councillors, including Elphinstone, who had been a contemporary of

Gladstone's at Eton. Derby said he was not up to the job. Victoria sent for Lord Aberdeen. He wanted a 'Liberal–Conservative' coalition. Victoria bristled at this. The word 'Liberal' was synonymous with Palmerston. The idea was rejected. Aberdeen bustled away to see if he could stitch up a suitable team. He came back on Christmas Eve with a line-up that included Palmerston as home secretary. Victoria was miffed, but hearing that her nemesis was almost incapacitated with gout and not likely to be fit enough for the job for long, she vacillated. Victoria put a list of demands to Aberdeen, including the desire to have Elphinstone back in the royal court and close by as lord-in-waiting. Aberdeen agreed to most of her requests and she then accepted his political squad. Uppermost in Victoria's mind was not wanting the nation to be dragged into the new year still without government.

23

THE BLEEDING DISEASE

Peelite Lord Aberdeen, George Hamilton Gordon, 68, promised better government but Victoria's journal reflected her pessimism. At 33, she looked back nostalgically for better times rather than forward. The first confirmation of her sixth sense of foreboding came in February 1853 when the dining room at Windsor Castle caught fire. She remained calm while the prince fretted. Predictably he called for an overhaul of the whole palace.

On 7 April Victoria became a guinea pig for medical science when she allowed chloroform to be administered to her during childbirth. Clark called in the renowned anaesthetist Dr John Snow of Edinburgh for this historic medical event. Victoria was not the first to use it, but she was the most high-profile patient. If she reacted well there was sure to be an upsurge in mothers trying it. Snow and the pioneer in the field, Dr Simpson, also of Edinburgh, had tried it in various doses on animals and humans. Victoria was not rendered unconscious, having barely an ounce applied to her nose and mouth. Clark observed that she was pleased with the effect and that she experienced her best recovery ever from pregnancy. She was amused by Snow's tale of the first ever patient to try chloroform: the woman in 1847 had been so excited by the ease of the birth that she called her daughter 'Anaesthesia'. Better, Snow said that another patient, who was troubled by incontinence during pregnancy, wanted to name her daughter 'Incontinentia'. Victoria had no dilemma over her choice of name: she called her latest son Leopold after her uncle. The King of the Belgians had for some time been back in her good books. But the boy had a problem. He was thin and delicate.

'I'm afraid that the poor lad has the bleeding disease,' Clark informed Victoria. 'If he knocks himself on any wee object he will bruise.'

'How does this happen?' she asked in despair.

'The science of it is unknown. But it is suspected that his blood lacks a clotting agent.'

'He will just keep bleeding?'

'It's most serious if he gets a heavy knock.'

'He will bleed to death?'

'That is what happens. We must make sure he wears padding, on his legs and arms; his body in general. The nursery must keep a wee eye on him all the time.'

Victoria was upset and vexed by the news.

'The disease is not derived from my family! We have never had bleeders.'

'It is not quite that simple, your majesty. Studies suggest females do not get the disease, except in very, very rare cases. But they are carriers. Only males suffer from it. But they can't pass it on to their sons.'

'Have you spoken to Albert?'

'Yes, like you, he is adamant that none in his family have ever had it.'

'It has to come from somewhere!'

Clark remained silent.

'Are you suggesting I am a carrier?' she demanded.

'Not necessarily,' Clark replied.

'If...I repeat *if* I am a carrier that would mean I had to have received it from either my mother or my father.'

'My research already suggests that neither your mother's side of the family, nor your father, had the disease.'

'What are you saying, doctor? That my father was not actually my father?'

Clark avoided any more discussion. He was aware that Victoria's father, the Duke of Kent, Edward Augustus, was a dissolute 50-year-old when he married with the explicit mission to produce an heir to the British throne. His mistress of 27 years had borne him no children. It was possible that another man, a haemophiliac, had been with the Duchess of Kent after her trying and not succeeding with her husband. There had been a race against time to get from Germany (where the duchess lived) to England for the birth. The duchess could have become desperate and 'had' the most suitable available well-bred male. Even John Conroy was rumoured as a possible 'supplier', although he was *not* a haemophilic, ruling him out.

Victoria was devastated by little Leopold's condition. She blew up at Albert, who seemed detached from the reason for her anguish. He had no idea why she was 'so combustible'. He wrote a 'rational' letter to her. She responded with an emotional reply. His clinical manner was not adequate for this moment, although her depression would have been unmanageable for anyone and only countered by medication. Albert became concerned more about her condition than Leopold's sickness, which had brought on Victoria's reaction. He resorted to correspondence with his wife as if they lived in two different countries or worlds. Albert was confused. He did not like her tirades but advised her not to control or hide her emotions. Victoria wanted to blow up, have a good cry, kiss and make up, preferably with sex. Albert wished to avoid all that. His idea of 'bringing it all out' was for her to express it on paper. He could then respond *on paper*. Victoria tried to honour and obey this dictate to scribble in order to unscramble her feelings but this only exacerbated her problem. Her emotions were tumbling like waves in a wild sea. Struggling with them in letters caused her more fury, even though she found her daily discipline of attending to her journal a joy. Albert hated the confrontations; perversely, she seemed to need them; she thrived on them. Her mental problem made her 'gun-fire' far more intense than 'normal'; his attempt to encapsulate, correct and tackle any issue like a daunting maths problems was inadequate.

As an escape from their feud, he busied himself with 'house-keeping', which in this case meant creating a special abode at Swiss Cottage in North London for their children. It appeared as much a witch's house as a children's playground. Albert also began building a new castle at Balmoral. He kept occupied while Victoria fretted over making sure little Leopold was organised not to receive any bruises. She knew that the torment over the 'bleeding disease' would stay with her as long as the victim lived. Clark informed her that her boy's existence was precarious. He could live another day or thirty years. The case studies were brutal in their simplicity: somewhere, somehow, no matter how well he was padded and careful, he would receive a knock that would cause him to bleed to death. Victoria in 1853 vowed to care for him more than any of her brood. Prince Leopold redefined the meaning of 'precious' when applied to life.

24

CRIMEA FEAR: INDIAN CHALLENGE

In July 1853, Russia invaded Turkey. Palmerston persuaded Aberdeen to make a demonstration against the Russians by having the British Fleet enter the Black Sea. Victoria was in Balmoral and stunned that she had not been informed. She hurried to London and experienced one of her most telling moments of helplessness as the monarch. Victoria huffed and puffed in private and to Aberdeen but it was too late. Had she been at Buckingham Palace she may have been able to intercede with Palmerston. International diplomacy had failed. Palmerston was urging support for the Sultan of Turkey in a joint action with France against Russia. On 23 October a beleaguered Turkey declared war on Russia. That day Victoria had afternoon tea at Buckingham Palace with Elphinstone. Because of servants hovering, they addressed each other formally.

'Do you think Palmerston has committed treason, my lord?' she asked him. 'He has not consulted his queen. And he has rejected her position!'

Elphinstone had for years now been a key sounding board on Victoria's and Albert's political positions. His views were always measured and usually apolitical. For once he didn't appear to have an answer.

'Well, my lord?' she prompted.

'Your German background and Russian connections put you in an awkward position, ma'am,' Elphinstone said.

'Spoken like a true Scot!'

'You asked my opinion, ma'am, not words of false comfort.'

Victoria scowled, then asked: 'So you are siding with Palmerston?'

'I believe it would be wise for you and the prince not to appear to be divorced from your government and your people.'

'Do you think we are?'

'No. But if you are *seen* that way, then *you* could be judged the way you have judged Palmerston.'

'What are you saying?'

'That your acts and views behind the scenes or in public in not supporting your government could be construed as treasonable, if Britain goes to war.'

Victoria looked stunned. She had never imagined that she could be viewed that way.

'Well I don't want Britain to support Turkey!'

'But you will have to want this, if your government does.'

Victoria's expression clouded. 'If the Russians have a quick victory on land that will be the end of it,' she said indignantly.

'Perhaps.'

'The Russian emperor would be magnanimous.'

Elphinstone didn't respond. Victoria added: 'Then the Turks would be amenable to reason, don't you think?'

'I hope that scenario plays out.'

'But you don't believe it will.'

'Sadly, not necessarily, majesty.'

During this time, Elphinstone became restless with his role as a courtier. War loomed in the Crimea; India was a potential hotbed of rebellion. He was fed up with the inaction and lack of challenge. His views were listened to and he had the queen's ear on most issues, yet his influence was limited. His experience over a decade in India was still strong within him. He wanted to return in the next year in the prize position as Governor of Bombay where there would be a vacancy. Elphinstone had canvassed Aberdeen and Palmerston; they supported him. All he needed was Victoria's blessing.

It was not a good time. Victoria was not enjoying her private life with little Leopold or her 'work' where she was dealing with a government she did not think was strong or trustworthy. Elphinstone's request to leave was met with stony silence. The most distressing departure in her life short of people dying had been that of her former lover himself. Elphinstone had been removed from her when she needed him most. Then he had been forced to go. Now she did not quite understand why he wished to exile himself once more. Victoria would have never considered what such a motivated individual might have been thinking about the role at court. But Elphinstone was 45 and had a different perspective. He was fit, but did not trust longevity. It was not a luxury in his family. Most of the Elphinstone men down the centuries had died between 50 and 60. This told him he had to take up a challenge or die wondering about what he might have achieved. If he said as much to Victoria, she would have been dismissive. She was queen. He and all her courtiers should do what *she* desired or commanded. Elphinstone had predicted her reaction and had prepared for it. Aberdeen was asked to tell Victoria that someone with Elphinstone's diplomatic skills and long experience of Indians and Indian conditions should be appointed to the plum Bombay job. He had received a cold response again and this caused him to ask for a private audience, which was granted in her study. She ordered the door locked. Victoria sat on a couch with Elphinstone on another opposite her. She began by trying to talk him out of the Bombay appointment.

'Surely at your age, you deserve a more comfortable existence, without the dangers?'

'With respect, majesty, I've had that for many years at court. I need the challenge.'

'You men!' Victoria said with a shake of her head. 'If it's not war, it's something else.'

'I do love India, majesty. That has a bit to do with it.'

'And not me?'

Elphinstone smiled gently: 'You know the answer to that.'

Victoria fell silent. After a few moments she said softly: 'I really wish you would stay, Elphi.'

'I must go.'

'I could command it!'

'And I could defy your command.'

'I could send you to the Tower!'

He smiled. 'Better to have me serve in India.'

'Where there is already unrest and matters may become worse!'

'That is a reason for me going, majesty.'

Elphinstone was away on a steamer to India late in December 1853, much to the sadness of Victoria. She recorded his parting in her journal, referring to year 1853 just gone as a metaphor for her former lover: 'We say goodbye with regret to an old year, which seemed to have become an old friend.'

After some jostling to push Palmerston out of the Cabinet, the former prime minister bounced back thanks to strong support from powerful individuals, such as Liberal statesman William Gladstone and Tory Lord Aberdeen, who could not afford to let go his most popular minister. Victoria saw this as meaning war with Russia in the Crimea was inevitable. It also meant hostility from the public towards Albert (and to a lesser extent Victoria), fuelled by press attacks on him, which were orchestrated by Palmerston. They were saying that Albert had assumed too much power and influence over the queen, which was an inference that he was steering her against perceived British interests, especially in foreign affairs. Criticism suggested he had become her private secretary, prime minister and commander-in-chief rolled into one. Albert was accused of plotting Palmerston's resignation and of being pro-Russian. With war looming, xenophobia increased. Crowds became hostile with boos and hisses when a carriage conveying Victoria and Albert passed through the Traitor's Gate. Victoria reacted, asking Aberdeen to refute the accusations in parliament with positive commentary about Albert by several representatives. The press reported the speeches that countered the attacks.

Stockmar didn't help early in January 1854 by writing a critique for Albert of why the court was unpopular. He blamed a corrupt party system, in which both parties were undermining the crown. The Tories had become 'degenerate bastards' since the introduction of the Reform Bill in 1832. It was against most of its members' interests. According to Stockmar, the Whigs, dominated by Palmerston, were 'republicans'. They viewed Victoria as nothing more than a 'Mandarin figure'. For once the wizard could not weave magic. The assessment was too general and simplistic. He was also out of touch with the shift in the power relationship between the monarch and her prime minister. Stockmar reminded Victoria that she in effect was 'a permanent Premier' where the prime minister was merely a 'temporary head of cabinet'. This was cute phraseology but delusional. It reinforced a false sense of power, intrinsic or otherwise, and drove Victoria to push Aberdeen to make Albert officially 'prince consort', or even 'king consort'. She believed this would further quash attacks on him and demonstrate how much the government favoured and endorsed him. Aberdeen was agreeable to this upgrade, but shrewdly advised that the timing was 'not quite right'.

With conflict now certain in the Crimea, Victoria saw the chance to shore up her support, and indirectly that for the prince, by backing the armed forces and war. This put to bed rumours about how much royal connections and friends interfered with her role as Queen of England and the empire. After writing in her diary that her heart was not in 'this war' she hardened her attitude when the humane Aberdeen declared to her that he found war repugnant 'in all its forms'. Victoria thought that having such a squeamish prime minister under the circumstances 'will never do'. Spurred by Stockmar's fantasy about her being 'a permanent Premier', she began acting as she perceived she should. In an about-face over not taking on the Russians, she advised Aberdeen that it was better to have a 'small' war now than a bigger one later, where he was all for 'patching things up'. Victoria would have none of it. She was prepared to rattle the sabre and then use it. Acting in her role to 'advise' her prime minister, she suggested the country should go to war. Aberdeen took this as a directive and much against his instincts had to agree. A stronger prime minister may have challenged her power prerogative, which was largely illusory. But even a tougher individual would have been aware that the nation was feverish about going into conflict, although there had been no rational discussion or justification for it. The press was for it; the public mood had to be taken into account. It was almost as if, after a long peacetime period, it was *necessary* to appease some manic or restless mood in the country. On 28 February 1854, three days after Victoria's discussion, Britain declared war on Russia in support of Turkey and in alliance with France.

The Crimean War had begun.

25

OLD FEELINGS, NEW CHALLENGES IN BOMBAY

Elphinstone arrived early in 1854 at Bombay, the west port of entry to India, which was far more attractive than the other gateways of Madras in the south and Calcutta in the east. Bombay's curved harbour, with its modest hills rising behind it, rivalled Sydney Harbour and Italy's Bay of Naples for sheer physical beauty and it was made even more familiar by the line of impressive European buildings along the waterfront. He was thrilled to feel the sense of freedom that this exotic country brought to him once more. The aromas, as ever, were there with the accompanying heat. The colours struck him more than ever, especially with the women in their saris—purple, orange, pink, red, all shades of blue, yellow and mauve. 'Such a contrast to the drab grey of London,' he noted, 'and I feel at home and liberated already.'

Writing to the Duke of Cambridge, he observed:

> elegant [Indian] women in short satin skirts, the like
> of which I have never seen in England, or quite as
> short in India for that matter. The dominant color
> in fashion seems to be green, but a special emerald
> variety that adds to the wearer's appeal. One very tall
> woman in pale cherry threw me a wonderful smile
> and a garland as we headed towards the governor's
> mansion. She had a white flower in her glossy black
> hair and she was well adorned with many-colored
> wrist bands...How I wish I could have stopped the
> carriage and spoken to her! But of course, the dignity
> of my new office would not allow such a liberty.
> Her full smile reminded me so of another.

The noises too were familiar—the chatter and laughter of the women; the industrious activity of men on bullock carts with squeaking axles; the clatter of carriages on cobblestone or gravel; and the continuous music with which he was not unfamiliar.

'Did I hear a harp?' he wrote. 'If so it seemed fitting at that moment, along with ever-present drums and gongs. It was cacophonous but still charming.' Overhead, birds cackled incessantly and he noted the endless stream of seven sisters—groups that flew always in formations of seven. Red-and-white parrots swooped low across his carriage's path.

Along the route to his residence, people waved and greeted the new governor, if not like a king, then someone important at least. East India Company officials had organised the city's greeting, but the cheering and reaction seemed genuine. He noticed, too, the bigger population of Bombay compared to his last presidency in Madras. The images were familiar: smiling faces, dirty white garments alongside spotless uniforms. In the crowds, women wandered in a variety of brilliant head-covering scarves and other headgear, and men wearing variously multicoloured turbans, skullcaps and cotton clothes, stopped, shaded their eyes and gawked. 'I wanted to bring out my sketch book even on the ride in,' he told Cambridge:

as everywhere I looked there was life and industry.
Craftsmen in alleyways worked in leather, brass and
precious metals. Brilliant mosques caught the eyes, as
did the pyramid-shaped Jain temples emerging from
high-walled compounds, and the Hindu temples
featuring copper idols, presumably instances of their
many gods...and knowing how much you loved
my talk of markets in Madras, the Bombay examples
out-shine them with the stunning flowers—roses,
marigolds, jasmine, and tuberoses.

He added in closing that 'as I begin my new post you will be at ease
to know that I have my affairs in order, just in case on the very outside
chance, as you feared, I do not survive my tenure.'

Elphinstone's governorship would run at least five years and would be a
considerable challenge, the greatest of his life. The western, or Bombay,
presidency of India was a long, narrow strip of country, including the
province of Sindh. It occupied the western coast of the peninsula from
the mouth of the Indus River to the northern tip of Goa, and from south
of Goa to the border of Maisur. The new governor controlled 347,400
square kilometres in which there were fouteen million inhabitants.
Elphinstone also had power over native states covering 184,700 square
kilometres, including a further six million Indians. On the surface
his new posting would have looked inviting. Bombay, a city of seven
islands on India's west coast, was one of the nation's most thriving and
populous centres. City elders and British bureaucrats were well disposed
to him because of his record in running Madras, his touring of remote
parts and his love and knowledge of the country. The achievements of
his uncle, the former Governor Mountstuart Elphinstone, from 1819
to 1827 also raised expectations of the new appointee. Mountstuart
had set a standard in organising education in India and this influenced
his nephew's efforts in the same field in Madras. On his first day in
residence in Bombay the new governor visited Elphinstone College,
an endowment of local communities in honour of Mountstuart. He

also attended a modest ceremony at the foot of the marble statue of his uncle, which had been erected by local Europeans. It meant that Elphinstone walked tall from the beginning of his stay in Bombay and it was also a spur, if he needed one, to stamp his own mark on the governorship, Bombay and the Indian nation.

Education would be a cornerstone of Elphinstone's ambitions, as it had been in Madras. Elphinstone's aim was to establish a university in Bombay as he had in Madras before his scheduled tenure of five years ended in 1857. Within a week of arriving Elphinstone was tackling a second area: train travel. In April 1853, a year before he was governor, the first railway in India began operating between Bombay and neighbouring Thane. It only covered 34 kilometres, but it was the start of a bigger system. Elphinstone was involved in the early development of the Bombay, Baroda and Central India Railway Company, which would be incorporated in 1855. He began the demolition of the walls of the fort, which had been a symbol of imperialism. Elphinstone also initiated plans for the Vhar waterworks, which were due to start in two years.

Modernising by the British was viewed with suspicion by some locals. The train running out of the city was looked upon as a 'demon'. The capitalist methods of financing and banking were disliked, especially the use of interest on money lent, which was frowned upon by Muslims, and always seemed to favour the Raj and not Indians. But it was 'progress' and the British felt, without broadcasting it, that their technical skills in modernising were superior to those of the Indians.

Elphinstone was more aware of local sensitivities than most, yet he was now part of the relentless imperial expansion in the empire's prize colony. He was at work continuing the development of a modern banking system, overseeing the build-up of the cotton trade, and improving road works and hospitals. Elphinstone further showed his abilities as a conciliator when dealing with the Bombay Association, a group formed in 1852 that vented public grievances to the governor. Negotiation was one way of dealing with unrest, which had simmered on the surface since the Sikh Wars he had experienced in 1845. Thwarting rebellion was not simply a choice between using a sledgehammer or fine diplomatic skills. Elphinstone had to deal with diverse political, economic, military, religious and social issues. Each area had delicate balances to maintain. Sepoys (native Indian soldiers) were under the command of British soldiers trained in the East India Company College in England. Elphinstone had his own army of about 100,000 sepoys with a commander-in-chief who reported to him. Along with similar armies in Madras and Bengal there were about 250,000 sepoys under command in the East India Company, which was more than the official army of the British Empire. The sepoys of the Bengal Army proved the most difficult to manage. They had their own list of grievances against the company. Caste privileges and customs had once been encouraged within the Bengal Army, but modernising regimes in Calcutta threatened some sepoys' ritual high status. Indian soldiers became unhappy about their treatment by British officers, who wished to entrench and deepen the divide between them. A few years earlier, in 1851 and 1852, sepoys had been required to serve overseas during a war in Burma. Hindus were upset. Tradition laid out that those who travelled 'the black waters' (away from the Indian homeland) would lose their caste. Low sepoy salaries caused disputes. After the British troops conquered Awadh and the Punjab, soldiers no longer received extra money because those missions were not considered 'foreign'.

There was also disgruntlement from the old Indian aristocracy, which saw its power eroding under British rule. The public auction of the Nagpur royal family's jewels did not help the demeanour of the local elite. An anti-company Raj attitude reinforced the belief that the British intended to convert them either by force or deception to Christianity. Elphinstone spoke individually to religious leaders in Bombay, assuring them that under his watch there would be no such intrusive development. He admitted that a surge in evangelism had occurred, but he would not encourage or court it in his presidency. Elphinstone let it be known in the army that he was against any officers attempting to convert their sepoys, yet it still went on. The company agreed with his assessment that such proselytising could lead to a flashpoint. At his instigation, the British made moves to ban it. But they refused to slow down expansion and westernisation, which the new Governor of Bombay endorsed. In general the company embarked on rapid change, banning many Hindu and Muslim religious practices, which were viewed as uncivilised. Elphinstone could slow the pace of change in Bombay but not the unrest it caused elsewhere, such as in Bengal. He was against Sati, a Hindu ritual in which a recently widowed woman was put on her husband's funeral pyre and burnt to death, either of her own volition or by force. It had been outlawed since 1829 but still went on in certain communities and regions, including those in Nepal and Bengal, where there was outrage over British 'interference'. Elphinstone wished sati banned altogether, preferring reason over force to ensure change. Predecessors, such as former General Sir Charles Napier, commander-in-chief in India, had been tougher, telling Indian leaders that the British too had their customs in response to burning a woman alive: 'We tie a rope around their [the killers'] necks and we hang them. Build your funeral pyre; beside it, my carpenters will build a gallows. You may follow your custom. And we will follow ours.'

As tough as this talking was, it did not stamp out sati. Elphinstone's approach was more effective. He also supported the abolition of child marriage and female infanticide. He backed efforts by the British to ban the Thuggee religious cult that had so intrigued young Bertie. Its members would insinuate themselves into other groups, and then murder them.

The Indians complained about the justice system, which they said was unfair to them. East India Company officers were allowed an extended series of appeals if convicted or accused of brutality or crimes against Indians. There was also anger over heavy taxation. It was seen as extortion. If taxes weren't paid, property was appropriated. Elphinstone moved early to buy more land for himself. But it was nothing compared to the Governor-General of India, Lord Dalhousie, who annexed, without compensation or payment, more than two and a half million square kilometres of land as the company's territory. This British expansion outraged local rulers, who viewed it as imperial greed on a grand scale.

Despite all the problems and attitudes to the Raj, Elphinstone in his first year as governor managed to gain the goodwill of the locals, the Europeans and the military. 'He brought to the office experience that few men could command,' historians Kaye and Malleson wrote. 'His knowledge of men, his courtesy, his genial bearing, gave effect to that experience...

His conduct as Governor of Bombay was invariably marked by temper, judgment and discretion. Calm and dignified in manner...he evinced on every occasion likely to test his action, the possession of a guiding mind, of a will not to be shaken, a resolution that went direct to its aim.' The mood of the population after the first Afghan War had to be handled with 'tact and judgment on the part of the rulers...Lord Elphinstone ... displayed them.' At first he had to show his administrative skills, which gained the confidence of the Indians. 'His measures for improving the resources of the country, and for establishing means of communications in all directions, are spoken of to this day.'

Four months into his presidency, an army officer asked him to come to a field a few kilometres from his residence to witness a game of polo, which the officer deemed to be played too vigorously. There were 30 horses and riders on each team competing on a dusty, crude playing area of about 200 metres long by 120 metres wide. About half the players were British officers in one team wearing red shirts and the other team had mainly Indians in green shirts, some of whom were also serving in the British army. The game was rough and dangerous with the mallets wielded freely.

'It's willing,' Elphinstone said, 'but I'm not going to ban it. In fact, it looks like fun.'

'The problem is the illegal gambling,' the officer said. 'Quite a lot is being wagered on the outcome. That leads to some extraordinary clashes. One resulted in a duel a few months before you arrived. Both officers were mortally wounded as a result.'

Elphinstone watched as one particular horse crashed its way through a pack. Its rider swung the mallet so hard that it collected an opposition rider, who was thrown from his horse and then trampled on by other competitors. Several people ran from the sidelines to help the bruised and battered rider. The offending rider dismounted, ran to the stricken opponent and knelt down to examine the man lying face down in the dirt.

'That was too tough,' Elphinstone observed as he sat on horseback close to the field's edge. They watched as the aggressive rider, wearing a leather cap, remounted, wheeled into another melee, and caused chaos again.

'Who is that Indian?' Elphinstone asked. 'The one who examined the injured man like a doctor?'

'Oh, "that" is a woman, sa.'

'What?' Elphinstone said, doing a double take.

'Yes, sa. Name is De Crepeney, sa.'

Elphinstone departed but left a message with Husna to visit his residence in the old government fort the next evening for tea. She accepted but arrived an hour late. Husna wore a very broad hat, a white silk shirt and a long red skirt. Nearly nine years had passed since they had seen each other. The only sign that she was older were flecks of grey in her long black hair. Otherwise, Elphinstone thought, she looked as magnificent as she did when they last met. He was still attracted to her.

'What brought you here?' he asked as he kissed her on both cheeks.

'Not you, I assure you,' she said with a smile. 'A month ago, I took up as an assistant in a medical practice owned by a French friend of my father's. Women still struggle to be doctors, so I am what the French call a "para-medical". I can practise in this man's surgery, under supervision. I am to be seen as a glorified nurse but, in fact, I do everything he does, and usually *not* under supervision and, may I say immodestly, *better*.'

'That explains your failure to respond to my Christmas letter. It would not have arrived from Paris yet.'

'How long will you be away from your little queen this time?'

'Five years.'

'Did you take up with her again?'

'No. We are good friends.'

'I heard as much, but didn't believe a word of it. You were *Lord in Waiting*. What on earth were you waiting for?'

Elphinstone laughed.

'Husna, my dear, you have not changed.'

'I am not your "dear".'

'And you?' he asked. 'Are you married?'

'Was. He died of the fever that swept Paris last year.'

'I am sorry.'

'Don't be. I had left him. He could not keep his hands off a cousin of mine in Paris.'

'Oh.'

'A *male* cousin.'

'Oh!'

'Yes, "oh".'

They sat in silence. Elphinstone didn't know what to say. There was a veneer of bitterness in her manner that had not been apparent before.

Elphinstone was kept in touch with British politics via letters and newspapers that travelled to him more quickly than when he had first arrived in Madras. Then the mail had taken sixteen weeks to reach him; now via the overland route it could take just five or six weeks. He was not distressed to be away from the turmoil that was affecting Victoria. Aberdeen resigned as prime minister early in 1855. The queen, now 35 years of age, was finding that candidates tended to be too old for office. She was pleased to hear Disraeli's remark about Palmerston: 'He is an old painted pantaloon . . .with false teeth that would fall out of his mouth if he did not hesitate when speaking.'

Victoria was more than ever opposed to Palmerston, who over the years had become her main political nemesis. She was despondent when another candidate for whom she sent, Lord Derby, declined and then recommended Palmerston. Disraeli could not resist another swipe at him, saying he was 71 years old, deaf, blind and no good at business. This amused Victoria but could not hide the fact that Palmerston was looming as the main option. The press and people wanted him. Still she baulked at the possibility, given his history of disregard for her views, her role and her relatives. Victoria beckoned Lord Lansdowne, a 75-year-old Whig elder statesman. He also rejected her overture. He said he was too old and not well enough. Next up was Lord Russell. He tried to form a government but could not appease a long-term political rival, Lord Clarendon. Victoria was in despair. She had wanted her cousin the Duke of Cambridge to command the military; she may well have dreamed about asking Albert to do that job (Wellington had wanted him to do this) or even be prime minister, if he had been elected to parliament. Even Elphinstone's suitability as a popular, chivalrous character came into her thinking. He was governing India's most important city with a huge army at his disposal. All reports she was receiving were saying that he was excelling in the role, where he was showing tact, finesse and goodwill. He was relatively young at 47, but his appointment as prime minister would be out of the question.

Victoria finally admitted to herself that Palmerston had to be the next prime minister.

26

VICTORIA TRUMPS NAPOLEON III

As Elphinstone's departure slipped from months into years, Victoria clung to Albert more and more whenever he made time from his busy schedule. She dreaded him making even a fleeting five-day visit to see Emperor Napoleon in France. The prince had to cement relations with the French in their combined bid to defeat the Russians in the Crimean War. The royalty of Europe had been sceptical about Napoleon III. The Queen was pleased that Albert was satisfied with him, apart from his penchant for smoking. King Leopold had always been unkind, thinking his taking of Louis Philippe's throne 'as like finding a snake in one's bed'. The emperor wished to keep on the accepting side of Victoria and wrote her a note about Albert, which no doubt gave Napoleon a smirk when he signed it. He said he had never met anyone with such profound knowledge as the prince, and who 'imparted it so freely'. Victoria, who always saw her husband's cup as half-full, even if there were nothing in it, accepted this as a wonderful compliment.

Her enthusiasm for the fight with the Russians took another turn when it did not all go according to plan. There was the brave

Photographic portrait of Victoria's first lover, the 13th Lord Elphinstone. This was commissioned by Queen Victoria in 1853 just before Elphinstone's second tour of India as governor, this time of Bombay. He looks wary of the camera. Former Captain of the Royal Horse Guards, John Elphinstone and Victoria were 'good friends' and much more over 25 years from 1835 to 1860. Reproduced with permission of *Royal Collection Trust*/© *Her Majesty Queen Elizabeth II 2014.*

Second Love. Portrait of Princess Victoria and Prince Albert at the time of their wedding. Their marriage lasted from 1840 to Albert's death in 1861. From the collection of the State Library of Victoria.

Third Love. John Brown, the Scottish servant, who became Queen Victoria's partner, from 1872 until his death in 1883. Reproduced with permission of *Royal Collection Trust*/© *Her Majesty Queen Elizabeth II 2014.*

Fourth Love. Abdul Karim, the Indian servant and companion who charmed Queen Victoria in the last 14 years of her life—1887–1901. Reproduced with permission of *Royal Collection Trust/© Her Majesty Queen Elizabeth II 2014.*

Most intimate relative: Queen Victoria with her first born of nine children, Vicky. They were very close and wrote 4000 letters to each other. Photographic print from the collection of the State Library of NSW.

The Church of England's St Peter's in Limpsfield, Surrey, near the Kent border. The monument to John Elphinstone lies inside the church, and his grave is on the other side of the north-facing wall.

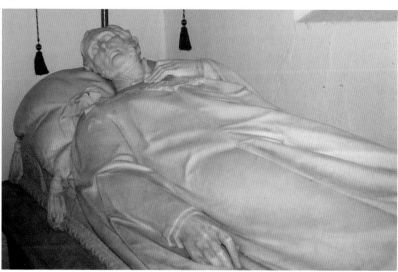

The life-size monument of the 13th Lord Elphinstone inside St Peter's was commissioned by Queen Victoria and created by royal sculptor Matthew Noble.

Author Roland Perry (left) interviewing KGB Masterspy Yuri Ivanovitch Modin in his Moscow apartment. Modin ran the infamous 'Cambridge Ring' of spies from 1947 to 1958, and was their KGB Control for the rest of their lives.

The notorious Anthony Blunt, a member of the Cambridge Ring recruited by the KGB in the 1930s. He became the Royal Art Curator in 1947 and was so for more than 30 years. In 1979 the Queen took away his knighthood when it became public that he had spied for Russia during and after World War Two.

but doomed charge of the Light Brigade, which made Victoria proud, yet then she heard about cholera, fever and diarrhoea striking her beloved troops. Victoria's cousin the Duke of Cambridge, with the army as commander-in-chief, caused her further grief when he had a breakdown at the height of battle. He was forced to take rest leave in Constantinople.

The duke wrote to close friend Elphinstone in Bombay. 'You will be surprised to see whence this letter is dated,' he said, 'but the fact is that I have just come up to recover from the fatigues of a very protracted and hard campaign...I regret to say it is not yet at an end.'

Elphinstone replied with a concerned letter. The duke wrote again from St James's Palace saying that he had recovered 'from the effects of a most hard campaign...good news from the Sea of Azofif lead me to the hope that ere long we shall have further great successes, and that the Russians will be driven out of the Crimea, in addition to the fall of Sebastopol.'

Husna ignored the governor's invitations to balls, building openings and exhibitions. But to Elphinstone's pleasure early January 1855, she turned up in a multicoloured sari at the Gymkhana Club during a cricket match between eleven East India Company representatives and a local squad of twenty Indians.

'I thought you had no interest in the game,' he said, shaking hands in front of the other guests in a marquee beside the ground.

'I hate it,' she said with a grin, 'but I was bored and, besides, I was intrigued to see inside this Gymkhana—such a British male bastion. This is a rare event in clubs to which women cannot belong, and especially Indian women.'

It crossed Elphinstone's mind that she seemed more like the sensual being he had known in Madras, rather than the cynical, apparently hardened individual he had invited to tea in his first months in Bombay.

They sat in wicker chairs and watched the game.

Husna looked around. Men in pith helmets were slumped in chairs, some asleep, others nearly so.

'It would be helpful if someone had a heart attack,' she said loudly to Elphinstone, who gave a mock frown of disapproval. 'It would surely liven things up!'

After a few minutes silence, Elphinstone leaned close to her and asked, 'Would you like to come to dinner at the residence?'

'No, *merci.*'

Elphinstone waited for some explanation. None was forthcoming.

Palmerston was sworn in as prime minister on 4 February 1855. His timing was good. The next month the old Tsar Nicholas died of a broken heart after the carnage of battles at Inkerman and Balaclava. He was succeeded by his son, Alexander II, who wished to make peace. Palmerston, a consummate politician, thought the peace terms were too soft on the original aggressor, Russia. There was a problem with the harmony between the French and British armies in the conflict. Anti-French sentiment, a hangover from Aberdeen's attitude, was holding back the harmony between the British and French armies. Vertically challenged Napoleon III, with his squat body, straggly goatee beard, big nose and eyes that seemed in permanent hangover, sought compensation, at least in appearance, from his tall, elegant Spanish wife, Eugénie. They made two visits to England. Victoria, now the pragmatic, more secure monarch, worked in tandem with her unfavoured prime minister, to finesse the pompous yet fragile French emperor. It helped that Napoleon was infatuated with her and she was pleased to learn that he had been a special French constable sent to London to help out the local police during the Chartist rising in 1848. He had been in Green Park to watch her on her way to open parliament for the first time. Napoleon had paid £40 to be at the opera just to lay eyes on her. These ingratiating revelations helped thaw any coolness at this high level of diplomacy.

A sticking point between their respective armies was Napoleon's bravado about leading them in the battles against the Russians. Everyone in the country knew that no British soldier would fight under him. He had to be disabused of this fanciful notion. Victoria was in her element and at the peak of her persuasive power since being crowned. First, she worked on Empress Eugenie, having her to lunch at Buckingham Palace. Using her charm as they ate, Victoria talked about everything else except the issue of her husband, but over tea in the garden her demeanour changed to one of concern.

'I would implore you to make him understand how important he is to France,' Victoria said. 'The country needs him. If the worst were to happen it would be a disaster for your country and so tragic for you . . . I can only think of how devastated I would be to lose my own husband. But it would so much worse for the emperor to be killed. I fear there would be civil war.'

Eugénie looked startled. 'We worry about it, your majesty,' she said softly.

'You must think too of yourself, as I have under similar circumstances,' Victoria went on as she sensed the princess's fear of losing her husband, her country and her head, literally. The guillotine was the nightmare of every member of a royal family.

'I would urge you to find a moment, a moment of intimacy, preferably, to influence him not to make a fatal error by leading his army in battle. It will be wiser and braver for him to show discretion. Remember a living, great emperor is preferable to a monument of one.'

The next day, Victoria made a point of being at a war council meeting between the British cabinet and Napoleon, despite Palmerston's ambivalence about her role. If he ever hesitated over her having influence, any traces of doubt evaporated at this meeting. Anticipating that Eugénie had softened up her husband overnight with at least pillow-talk, Victoria addressed Napoleon: 'I would implore you emperor, please, please do not go to the Crimea. It would be too dangerous for the most important commander in the whole of Europe to risk all.'

This was supreme flattery and tactical, and yet not surprising, as these two had a history of flirtatious friendship. Victoria had ever been susceptible to his charm that women enjoyed and men could not understand. This was in spite of him being the nephew of England's former arch-enemy, Bonaparte, and the way he had taken office. In 1848, Napoleon had been elected French president after King Louis-Philippe had been thrown out. He then staged a coup and made himself emperor. His elevation had been at the expense of a monarch, always a fearful event for royalty. And yet Victoria had genuine affection for him, and him for her.

Now this comment about his military status, in front of a sceptical British government no less, left Napoleon unable to disguise his delight. The cabinet members were silent and in awe of their self-possessed queen as she drew breath and then continued: 'We are so aware of the excellent French and British generals ready to do their job.' She paused to glance at her ministers. 'It is no secret here for me to pass on our concern that if you left Paris our intelligence suggests your uncle Prince Jerome and his cousin Prince Napoleon would make mischief for you.'

Napoleon grimaced, and with a Gallic pout said: 'A commander must risk these things, your majesty . . .'

'With respect, emperor, someone as important to France and the stability of Europe as your highness should not risk being killed, for you surely would be a target on any battlefield.' Napoleon shifted his diminutive frame in his seat. Victoria added: 'For the sake of peace in France, for your wonderful family and beautiful wife, you should not risk everything!'

The impassioned plea had all eyes turning to him. At first his facial expressions, then his nodding head and finally more and more Gallic shrugs of agreement led everyone to believe that they knew what his response would be. Chuffed at Victoria's apparent concern, he picked up on the problems that members of his family might cause by attempted coups. Victoria had presented him with a substantial face-saving excuse.

'I understand your majesty's ever-so-wise words,' he replied, 'and it is very true that members of my family would love me to go abroad to command my army. They may well see it is a chance for a coup.' He paused, himself heavy on theatrics, 'I make you this promise, your majesty. I shall consider not going.'

He returned to Paris. A week later a would-be French assassin tried to shoot him. Victoria noted from her multiple experiences that the attempt was made with 'a pistol, thank God!—hardly ever seems to succeed'. But the effort capped off her diplomacy. Napoleon decided not to lead the two armies in the Crimea. The French were now onside but without their interfering, quixotic emperor. Palmerston then moved into his form of diplomacy and persuaded Napoleon to walk away from peace negotiations. Palmerston thought that if Sebastopol fell he would be in a tougher negotiating position. He waited. In September, half a year after Russia wished to have a peace agreement, the French captured Malakov just as the British were pushed back from the Redan with many casualties. On 27 February 1856, an armistice was signed. A month later, an agreement was reached at the Congress of Paris. Palmerston called for a demilitarised Black Sea and got it. But the Crimea was under Russian control and he could not push it back to the Turks' Ottoman Empire. The war and terrible carnage was over. Victoria had to acknowledge Palmerston's role in April by awarding him the Order of the Garter, the highest order of chivalry or knighthood. It brought prestige for Palmerston, and was good politics for her. Public sentiment that had waivered over the royal family now peaked in their favour again. Bestowing such an honour on someone she had despised showed a certain magnanimity on Victoria's behalf. It was also shrewd. Palmerston was very popular in the country. But now he was disposed towards his monarch and would be less likely to upset her.

27

IN THE BARREL
OF A GUN

The escalated troubles in India in 1857 were triggered by a gun.
Sepoys throughout the country were issued with a new rifle, an
Enfield percussion cap musket. It was a far more powerful and accurate
weapon than the smoothbore Brown Bess that had been standard issue
throughout the British army for more than a century. The more modern
weapon had a couple of major innovations, but the loading process
remained the same. Soldiers still had to bite the cartridge open and pour
its gunpowder into the rifle's muzzle, then stuff the cartridge case into
the musket as wadding before loading it with a ball. The paper cartridge
case was coated with grease to make it waterproof. A rumour spread
through the sepoy ranks that the new rifle's standard issue cartridges
were greased with lard (pork fat) or tallow (beef fat).

The controversy even became the subject of discussion between
Husna and Elphinstone on a ride one morning to the ancient Buddhist
Kanheri Caves deep in a green forest on Bombay's western outskirts.
After continued invitations and rejections, she had agreed to gallop
with him as they had in Madras.

'Why are you so concerned?' he asked.

'You forget again! My family members here are all Muslim. It is a serious issue. They all talk much about it.'

After a minute, Elphinstone mused: 'Hmm, I can see that in the heat of battle it could be a problem.'

'That's what I've been saying,' Husna said. 'You have to do something about it.'

Elphinstone wrote to General George Anson, the commander-in-chief of armed forces in India, explaining the problem with clarity. But Anson was trenchant in his attitude.

'I shall never give in to their [the sepoys'] beastly prejudices!' he replied.

'Then make way for even beastlier consequences,' Elphinstone warned him. And he was right. The grease issue was the last in a series of grievances that had been simmering for years. The Indians took up the new weapons and found an acceptable way of breaking the cartridge without making mouth contact with the grease. They then aimed them against British occupation. The British wished to view it as a 'mutiny', which had the connotation of an unruly mob rising against 'authority'. Indians preferred to call it the 'First War of Indian Independence' or a 'freedom fight'. The declining Mughal dynasty rulers of the central state of Oudh had been friends with the British for a century but when it was annexed there was unrest among Muslims. This left central India a tinderbox of discontent.

The successor to Dalhousie as governor-general was Lord (Charles) Canning, aged 44. His appointment was controversial. Many in England viewed it as naked nepotism. His father was the celebrated statesman and former prime minister (1827) George Canning. Nothing in Charles's performances as postmaster general in Aberdeen's ministry (and later under Palmerston) suggested other than that he was a hard-working administrator, without the self-confidence, experience, courage, strength or intellect for the biggest job in the British Empire outside England. Canning was a nervous type, who also lacked the personal warmth, flair, finesse and character needed for such a monumental challenge. But still he was sent to India in 1856. Canning tried to impress early but his actions caused further discontent. He brought about the *Services*

Enlistment Act ordering all troops of the Bengal Army to be ready for service inside and outside India.

England's empire maintenance and world marauding had taxed its resources with wars in the Crimea, Persia and China. More contention arose from the fact that there were five Indians to every British soldier, and the natives were paid less than the rawest European recruit. It was an unequal equation on both counts and encouragement for sepoys to revolt. In January 1857 there were minor outbreaks of arson in cantonment areas. At Barrackpore near Calcutta an Indian soldier shot dead a British officer and was hanged. Indian troops were court-martialled and imprisoned. There was more unrest at Berhampore in Bengal. But that too was repressed and rebels were punished. Canning had a poor first year. He did not have the skills for such a demanding job, which he made tougher by being too heavy-handed and dictatorial.

For Victoria, giving birth seemed often to coincide with war or a disturbance in some part of her empire. In late March 1857 the mail brought her news of problems in India and on 14 April Beatrice was born. Vicky had been born in October 1840, seventeen years earlier. Victoria was a month off her thirty-eighth birthday and Clark thought it might be wise to make this her last child. Victoria's reaction was typical. 'What?' she said to her long-term physician, 'no more *fun?*' Despite the impressive royal production line, Albert remained sparing, if not stingy, in his sexual affections; so much so that he equated sex with pregnancy, unlike Victoria who saw it for its own sake as pleasure. This led to 'fun' being limited to bursts after long intermissions. When she registered 'pregnant', Albert continued to withdraw his services. By 1857, he seemed to be becoming weary of every exertion as he worked longer hours and enjoyed life less. He invented and installed a bedside switch to activate mechanical locks on the bedroom door.

When Victoria asked why he had made it, Albert said it was to stop his children coming in when 'you and I are in here'. In reality it was another excuse to avoid her 'assaults', which were still frequent. They wore him out and caused stress. Another way of surmounting Victoria's insatiable lust was to spend more time with the seventeen-year-old princess royal, Vicky, as she drifted towards an arranged marriage with a Prussian prince. Victoria became fed up with her daughter always dining with them until 10 p.m., which did not allow for the parents to spend time together before sleeping. Vicky was Albert's favourite child. He hated the thought of this special daughter leaving, if only because she was a buffer against Victoria's exuberant demands in his boudoir. Vicky had all the gifts. She was sympathetic and more understanding of his foibles than his wife. Vicky was clever, like him, and interested in the arts and sciences. It was a case of 'like father, like daughter' down to her capacity to concentrate and absorb a verbal or written brief with complete retention of its meaning and its integrity. These were all the qualities wished for in Bertie, but which he lacked.

'Certainly the Prince of Wales did not take after his father,' Strachey observed. This applied to his intellect, interests and appearance. He looked nothing like Albert but was 'a true scion of the House of Brunswick'. Bertie at fifteen had a long nose, which neither Victoria nor Albert had. He had a chin more like that of his mother. Bertie did not have prepossessing looks, but his expression was sympathetic. He liked to laugh, but there was not much opportunity to let forth this emotion, which was understandable given his suppressed life under rarified conditions that carried with it unreal expectations.

Bertie's parents had read him wrongly, assuming that he could be pushed, punished and pummelled into being what he was not by instinct, inclination or aptitude. Instead of backing off to let him develop and find his métier, Victoria and Albert applied endless pressure. Bertie was sent on a tour of Europe with a select group of tutors. Albert ordered him to keep a diary. Bertie obliged, only to the point of *keeping* it with him. His father inspected it on his return and was disgusted at how thin his observations were. There was no mention of meeting the Pope. His parents thought this was a moment to savour since it was a first for a Prince of Wales. Instead his demeanour on the trip was one of boredom to the point of sadness at his plight. This weight on Bertie was either going to crush his spirit or cause an explosive reaction. He took the buffeting, making understandable outbursts of petulance against the regimen foisted on his life. Albert complained about Bertie to his old mentor Stockmar, but he could offer nothing new on how to turn him around. Besides, the baron, at 70, was on his last visit to England after twenty years of, as he put it 'the laborious and exhausting office of a paternal friend and trusted adviser' to Albert and Victoria. Stockmar had done more than anyone else to put them together, and to bolster, support and advise them. Albert was very much his creation, presiding as far more than a figurehead over the greatest nation and empire the world had so far seen. Albert was the toiler behind the throne. That Bertie in turn was not in any way the creation of his father was not Stockmar's fault, or now his concern.

Victoria wrote to Vicky several times a week. Her daughter had become her most important family confidante:

> I have been shamefully deceived [by Albert] about
> Alfie [her second son]. It was promised me that the
> last year before he went to sea, he should be with
> us; instead of which he was taken away and I saw
> but very little of him. And now he is to go away for
> many months and I shall not see him [until] God
> knows when! And papa [Albert] is most cruel upon
> the subject. I assure you it is much better to have no
> children than to have them only to give them up! It
> is too wretched...I look forward with horror to the
> separation...Two children in one year. It is horrible.

The difference now that stopped her slipping into an abyss was the prospect of Albert showing her and baby Beatrice some affection and him being there for Victoria and not so wedded to his work. Clark feared for Victoria's mental condition, having warned Albert a year earlier that she had told him that having another child would 'sink her'. But it proved the opposite with Beatrice, on whom she doted, and her first year proved to be a blissful period. Victoria found new energies and a result was to push again for Albert being made prince consort. But the nation was more interested in developing democracy than rewarding and embellishing the prince, whose aloof and cold image still saw him branded as 'different' and 'foreign'. Victoria was hurt that the public could not see her Albert as she did: noble, hard-working, dedicated to Britain now more than even his beloved homeland, and most importantly his unfailing support for the monarch. She stepped in and by 'letters patent'—royal decree—made him prince consort. *The Times* was apathetic, editorialising that the epithet was of no importance. The flexing of monarchical muscle had a benign impact. But it was of import to Victoria as queen. It meant that when Albert next gathered with other royalty in Europe only King Leopold was superior to him.

28

ELPHINSTONE
STEPS UP

In May 1857 large-scale rebellion flared in Meerut, Bengal, when sepoys broke open a prison and released comrades. They then galloped to Delhi and took it over. The revolt then spread to other areas, including Lucknow, Bareilly, Cawnpore, Agre, Jhansi, Benares, Central India and Bundelkhand. The Sikh leaders in the Punjab, the Nizam (ruler) of Hyderabad, the Afghans and Gurkhas (of Nepal) remained loyal to the British. The Madras and Bombay armed forces sat still, for the moment. Governor-General Canning was having trouble in Calcutta, especially with some of his own countrymen who had lost either their nerve or will over the prospect of an uprising. Either way, the pessimism was disturbing to Canning. But he was buoyed by Elphinstone, and also Madras's governor, Harris, who responded on 18 May by sending a contingent of Fusiliers on a ship north along the East India coast to Calcutta. Elphinstone's immediate reaction was to think of the crisis as one for the British Empire first, and his presidency second. He was already strategising like a supreme commander or governor-general, whereas Canning demonstrated indecision and self-doubt, which led to him dithering in the initial months when a sense of purpose, a national perspective and strength were needed.

'Elphinstone deserves the fullest praise from the start,' according to Kaye and Malleson. '[He] possessed this advantage over Lord Canning; his previous experience in India had given him a thorough knowledge of the country and the people. When the Mutiny broke out he saw it as it really was. It was no isolated outbreak, no local discontent, but part and parcel of an organized rebellion, which had its main roots in the North-West Provinces.'

It would move towards Bombay unless stopped early. Elphinstone's presidency was vulnerable because its army was in part made up of Indians from the troubled Oudh province of central India. Elphinstone had studied the Napoleonic Wars and adhered to Bonaparte's strategy of concentrating maximum force at key positions.

The Bombay governor demonstrated he had a head for organisation. An early move was to collect horses, mainly the hardy 'Waler' from Australia, and also others from the Cape and the Persian Gulf. This was in anticipation of cavalry and artillery being sent from England. Elphinstone hired horsemen to break in the animals in time for the cavalry's arrival. His closeness to the Duke of Cambridge, the commander-in-chief in Britain, was vital and they were in constant correspondence. The duke was disposed to meet his every wish in cooperation with his commander in Bombay, General Somerset. Elphinstone dispatched all the European troops he could muster to places most exposed in his huge presidency and beyond.

'From the very hour of the news of the uprising,' Kaye and Malleson wrote, 'Elphinstone displayed a power equal to every emergency...He urged General Ashburnham to proceed to Calcutta with troops he had been taking to China; he chartered steamers; he asked for troops in Mauritius and the Cape [to transfer to India]; he sent a column of troops to Central India.'

A relieved Duke of Cambridge wrote to Elphinstone in June 1857: 'Thanks to your admirable arrangements you have been able...to obtain troops from Cape and Mauritius just at the moment when their services are most needed...Doubtless you have saved your Presidency from joining to any extent in the mutiny of their Bengal neighbours, which it is clear that they were disposed to do.'

Elphinstone appreciated his friend's praise but in his mind it was only the beginning of the effort to curb outbreaks. The column he was directing to central India was commanded by Major-General Woodburn and made up of troops of Elphinstone's previous outfit, the 14th Light Dragoons, along with the 25th Bombay Native Infantry. On 8 June 1857, it left on a long trek towards Mau in the country's north-east where there was trouble. This swift and decisive action may have left Bombay exposed, but the governor used his best officers to secure the city. The experienced and intelligent Brigadier-General Shortt was given command of the entire Bombay garrison. It was made up of 400 Europeans, three Indian regiments, the 10th and 11th Naval Infantry and a Marine battalion. In addition, Elphinstone had a police corps made up of 50 Europeans and 200 Indians controlled by William Crawford, the senior magistrate of police. The governor had surrounded himself with sharp, disciplined and authoritative leaders, who, like him, thrived in a crisis. Then there was the shrewd, brutal Charles Forjett, 43, the superintendent of police. He was the subject of discussion when Husna finally agreed to breakfast with Elphinstone at the residence after they had completed a two-hour-long ride by 8 a.m.

'Are you concerned?' Husna asked. 'The independence movement seems to be spreading.'

'There is no panic with Bombay residents. We will contain the mutiny.'

'Mutiny? It is an attempt to end the Raj—a real fight for independence.'

'We see it as a quasi-unified rebellion. It doesn't help that the newspapers are reporting the massacres by Muslim sepoys in other provinces, but so far there is calm in Bombay.'

'I am not sensing that. I hear "Wahhabi Phobia"—a fear of Muslims.'

A dozen servants fussed about. Coffee was served.

She sipped her drink in contemplation, admiring the wonderful view of the sea, which was providing a cool, relieving breeze.

'What are you proposing to do about the Muslim community?' she asked.

Elphinstone leaned back as tea was poured for him by a servant watching his every move.

'We are consulting with it,' he said.

'You, personally?'

'My chief of police.'

'Forjett? He is hated.'

Elphinstone nodded. 'I know. But he is effective.'

'When you say 'consult', what have you in mind?'

'He'll meet the leaders and mention that peace has to be maintained during the Buckree Id festival.'

'Why that one?'

'I have attended others. Let us say, 'excitement' at them has provoked violence.'

'I've heard you plan to ban the festival.'

'No. I wouldn't do that. But I want no nonsense at it.'

'I shudder to think of Forjett's methods. I've heard he has already warned some leaders that they will be shot if they cause mischief.'

'That doesn't surprise me.'

'You condone his tactics?'

'If they are effective, yes.'

Husna stood up, collected her shawl and hat and walked out.

Forjett had a sepoy spy in the army's ranks, which annoyed its commander, Brigadier Shortt, who claimed he had complete faith in his officers and the rank and file. They did not need any special attention. Forjett was not convinced. He consulted Elphinstone at the governor's mansion.

'Shortt is a good man,' Elphinstone said, 'but perhaps a little naive. We should be wary. See what you can find out from your informant. There are 150,000 Muslims in Bombay and any trouble with sepoys rebelling would soon influence many of the rest. Then we'd have real issues.'

'You're right, my lord,' the straight-backed, square-jawed Forjett said. 'My man is due to report tonight.'

'I've heard from my friend Husna de Crepeney that the Muslim community is most concerned about you.'

Forjett stroked his turned-down, handle-bar moustache and grinned slyly.

'I am pleased to hear it,' he said.

'So am I. Bluff is an important factor here.'

'We may have to go further than that, my lord. We have no serious defence if the uprising spreads here.'

'It won't spread here, if you handle it correctly.'

'Will the Muslim community be public in their support for your presidency?'

'We'll know soon.'

The governor agreed to place 50 mounted Europeans with the garrison soldiers. Bombay citizens reflected the relative harmony and goodwill between them and the Raj when they began seeing Elphinstone and expressing support. First, David Sassoon, heading up the Jewish community, came forward on 15 June and condemned atrocities by the Bengal Army. On 20 June, 400 of the British and Indian elite, representing almost all religions, turned up at the residence. Three days later the Bombay Association, allegedly speaking for a broad cross-section of the community, told the governor how it would muster a civil peace-keeping operation if troops had to be sent away from the city. The press editorialised with suggestions for creating a volunteer force of civilian Europeans, and even a Parsi (Persian) militia.

The spread of the rebellion was very much on the minds of Elphinstone and Husna on a ride out one morning to the Elephant Caves near where they visited the Kanheri Caves. They had to stop several times as elephants and lions wandered near them. When they reached the caves, they dismounted, sat on rocks near the cave entrances and sipped water. It was 7 a.m. but already their clothes clung to their bodies.

'The Muslims have not yet voiced their support for me,' Elphinstone remarked.

'Should they?'

'Would be helpful. It would reassure me that they will not condone disruption. The news from Puna is not good. I am reliably informed that Muslims are plotting to kill Europeans. I've been warned that something unpleasant may happen at Buckree.'

'What will you do?'

'I would not let anything upset the festivities.'

'But how will you go about ensuring that?'

'I shall leave that in Forjett's hands.'

Buckree Id was heavily policed. Forjett made some early arrests and there were fewer incidents than in previous years.

Elphinstone had never been busier in his career. He was preoccupied by keeping Bombay safe, but, in adhering to his dictum to hold rebellion throughout the nation first, he also had to attend to matters outside his presidency. He maintained his position as a far more effective leader in a big crisis than any other member of the Raj, including Lord Canning. Had the British government been closer to events it would have replaced Canning with Elphinstone by June 1857, but it was not in a position to comprehend the fluid and fast-moving dynamics of spot-fire uprisings over India's vastness. The tyranny of distance and unreliability of the still new, but lately improved, telegraph system produced shortcomings in dealing with issues.

'I am persuaded,' a frustrated Elphinstone wrote to Woodburn on 22 June 1857,

> that the local officers greatly exaggerate the danger
> of a rising in our own provinces. I have no fear of
> anything of the sort; and, if it should happen,
> I trust that we should be able to put it down
> speedily. But I feel confident that it will not
> happen—at all events, for the present. If you allow
> the insurrection to come down to our borders
> without attempting to check it, we shall almost
> deserve our fate; but if by a rapid advance you are
> able to secure Mau, you will also, in all probability
> save Mehidpur, Sagar, Hoshangabad etc.

This letter summed up the Elphinstone mentality, which was not replicated by others. Their dithering caused mutinies in Mau and Indur.

These mutinies had to be put down. This promised much bloodshed, which would have been avoided had the governor's initial instruction to restore British authority in central India been carried out.

'The column's march beyond the Bombay frontier was due solely to Lord Elphinstone,' according to Kaye and Malleson. 'Had he been unfettered, and had its first commander been a man after his own heart, it would have taken place in time to prevent much evil in Central India.'

Elphinstone's risky yet brave move to leave Bombay and his presidency without its usual defence strength had been based on the gamble that his request for support troops from Mauritius would be fulfilled. It was in mid-July when the 33rd Regiment arrived and appeased further worries about insurrection in the city, especially concerning another Muslim festival, the Muharram. But just when he had more security, he was under orders to whittle his defences further when Canning's agent in Rajputana province asked for a further column of troops to be sent to central India, along with reinforcements for the first column, which began putting down the rebels at Mau.

The thinning of his armed force caused Elphinstone to further concentrate his thoughts on how to prevent a riot or even an uprising in Bombay. He told Forjett to address a gathering of 500 influential Muslims on 8 August 1857 at the home of their leader, Mohammed Ali Rogay. The governor told the superintendent to be firm and direct. Forjett's subsequent speech was masterful yet vicious. He began by congratulating the Muslim community for maintaining a sagacious 'tranquility'. Then he boasted of the Raj's handling of the crisis and how it had withstood all challenges or efforts to subdue it. The British rulers, he claimed, 'had, as usual, emerged as the victors...only persons fit to be inmates of the [Bombay] Colaba Asylum would attempt to threaten the peace, for *every guilty man will be strung up before his own door.*'

Forjett trusted that the Muslim leaders would use their influence to ensure that the upcoming Muharram festival was incident-free. If this were done they would benefit by safeguarding life and property and 'gain the good graces of the government'. Forjett reminded them of the benefits received from the British, including religious tolerance.

He then quoted a passage from the Koran that said there should be gratitude for such a government. Forjett's performance was quoted in full in the papers the next day.

At noon on 16 August, Husna rode from her apartment to the governor's residence and insisted on seeing Elphinstone. He was at his desk working when she barged into his office. She opened *The Times of India* and pointed to the report of Forjett's comments.

'Are you behind this?' she demanded.

'Forjett was charged with making the Muslim community, in fact, all communities, understand the consequences of rebellion,' Elphinstone said, standing. He gestured for her to sit on the couch near his desk. She remained standing.

'I believe he is inciting problems, not calming them down.' She pointed to the paper. 'This is all so inflammatory! It will make matters worse!'

'Let me be the judge of that,' he said, keeping his equanimity. 'I am waiting for all the leaders of the communities to report in to me. So far the Muslims have not.'

Husna was distressed.

'Don't be so concerned,' he said, coming around his desk.

'I may go back to Paris!' she said, looking tearful. 'This is no city for a Muslim!'

Elphinstone held her close.

'You'll be safe. I assure you of that.'

On 17 August, the Muslim community's key representatives finally came to Government House to pledge their support to Elphinstone, giving assurances of loyalty and devotion to peace. They were the last religious group to do so.

'Better belated than never,' Elphinstone wrote to the Duke of Cambridge. The governor commended Forjett 'for not mincing his words'. Elphinstone's message had a desired effect. Forjett called on the governor early one morning and joined him for breakfast.

'One of the most eminent Muslim leaders, Sheikh Ahmed Kubbay, has told me about nearly 600 troublemakers,' Forjett informed him.

'What do you propose we do?' Elphinstone asked.

'I am here to ask you, governor, but I think we should make an example of the ringleaders.'

'How?'

'Execution.'

'The Muslims are not so hierarchical,' Elphinstone said thoughtfully. 'You would be killing quite a few of them. What are the alternatives?'

'Well, incarceration, governor, but putting so many behind bars would be inviting more trouble.'

'What about shipping them out of the city?'

'Hmm. It could be done.'

'Then do it. Make sure it's in the middle of the night.'

29

THE PRESIDENT'S ENFORCER

Elphinstone next met with Bombay's Lord Bishop. They decided that the city should hold a 'Day of Humiliation'. The bishop announced that it would be on 14 August 1857 'in view of the dreadful judgement with which God is visiting on the land'. The result was people flocking to their houses of worship. They dreaded that the outside terror would strike Bombay, yet the population was unaware of how Elphinstone was manipulating all levers of state and the military to ensure that the city could withstand any assault. By 17 August he had the bulk of European troops stationed at Colaba, protecting government offices, the mint and banks at the city's fort. This also ensured the safety of the nearby docks and harbour. He had a small military guard supported by the police defending the hospitals and the barracks at Colaba. Army units were posted around the town at the entries to the main European residential areas of Malabar Hill, Breach Candy, Byculla and Mazagon. The Indian Navy was called on to send armed sailors to the British Peninsula and Oriental Company office at Mazagon, the powder works at Sewree and Rowlee Hills at Parel. Elphinstone ordered that a train be ready to bring in troops from Bori Bunder on the coast east of Bombay. He directed Brigadier Shortt and Forjett to station armed civilian volunteers at strategic points around Bombay. The governor did not seem to miss anything. He even had suspicious letters that were written in local vernacular sent to a translating department to be checked. This proved fruitful. More would-be troublemakers were rounded up. Elphinstone also made sure that there was some fanfare for the arrival in Bombay of a second detachment of the 33rd Regiment from Mauritius.

'Every scoundrel in the town was closely watched and kept in a state of terror,' Forjett told Elphinstone. He made police rounds in disguise throughout the city at night. If he found anyone speaking of the success of rebels in other parts of India 'in anything like a tone of exultation, I seized him on the spot.' He would blow a whistle. Police would come, bind the 'culprit' and take him to prison. Elphinstone was informed that there would be an uprising from the sepoy ranks in Bombay. Brigadier Shortt and other British officers, certain of the soldiers' loyalties, refused to believe it. The governor sent the more-than-willing Forjett in search of evidence before the beginning of the Muharram festival. The community still feared a Muslim uprising and Forjett responded by stepping up the psychological pressure, which the public knew he coupled with direct, sometimes muscular action. There was always a fear that he would push the governor for martial law, but before such a drastic decree, he had a gallows built in the police station yard. Then he rounded up some of the more criminal and notorious types in Bombay and escorted them down to have a look at the frightening wooden structure. He forced them up the steps to the platform. Then he urged the toughest potential 'subversive' among them to put the noose around his neck to see how it felt. Forjett had a big bag attached to the noose. He asked a hangman to demonstrate what happened when the trapdoor was opened. No doubt more than a few onlookers went a little dry in the throat. The demonstration affected the more dangerous of them. Finally, Forjett reminded the gathering that he knew every single one of them and their whereabouts.

'Like the Indian elephant,' he told them chillingly, 'Forjett *never* forgets.'

The pressure was kept on when actual arrests were made and the men were taken to gaol in view of the gallows. Some were given the choice of hanging or agreeing to be deported during the night. No-one took the former offer. This way some of the more dangerous elements in Bombay were again shipped out under the cover of darkness without fuss or public knowledge. Elphinstone was demonstrating a ruthless side in endorsing Forjett's terror tactics.

Husna's contacts among Bombay citizens told her with more urgency than ever of the fear running through the Muslim community. She accepted an invitation to play golf with Elphinstone at the Royal Bombay Club. When no others would tee off with him because of his partner, they played the course alone together.

'Sorry to cause you so much embarrassment,' she remarked. 'Pardon me for being a woman, a quasi-doctor, an Indian and a Muslim.'

'And not a member!' Elphinstone said with a relaxed smile, handing their clubs to a turbaned servant. 'You are pardoned for all five deficiencies, but I am governor of this presidency and I play with whom I like.'

As they walked the velvet green, one of the most beautiful links in India, her continuing disdain for Forjett's tactics emerged.

'It is all brinkmanship,' she said, as they lined up shots on the fifth green. Elphinstone's shot meandered off the green and into rough. Hers went close to the hole. 'His approach will precipitate problems, not stop them.'

'Perhaps,' Elphinstone said, bending to line up his next shot. He played it and took two shots to reach the hole. 'I believe in firm action early, to nip any disturbances in the bud.'

'At the expense of lives?' Husna asked, hands on hips before she sank her own putt.

'If we stop the massacres occurring,' he said, 'yes.'

Rumours of an uprising persisted. Forjett, with Elphinstone's acquiescence, went more on the offensive rather than waiting for something to happen. The zealous superintendent attempted to break into a home in Sonapore that the governor had been tipped off was a rendezvous point for a clandestine meeting of sepoys. Forjett abducted the house's owner, Ganga Prasad, and took him to a police station for interrogation. Forjett offered bribes for information. When that failed he made threats. Prasad opened up and disclosed the barest facts about a plot for an uprising in sepoy ranks. Forjett forced him to set up a 'sting' operation in which he would lure rebel sepoys to his house. Forjett, his assistant Captain Eddington and an Indian policeman, waited in the house hidden behind wooden panels. They watched the sepoys arrive and then listened to their conversation. There was no doubt in Forjett's mind that these men were hell-bent on trouble. But he knew that Brigadier Shortt would not accept that any Indian soldiers under his command would plot rebellion. Forjett demanded that Prasad set up a second clandestine meeting of sepoys. This time Forjett took with him Major Barrow, the officer commanding the Marine battalion. They approached the house in disguises and took up their hidden positions once more. Barrow was shocked to recognise men from his 10th and 17th regiments.

Forjett and Barrow learned that the sepoys planned an outbreak on the last night of the Muharram festival. Elphinstone's clinically thorough and efficient measures, coupled with Forjett's intimidation of the would-be rebels, had forestalled any immediate trouble in Bombay. Brigadier Shortt was the only weak link. He accepted the evidence of mutineers in the ranks but hesitated over how and when to react. Two days after the rebels were witnessed in Prasad's house, Elphinstone received more intelligence about an uprising, which was passed to Forjett. It was set for 15 October 1857, the night of Diwali—an important Hindu festival. Shortt at last cautioned the officers commanding the 10th and 11th regiments. The ringleaders were arrested and court-martialled. Their punishment was as bizarre and spectacular as it was barbaric: they were sentenced to death by being blown from the muzzle of a cannon.

Husna tried to see Elphinstone. For the first time in their mercurial relationship, he refused to see her. She turned up at another cricket match, this time uninvited. Police would not let her near the member's marquee. Husna waited until Elphinstone sat in a deck chair next to

Forjett to watch the game and then yelled from behind a fence near the guarded entrance: 'Are you not going to see me now, governor?'

Elphinstone got up from his chair and walked to her. When he was a few metres away, he said: 'Not here, not now.'

'How can you sit here, watching a pathetic game of cricket, while your chief of police fires people from a cannon!' she said raising her voice. 'What are you? A monster?!'

Elphinstone looked ruffled. He glanced around to see Forjett striding towards them. 'If you continue like this, I won't speak with you,' he said, as guards moved close. Most of the game's watchers turned their heads to the disturbance near the ground's entrance.

Husna spat in their direction as Forjett reached them.

'I told you that I would not allow the rebels to upset Bombay,' Elphinstone said, his composure returning, 'our approach has worked.'

He turned and walked away with Forjett, leaving Husna crying as she mounted her horse.

'Don't take any notice of her,' Forjett said. 'She is hysterical. Muslim women tend to overreact.'

'I am most fond of her,' Elphinstone said softly, glancing back to see Husna riding away.

'My lord, happy it is for Bombay,' Forjett said, 'happy for western India and happy for India itself that you are Governor of Bombay during this period of the mutiny. Otherwise tens of thousands would be massacred in this city. Just remember that, my lord.'

Elphinstone looked at his police chief, but said nothing.

On 25 January 1858, seventeen-year-old Vicky married 26-year-old Prince Frederick William of Prussia in London. Victoria insisted that the ceremony take place at the Chapel Royal, St James's Palace. It was a love match and the first of the dynastic alliances that the queen and Prince Albert both craved and had crafted from their own union. This new match would, hopefully, cement ties between London and Berlin. Even more sanguine was the desire that this marriage would lead to a unified Germany.

The people of London knew the game in progress. Wherever Vicky ventured a chant went up: 'God save the prince and bride! And keeps their lands allied.'

Victoria was overjoyed at her daughter's wedding, now writing some-times up to three, even four letters a day to her in what was already a copious, ever-flowing two-way communication. Vicky over the last few years had become an even greater confidante of the queen than Albert. In letters, Victoria let go feelings that she would not express in her diary. Vicky responded with as much enthusiasm as her mother, sometimes even out-writing her in letters.

30

THE BRITISH
PREVAIL

By early 1858, the British had begun to take India back under their control using sometimes brutal methods. Massacres occurred in some cities, such as Delhi, adding to the millions killed in the uprising across the nation. The rebels lost ground. They lacked a unified purpose and standout leader to wrest power from the Raj. Their rebellion too was not widespread. Elphinstone had managed to nip any reaction in the bud in Bombay and to maintain vigilance. Madras too was kept quiet. Sikhs and Afghans continued to stay out of the uprising in 1858, while Gurkhas stepped in to help the British suppress rebels. Mutineers ran out of money and men, which forced them to give up on several occasions. They were simply out-resourced by their colonisers. The British battle operations and preparation were at last made easier by the use of an improved telegraph and post, which helped in deciding how many soldiers should be sent where. Mastery of the seas also aided the British in bringing troops from England and, in Elphinstone's case, from South Africa and Mauritius.

In April 1858 after central India (Oudh province) was almost under control, Canning proclaimed that the entire province's land would be confiscated by the British. A former governor of India, Lord Ellenborough, was now president of the Board of Control for India. He drafted a new scheme for governing the country after the rebellion. Ellenborough, known for his impetuosity, sent a caustic dispatch to Canning, censuring his Oudh ruling, and allowed his missive to be published in *The Times*. His colleagues in the Derby government were displeased and let him know it. Ellenborough was forced to resign. His thoughtless act in condemning Canning in public allowed the governor-general to keep his position when otherwise he would have been brought back from India. Canning also wished to impose income tax in India. Elphinstone objected firmly in private correspondence with Canning. The Governor of Madras, Sir Charles Trevelyan, went further and published his own condemnation of the policy in the Indian press. Trevelyan was forced to resign. There was now a renewed unease in England about Canning's capacities. Elphinstone, who was due to return to England by the summer of 1858 after a five-year tenure, was asked to stay on in his job. He would be a back-up should Canning's governorship cause further unrest in India. If Canning was forced out, Elphinstone was recommended by three successive secretaries of state—Vernon Smith, Lord Ellenborough and Lord Stanley—to take over as India's governor-general.

Historians Kaye and Malleson summed up Elphinstone's impact:

> Only those who have enjoyed the privilege of
> reading his voluminous correspondence during
> the 1857–58 Uprising can form an idea of the
> remarkable perspicacity which characterized Lord
> Elphinstone's views on every point connected with
> the stirring events of those years.
>
> The strong and weak points of a case; the true
> policy to be pursued; the proper timing for putting it
> in action; when to withhold the blow, when to strike;
> the reasons for withholding or striking are laid down
> in clear and vigorous language in his letters . . .it
> seems marvellous how a man standing alone should
> have judged so clearly, so truly. Many of the military

movements which tendered to the pacification of
the country had their first inspiration from Lord
Elphinstone...no man in India contributed as much
as him to check the mutiny at its outset; no man
contributed more to dominate it after it had risen to
its greatest height.

In the glory of the victory, amid the bestowal of
well-merited rewards for military service, the great
desserts of Lord Elphinstone received but small notice
from the public...it now becomes the duty of the
historian to place him on the lofty pedestal to which
his great services, and his pure and noble character
entitle him.'

Elphinstone never sought 'notice from the public'. It was not in his
nature. He just wished to do his duty for his queen, to whom he was
dedicated with passion, and the empire, of which he was a prominent
creature. The Bombay experience had given him a sense of fulfilment,
which he had craved while carrying out his duties with diligence at
the docile House of Lords and parochial royal court. All his exceptional
skills were drawn out in India. Elphinstone was exhausted but content
that he had taken on a huge challenge and won. He would not now go
through life wondering about his capacities or the depth of his courage.
But his successes would soon be subsumed by the need to better govern
India.

With peace breaking out, the British government and press
concentrated on what should be done with this vast, unsettled land.
Elphinstone warned Victoria, the prime minister and others in private
that it had to be organised and led far better. He was not alone but still
a strong voice in persisting with the view, expressed a decade earlier
to the queen, that the East India Company should be disbanded. He
had always advised that India would be better off if the crown took
it over. The thought titillated Victoria, whose passion about India had
been kindled then kept up by Elphinstone over more than two decades.
Albert also began urging the transfer of power where India would

come under the control of the British government rather than that of a private company.

Victoria knew that something had to be done. She wrote of her 'feelings of horror and regret at the result of the bloody civil war', then announced that the transfer of power from the company to the state should 'breathe feelings of generosity, benevolence and religious toleration'. At her behest, a reference in the Queen's Proclamation of 1858 that threatened the 'undermining of native religions and customs' was replaced by a clause guaranteeing religious freedom.

It was seen as a further step in the democratisation of the empire, although Indians who understood what was happening would remain disgruntled. It was about British Empire maintenance, not Indian independence. The proclamation set out the changes. Canning was made India's first viceroy. As such, he was in an environment that suited him far better than the pressures of war. He could apply himself as a diligent administrator without the anxieties and huge challenges that the rebellion had created. The East India Company was dissolved by a special British Act of parliament. Britain's possessions and protectorates on the Indian subcontinent were formally incorporated into the British Empire. A fifteen member council was created to run India. Indians were promised more prominent positions in government. Princes were to be paid off to keep them content, even more than they had been with the company. Ancient rites and customs were to be encouraged and retained to keep the natives happy and distracted from further rebellion, although small 'out-clauses' would allow the British to move against more extreme rituals. Rebels, except for those who had murdered British subjects, were to be granted pardons.

31

A 'FRIEND' IN TROUBLE

Victoria wrote to Lord Stanley early in 1859 about the British governors who had survived the Indian uprising with distinction: 'Lord Elphinstone also ought not to be left unrewarded, and a step up in the peerage...does not appear too high an honour for him, for he has greatly contributed to the saving of the Indian Empire.'

The Prince of Wales's biographer, Stanley Weintraub, noted that during the uprising Elphinstone had 'demonstrated courage and resourcefulness when panic was more common'.

True to her word, Victoria followed through. In May 1859 Elphinstone was rewarded with an important civil award—the Knight Grand Cross of the Order of the Bath—and made a peer of the United Kingdom with the title Baron Elphinstone of Elphinstone in the County of Stirling. These were most important honours to him. He had inherited his Scottish Baronetcy; he had more than earned these British citations. The Duke of Cambridge congratulated his great friend and informed him there had been a vote of thanks in parliament. 'I felt a real pleasure in bearing my tribute,' he wrote, 'to the great powers of government and organisation which you have displayed in those eventful times.'

Victoria could not have put it better. She had resumed some discreet, occasional correspondence with Elphinstone after not having quite forgiven him for leaving the royal court for India again in 1853. But when things hotted up in India, she was concerned for him, and began to understand his decision. Victoria was proud of his outstanding service and the fact that it had been recognised by her government, albeit after a nudge and intervention from her. If she had been the prime mover in awarding him so highly after his first stint as governor at Madras, there would have been questions asked about their relationship again. Even in 1859, there were still many in parliament, the royal court, the public and the press who recalled the whispered, rumoured 'scandal' about the young princess and the captain of the Horse Guards of nearly a quarter-century earlier. Elphinstone had achieved on merit in Bombay, which was the way he wished it to be.

He wanted to come home to sort out some minor issues over his estates in Scotland but the British government asked him to stay on in India into 1860. In February of that year, he felt poorly and was soon in bed with a reoccurrence of the fever that had struck him in Madras, and an extra problem with heart palpitations. His personal surgeon and closest friend in India, Richard De Courey Peele, was at a loss on how to treat him. Elphinstone asked him to contact Husna, who had not spoken to the governor for two years since their falling out over the uprising. She turned up at the residence and examined him in his bed as if he were another patient and not a former lover.

'The palpitations can be eased by chest massage,' Husna told him, 'and I can probably alleviate that. But the broader problem for you is the heat. This time I do endorse that you go to the hills to recover. The air is better. It's cooler.'

Elphinstone was taken to a hill resort outside Bombay and after a month's seclusion under the supervision of both De Courey Peele and Husna, he made an apparent recovery. In early April 1860 he returned to the residence to applause from his big staff. He took up duties for a few hours a day, and in late April announced to Husna that he would ride with her again in the morning. But after a week of rides, she noticed that he was pale, sweating and having trouble breathing. She ordered him to bed again. Both she and De Courey Peele became concerned with his weight loss. Husna recommended Elphinstone imbibe hemp oil. De Courey Peele overruled its use. They argued over it in front of the governor.

When De Courey Peele insisted it not be administered, Husna secretly put the oil into his food and it seemed to improve Elphinstone's condition and feeling of wellbeing. He felt fit enough to travel for the first time in months.

'I think it better I return to London,' Elphinstone said to her one morning. 'I'll go to the German spas after that.'

Husna stayed at the residence in the room next to him on his last night in Bombay. In the middle of the night he was awoken by his bedroom door opening.

'Only me, my lord,' Husna whispered. 'I want to be close to you.'

She slipped into bed next to him. He turned to her.

'I don't want you to get this bloody fever,' he croaked. 'It's contagious.'

'I'll risk it,' she said, snuggling close as they embraced.

He was sweating. His nightshirt was soaked. Husna got up and poured some water from the jug on the wash-stand into the basin. She removed his shirt and gently ran a sponge over his entire body. She then dried him with his towel, found a clean nightshirt and helped him put on the fresh garment.

'You're so soothing,' he said, with a wan smile, 'so . . .'

'Loving?' she asked, kissing him softly, letting her lips linger.

'Yes, loving,' he said, his voice a whisper.

'I love you, my lord. You are the only man, save my father, that I have ever said that too.'

He turned to her.

'I have that feeling for you too,' he mumbled.

'More than your little queen?'

'Different. . .'

She kissed him lightly and settled to sleep.

When Elphinstone was ready to be taken on the first stage of his journey home the next morning by De Courey Peele, Husna embraced him and through tears said: 'If you want me to come to London to care for you, I shall, happily.'

'I'll write,' Elphinstone said, as servants waited to carry him from the residence, 'and you can meet me in Germany.' As they embraced, he whispered in her ear: 'I do love you.'

3 2

LAST WRITES

The journey over land and sea was agony for Elphinstone. His condition worsened and by the time he reached London on 12 June 1860, he knew his time was almost up. There would be no trip to freshen up at the German spas. De Courey Peele attended him daily and took up residence at Elphinstone's home at 29 King Street St James, London. Elphinstone wrote to Victoria first, telling her of his plight. She was distressed. She wrote to Lord Canning in India: 'Alas! Another most valuable public servant and friend of ours, Lord Elphinstone, only returned [to London] to die.'

After a hectic day of writing and review of his last will on 18 July 1860, Elphinstone was deteriorating rapidly. He signed the will in front of witnesses, including De Courey Peele. The thirteenth lord's signature was spidery; the last intellectual effort of an accomplished human being. Sedated, he spent a comfortable night, sleeping on into 19 July 1860.

Victoria, a few minutes ride away in Buckingham Palace, spent a restless night waiting for news on the inevitable demise of her former lover. At 6 a.m. she got up and asked one of her staff to visit Elphinstone.

Then she changed her mind. 'Have a common carriage prepared,' she said. 'I shall visit him myself.'

She rode with a lady-in-waiting and two guards out a side entrance to Buckingham Palace Road, past the front of the palace, along The Mall, left into Stable Yard Road, and then into King Street and Elphinstone's home. She was met by a startled De Courey Peele at the front entrance.

'How is the lord?' she said softly, as he bowed and ushered her in.

'Close to parting, your majesty.'

'May I see him?'

'He is barely conscious,' the doctor began but on seeing Victoria's expectant look added, 'yet he would be honoured, ma'am.'

He led her along a passage to the bedroom. Victoria was stunned to see how thin Elphinstone had become. He was lying on his back, his cheeks hollow, his mouth open, sucking in his last hours, perhaps minutes, of breath. De Courey Peele leaned over him.

'My lord,' he said, 'the queen is here to see you.'

Victoria moved close and took Elphinstone's hand. It was ice-cold. She squeezed it and could not fight back tears, yet she kept her voice steady as she whispered:

'Elphi, my love, Elphi.'

Elphinstone's eyes opened. He turned his head and squinted. Making out Victoria, he smiled wanly but warmly. Victoria leaned close and hugged him. She whispered: 'My beautiful, darling Elphi. I always loved you, my first love.'

His hand responded by clasping hers with the last ounces of strength in him. He then went limp and turned his head away. Victoria gave a yelp. Her hand went to her mouth. 'Is he . . .?'

De Courey Peele touched his wrist, feeling for a pulse. It was weak.

'He will not last the day, your majesty,' he said quietly. 'But it is wonderful you have come. You could see how much he appreciated your presence.'

Victoria wept as she was accompanied by the doctor back to the carriage. Her lady-in-waiting comforted her on the return to the palace. Victoria was taken to her bedroom where she planned to remain for the rest of the day. In the next few hours, close friends and confidants gathered at Elphinstone's home. Apart from De Courey Peele they included Colonel Bates, his former military secretary, and a relative, Mr Adam, who had been his private secretary throughout the seven-year Bombay presidency. Elphinstone lost consciousness in the afternoon and died in the evening. He was 53. His cryptic death certificate put down the 'cause of death' as 'intermittent fever, with enlarged spleen'.

The 13th Lord Elphinstone's last words were to De Courey Peele: 'Let it be known, my good friend, that through the pain I died fulfilled—in life, in love and in achievement.'

33

NOBLE INTENTIONS

Elphinstone was buried in the quiet Church of England graveyard of the elegant and beautiful St Peter's, Limpsfield, in Surrey near the Kent border. He was placed next to the grave of his uncle Mountstuart Elphinstone, situated under the church's window on the north-facing wall. Victoria pondered going to the funeral, but decided she would be overcome by grief and her reaction would be noted. Instead, she sent a large wreath.

Victoria remained sorrowful over her former lover's death. She remarked to any close to her of the loss of her 'good friend', but she could not avoid the continued grief created by the memories that flooded her mind on Elphinstone's demise. He would leave a hole in her life that could not be filled by another. She had known, loved and respected him for 25 years. Ever since her early years, Victoria had been smitten by the handsome captain of the Horse Guards. Now he was gone and she felt empty, abandoned and unloved. She needed someone to talk to about the loss but there was not a soul to whom she could turn to unburden her feelings. She began something in her diary but then ripped out the page and burnt it. There was always the fear that her diaries would be made public posthumously and she was aware that in her exalted position every scribble, however absent-minded, pointless or simplistic, would be pored over by future historians. She had seen it countless times before with royalty everywhere and knew that as queen of the world's greatest empire her every utterance would be analysed perhaps for centuries to come. At times like this it unnerved her. She could not rely on her diary, which was her silent 'companion.' It might one day turn on her.

Instead, Victoria decided to write to the one confidante she could trust implicitly to keep secrets: nineteen-year-old Vicky. Vicky was mature for her years and devoted to her mother, father and children. Victoria was at Osborne House on 25 July, six days after Elphinstone's death. She planned at first to write to congratulate Vicky on the birth of her second child, Charlotte. It was a stunning mid-summer day. The sea was calm, the sky cloudless. Victoria sat alone in the pink-coloured alcove overlooking the beach where she had entertained Elphinstone. She wrote:

> Thousand, thousand good wishes, blessings and congratulations! Everything seems to have passed off as easily (indeed more so) as I could have expected though I always thought it would be very easy, and totally different to the last time, and the darling baby, such a fine child. I am delighted it is a little girl, for they are such much more amusing children. This [Charlotte] will be another Beatrice. How I long to hear who she is like and what she is called!

Victoria went on to confess her affair with the thirteenth lord, whom her daughter knew and admired from his court days. This purging on paper was a considerable release for Victoria from an experience that had played on her mind since those turbulent days. Now that the secret was with someone she loved and trusted so dearly, she discreetly commissioned the Yorkshire-born royal sculptor Matthew Noble, 42, to create a larger than life-size marble monument of Elphinstone, which cost £3235. Noble was her favourite sculptor. He had exhibited scores of works at the Royal Academy, starting with the bust of the Archbishop of York in 1845. In 1847, she and Albert had been most pleased with the bust he did of Victoria. She came to know, like and trust Noble in the few sittings she granted him when he did the preparatory drawings and measurements. It led her to commission a bust of Albert, which once more pleased the royal couple. In 1856, Noble entered and won a very keenly fought competition to do the Wellington monument at Manchester. In 1858, he was asked to execute a huge marble bust of Albert, again for Manchester. That city's mayor, Thomas Goadsby, also commissioned a nearly nine-metre high marble statue of Albert.

In a private meeting with Noble at Buckingham Palace, Victoria discussed her requirements for Elphinstone's image. They stood near a table in her study.

'I want a dignified marble monument to this man as I remember him,' she said softly and sombrely. 'He should be in the robes of the Knight Grand Cross of the Order of the Bath, with his left hand over his heart.'

'So I was informed, your majesty, in the note from you and I have taken the liberty of creating these sketches.' He removed drawings from a leather folio holder and handed them to her.

'Wonderful...remarkable...' she said examining the drawings. 'This is as I recall him!'

'"Recumbent, but not deathly,"' was your instruction, your majesty.'
'Yes, you have done well, Noble, so very well.'
'And the dedication?' he asked as he took out a quill and paper.
'Ah, yes,' she handed him a sheet.

TO THE MEMORY OF
THE RIGHT HONOURABLE JOHN
13th LORD ELPHINSTONE
BORN 1807. DIED 1860.
THIS MONUMENT IS ERECTED
AS A TRIBUTE OF SISTERLY AFFECTION'

Noble read it out and nodded. '"Sisterly affection", your majesty?'
'I wish the memorial to be discreet in every respect, Noble.'

'I understand, majesty,' he said. 'The question is where the monument should be placed. At that size, and using marble, it will have to be sculpted where it will be located.'

'So I was forewarned. It should be at the lord's burial place at St Peter's, Limpsfield.'

'Has the priest there been informed?'

'No. Just in case he is...er...difficult—a situation which might draw unnecessary attention to the monument—he is to be sent on a sabbatical.'

'Oh,' Noble chuckled, 'where?'

'France, for a year.'

'That will be plenty of time, majesty.'

Victoria handed him a plan of the church.

'You should create it inside the building,' she instructed. 'It should be near the wall outside which Lord Elphinstone is buried.' Victoria pointed to another sketch on the table. 'There is another request. I want two stained-glass windows placed in the wall between his grave outside and your creation inside.' She pointed at a drawing on the left and with her eyes down added: 'In this window in the bottom part I wish to see er...a queen knighting a kneeling man in full regalia. The top part can be some other religious depiction. I'll leave that to you, Noble. The top part will take away the significance of what I actually wish in the bottom half of the panel.'

'Yes, majesty, I can see to this with a very special glazier friend,' Noble nodded. 'But stained glass? The archbishop may not agree.'

'Oh, he will agree, Noble,' Victoria said, with a mixed expression of haughtiness and certitude. 'I am the head of the Church, remember.'

'Of course, ma'am,' Noble said with a nod which grew into a bow.

Victoria pointed to another drawing.

'It is this window in which I wish to see a second depiction in the bottom half. Again the top half may be of some other religious symbolism and, again, you may choose it.'

Noble leant over the second drawing and peered at it closely.

'It is the same...queen,' he said, 'with a...'

'A child clinging to her. Not a baby, mind you, a grown child.'

'Hmm. Unusual. Is there meaning here, majesty?'

Seeing her famous look of disapproval for the question, he added quickly: 'I only wish to have a sense of what I am to create, majesty.'

'Just do your very best, Noble, which I know will be brilliant. I want the light to shine over the lord's grave outside the church and onto the monument inside.'

'Of course, majesty,' he said, bowing again and aware that the consultation was over.

'Just one question, if I may, majesty. What happens if the priest objects to my handiwork when he returns from his "sabbatical"? If he wants to remove the monument, he will have to take the Church down around it.'

'If he objects he will have to live with it, Noble, or leave his parish.'

Husna received a letter from De Courey Peele, telling her of Elphinstone's death at the same time she heard from the deceased man himself. Even though she assessed he was dying in his last days in Bombay, she was devastated by the sad news. She decided to leave India and return to Sweden where she hoped she would finally be accepted as a qualified medical practitioner.

34

THE END FOR
ALBERT'S TORMENT

Exhausted by the emotion over Elphinstone, other family deaths and the usual issues of state, in the autumn of 1860 Victoria took time off with Albert to visit Prussia for the first time. A few weeks into the stay Albert was in an accident when he jumped clear of his runaway four-horse carriage just before it collided with a wagon at a level-crossing, He seemed to recover but Stockmar, whom Victoria and Albert visited, made the stark observation that Albert had been affected by the incident more than anyone realised. The prince, he believed, was not a resilient enough soul to overcome a serious illness if one were to befall him.

Stockmar's private comment showed some prescience when Albert was about to leave Coburg. The prince broke down in front of his brother, saying he would never see his birthplace again. Albert was a sad figure, who had let his body and spirit go to seed. He was only 41 but physically and spiritually defeated. He teetered between hypochondria and real medical issues. A bright spot in his medical care was Clark's retirement, aged 73. Albert had never approved of him and could never understand why Victoria had ordered her husband to be his patient when others had deserted him 21 years earlier. Clark had been replaced by Dr William Baly, a younger man with a brilliant reputation. But late in 1860 he was killed in a train accident, leaving Albert bereft. Clark did his duty at Victoria's request and returned part time to find another doctor. He secured William Jenner, a pathologist. Albert continued to suffer ailment after ailment, from teeth problems to swollen glands, yet nothing, it seemed, would slow down his strenuous work habits. It was as if he had to keep proving himself in the special role that he had created as consort.

Matters were made worse for the royal couple when the Duchess of Kent died at Windsor on 16 March 1861. Victoria was present with Albert, who had done much as the mediator to bring mother and daughter together after years of bitter estrangement. Albert was upset. He had been close to his mother-in-law, aware that, along with Stockmar and Leopold, she had been instrumental in arranging his life with her daughter. Victoria had never completely forgiven her mother for her behaviour when she (Victoria) was ill at Ramsgate and for banishing Elphinstone from the kingdom. The duchess's siding with Conroy in taking her lover from her had made Victoria think that her mother did not love her. But, on going through her mother's papers, she realised that the opposite had been true. In recent years, the duchess and Victoria had been as close as any other mother and daughter in her circle, or perhaps even an average family. There were so many family events, births, deaths, marriages and birthdays among them that there was much to gossip about. They had been drawn together. But those private papers made Victoria realise that this love was not a late thing. Her mother had always had good feelings towards her, despite what the duchess perceived as Victoria's headstrong adolescent years. The duchess's death, Victoria's remorse about not being fully aware of how her mother felt about her all along, and now the sense that another powerful influence in her life had been taken from her, combined to cause a breakdown, a profound bout of depression.

Victoria wrote to Leopold, telling him she felt no longer cared for by anyone. Albert was too busy to fill the void or even be aware that he could give more to his wife at this moment of loss. Yet she dared not reproach her husband, who was forever under a tremendous workload. Instead, she went into months of mourning interspersed with bouts of melancholia and hysteria. It reached a point where many at court, including Albert, wondered once more if she had inherited the madness of her grandfather, George III. This amateur assessment of her severe and unmedicated depression had come up occasionally in her life. Now, as she matured and moved into her forties, it was more frequently a subject for discussion among the chattering classes connected with the royal court. Shielded from the gossip, Victoria wore black for months out of respect for her mother as much as sadness for herself.

Victoria longed to be closer to Albert. She needed his attention now more than ever but he seemed unable to recover from his riding accident. His own 'down' periods and prolonged listless spells made her concerned about him. The thought of losing him was unbearable.

On the way to Stockholm, Husna De Crepeney diverted by boat to London and visited St Peter's in Limpsfield to mark the birthday of the thirteenth lord on 23 June 1861. She arrived wearing a long black dress and hat, and could hear Matthew Noble putting the finishing touches to his creation of Victoria's commissioned memorial. Husna found Elphinstone's grave outside and placed a dozen roses on it. She ventured to the entrance and watched Noble chiselling at a huge marble block, his face covered by a gauze mask. He stopped working, took off his mask and approached her.

'Can I help, madam?' he asked. 'I'm afraid the church is closed for a renovation. I am just finishing this work. We have a very important visitor coming in two hours.'

Robed church figures were bustling about, looking nervous.

Husna smiled.

'It is pleasing,' she said, 'very pleasing that your little queen has sought to honour such a great man this way.'

'Who are you?' Noble asked impatiently, while still surprised at Husna's comment.

'I was Lord John's very good friend and lover,' she said, matter of factly. She stepped over to the marble figure and placed two roses in the finely honed hands.

'How did you know—' Noble began and then checked himself. His project was meant to be secret. Before he could say more, she had walked outside. He paced to the door to see her disappearing down steps to a waiting carriage on the road. Noble looked up for what he later described as the shock of his life. At the top of the hill running down to the church was an entourage of three carriages and several mounted and kilted guardsmen. He had no doubt that the gilded carriage in the middle of the halted procession was occupied by Queen Victoria. Noble went into a flap. He had been shaving off a few blemishes on the monument but now had to stop and have it swept up for Victoria, who was two hours early for the first viewing of Elphinstone's effigy.

Victoria and her entourage watched in silence as Husna's carriage clattered by up the hill to the road back to London. Victoria noted that, like her, its passenger was dressed in black and she was curious to know who had been in the church before her. Could it be that Elphinstone's half-sister come to pay her respects, she wondered.

Church dignitaries ran to the hill-top to greet, bow and beckon the royal procession down the hill. Victoria was helped from the carriage by two ladies-in-waiting and escorted by the stand-in priest, the rotund Reverend Arnold Potter, to the church's entrance.

'Who was that visitor, Noble?' Victoria asked sharply as she stepped inside.

'She did not give her name, majesty, but she did venture the most extraordinary comment.'

'Oh, and what did she say?' Victoria asked, trying hard to sound only vaguely interested.

'Well, she claimed to be a good friend of the thirteenth lord's, majesty, and . . .'

'And, Noble?'

'Er . . . um . . .' He began with a nervous giggle, 'She also *claimed* to be the lord's *lover*, majesty.'

'Lover? Poppycock!' Victoria gathered herself and with a wince added, 'Really, Noble, you should not have allowed such an odd stranger into the church.' She looked around and glared at the officials, who all examined their feet. Her eyes fell on the memorial, but she blinked at the two roses, which sat in the reclining statue's hands.

'Those flowers,' she snapped, 'get rid of them.' She turned to a lady-in-waiting and motioned for her to place a small bunch of mixed flowers on the marble hands.

'How . . . how . . . do you like the work, majesty?' Noble asked bravely.

Victoria wandered close and leaned over the face. She was making an effort to compose herself and said after a lengthy pause, 'It is remarkably good, Noble. Quite, quite special. Better than I imagined and so lifelike. I thank you.'

'I am most honoured and grateful, majesty,' Noble said with genuine relief.

Victoria admired the windows she had requested. She looked around and said: 'Now, please, take me to the graveside.' Reverend Potter, showing a certain presence of mind, scurried outside, grabbed the six roses on the grave and scattered them on other graves out of sight, just before Victoria appeared.

'He was a very loyal servant of the crown,' Victoria said, in an indirect effort to justify her being there, eyeing Potter and Noble. 'Saved India for the empire.'

At Elphinstone's graveside, she bowed her head for a moment, causing the entire entourage and the church officials to do the same. After wandering with everyone else in tow into the church's western graveyard, she spotted a couple of Husna's scattered roses. She turned to Potter and said with a momentary wince rather than a smile: 'Lovely roses, Reverend.'

Potter went red and swallowed before stepping forward to ask Victoria if she would like to stay for food and refreshment.

'We have come a long way,' she said, 'and, yes, we would like that very much, thank you.'

Prince Albert slid into a mental and physical abyss through 1861, culminating in distress over nineteen-year-old Colonel Bertie's dalliance with a prostitute, Nellie Clifden, at the Curragh military training camp, at Kildare, Ireland. Boisterous fellow officers paid Nellie to be in Bertie's bed when he returned after a bout of drinking with them. Her royal duty, she was told, was to give the prince and future King of England 'freedom from his state of virginity'. Nellie went about her mission diligently and so well that he wanted to secret her back to Cambridge where he was a student.

Word of the relationship filtered back to the royal court. When Albert heard of this event, he was mortified. It hurt him to think that his son had strayed so far from the godly life he had directed and instructed. The timing too upset Albert. A marriage was being arranged for Bertie. Victoria tried to placate Albert.

'It is such a vile and crude thing to do!' Albert remarked.

'He is sowing his wild oats,' Victoria said. 'Something not unknown in both our families.'

'Yes, but apart from animal lust associated with his pursuits, it is so dangerous! It opens him to blackmail, ridicule, *everything*. It reflects on you and me so badly. Such depravity could threaten the monarchy.'

'Now darling—'

'No, think of it. It is just what those awful Scottish and Irish republicans would love to see. Ammunition for their cause.' Albert buried his head in his hands. 'How could we produce such a thoughtless offspring?'

Hearing of her father's distress, Vicky, on a trip to London, met with Bertie at Kensington Palace when he was on leave from Kildare. The air was crisp when they walked the fields close to the palace.

'Papa is so distressed over your..."affair" with that notorious woman.'

Bertie was embarrassed.

'You must understand, Bertie, he is from a different background than Mama. Such matters are abhorrent to Papa.'

'Yes, "sex". It is so appalling to him. I often wonder how we got here.'

'But it's not the same with Mama. She is a Hanoverian. They have a different outlook.'

'She is an awful prude like him.'

'I am afraid you are wrong there.'

'What do you mean? How do you know?'

'I cannot say.'

'You can tell me. I thought there were no secrets between us.'

Vicky stopped and turned to Bertie, eyeballing him. 'If I tell you, will you never mention it to anyone?'

He nodded, intrigued. 'Of course,' he said, 'I'd never divulge anything you told me.'

Vicky knew this to be true. There was a strong bond between the siblings.

'Mother wrote to me a long letter about an affair she had before she met Papa.'

Bertie was stunned. His eyes bulged as he struggled to assimilate this information.

'Who was it? Not the Duke of Cambridge? Not one of those ghastly Dutch?'

'Lord Elphinstone.'

Bertie's hand went to his mouth. 'No! He was often at the court, but...'

'He was appointed by Mama. She wanted him there.'

'I remember being told that he was sent to India for something...'

'He was sent to Madras after his relationship with Mama.' She paused to let the astonishing news sink. Her brother was torn between revelation and incredulity.

'I liked the man so much,' Bertie mumbled.

'We all did, including Mama, very much.'

'I often wished he, or someone like him, was my father.'

'Mama was fifteen and very much in love before she met Papa. In that sense there was no betrayal of Papa.'

Bertie was deep in thought. 'You say she said this all in a letter?'

Vicky nodded. 'Yes. It is safe with me,' she said, 'as is all our correspondence.'

'She always wrote to you.'

Vicky touched his arm. 'Oh, Bertie, you know you are an appalling correspondent! If you had replied, she would have written much to you. She wants so much to know everything from all of us.'

'I know, Vicky. You're right.'

They strolled on. A shepherd was moving about fifty sheep close to them.

'Amazing,' Bertie said, shaking his head. 'I don't know whether to laugh or cry.'

'You know you are like her?'

'What?'

'Mama had admitted that she fears you are the male version of her.'

Bertie was surprised. 'She never told me!'

'It's not the sort of thing to tell a son.'

He smiled ruefully and said: 'I suppose not.'

'It might encourage you to think—'

'That cavorting with the likes of Nellie was acceptable?'

Vicky nodded. Then she stopped and turned again to him, her expression serious again. 'Could you consider dropping her?' she asked.

He stared. 'They haven't sent you to abort my relationship, have they?'

'No, of course not. But I do know that Papa has organised a wonderful woman for you to marry.'

Bertie clenched his fists and stamped his foot. 'They have been doing that for a year. I hate this!'

'You won't, dear brother, when you meet her.'

Bertie shook his head again. They waited until the shepherd had eased his herd past them.

'Who is she?' he asked.

'That I cannot tell you.'

'But you know her.'

'I've met her. She is easily, *easily* the most beautiful woman of royal blood in the world.'

Bertie's interest piqued. He tried not to show it.

'Why not tell me?' he asked.

'That is the privilege of our papa. But I would ask you to let go this whore—'

'She is no whore! She wants to be an actress. . .and I can help her.'

'That's in the future. She is now a common Irish prostitute, is she not?'

Bertie hung his head. 'I don't see her as common,' he mumbled. 'She. . .she is funny and amusing and interested in music.'

Vicky rolled her eyes. 'Get rid of her!'

Bertie looked defiant.

When St Peter's priest returned from France after a year away, he was not pleased with the large, elegant memorial to Elphinstone. He wanted the 'carbuncle of a thing' removed but was told by a higher church authority that this was impossible. The priest was never informed why the monument had been put there and who had commissioned it. Nor did he have much idea of Elphinstone's achievements, which had received modest mention in the press. The reverend father had to accept it for the rest of his term at Limpsfield.

The efforts of Victoria and Albert with Bertie were a repeat of the events that had happened to them twenty years earlier when they, as young adults, were manipulated into a relationship to satisfy the royal social engineering ambitions of the Duchess of Kent and Leopold. The difference was that the two callow youths were at least consulted en route to their coupling. Albert's dictation rather than consultation left Bertie confused. But this befuddlement was offset to an extent when he learned, as his sister had said with such certitude, just how beautiful his proposed bride would be. The young woman in question, Princess Alexandra of Denmark, would have no such luxury or compensation to look forward to. Albert wrote a 'carrot and stick' letter to his son. It demonstrated his shrewd mind by conjuring a picture of Nellie, now in London, becoming pregnant to one of her many 'admirers' in the burlesque halls. Albert warned that she would claim that Bertie was the father.

'If you were to try to deny it,' Albert noted, 'she can drag you into a court of law and force you to own it.' Once Bertie was 'in the witness box, she will be able to give, before a greedy Multitude, disgusting details of your profligacy for the sake of convincing the jury, yourself cross-examined by a railing, indecent attorney, and hooted and yelled at by a Lawless Mob! Oh Horrible prospect, which this person has in her power, any day to realize! And to break your parents' hearts.'

Given Bertie's sheltered life, tendency to stutter and unconfident character, this would have been a shocking letter, its emotional blackmail meant to leave him guilt-ridden and fearful. It was a cunning way of railroading him into the marriage he had been resisting. The message was *in* Albert's lines, not between them. His mother the queen and the monarchy itself, to which Bertie was intricately bound, had to be protected. He reacted predictably with shock, contrition and repentance and not a little horror that a bit of sustained fun, where two people appeared to do no harm to each other, should create such a ruckus. Bertie said he had ended the affair despite the boasts in London by Nellie, who was cashing in on the claim that she was Bertie's 'princess'. Unconvinced by his son's claims, Albert decided he had to visit his son to work things out and elicit assurances from him. Albert was in a sorry mental state. He told Victoria that he had lost the zest to live, which was in accord with Stockmar's recent observations in Prussia.

'If I had a severe illness,' Albert said, 'I am sure I would give up at once; I should not struggle for life. I have no tenacity for life.' This was strangely defeatist for a 41-year-old in a job that he had fought for and had built up. It reflected his overwork in dealing with his own and the queen's affairs. In this mood and with his constitution failing, Albert met Bertie at Madingley Hall, Cambridge. They walked outdoors until the early hours of 26 November 1861. It was cold. Albert coughed so much that Bertie suggested they return to the hall.

'Not until we resolve this prostitute thing,' Albert said, a handkerchief thrust to his mouth.

'There is nothing to resolve, Papa.'

'Are you still seeing this woman?'

'Occasionally, but as a friend only.'

'That is not good enough. You must rid her from your life. Then and only then will the rumours die.'

'Papa that is. . .is so. . .so,' Bertie began but was held up by a sudden stutter, something that had afflicted him less in the last few months.

'What boy? Say it!'

'Un–un–unfair!'

'Unfair?! That we ask you to desist from an affair that is a danger to you and the monarchy itself?'

'Does Mama know of this. . .too?'

'Of course and she is distressed, like me.'

'I d–don't believe. . .believe that.'

'Why? Do you think she approves?!'

'I thought sh–sh–she might be. . .un–un—'

'Understanding? Why? You are committing a morally outrageous and disgusting act with a common whore! Your mother is head of the Church, queen of empire!'

'B–b–but. . .'

'Spit it out,' Albert ordered and then went into a coughing fit. Bertie was suddenly angry.

'You should ask her how sh–she. . .would know how I feel.'

'What are you saying?'

Bertie could not bring himself to say more.

When he could speak without coughing, Albert said, in a more conciliatory tone: 'I want you to agree never to see this woman again or any other whore. Will you do that my son, please, if not for your sake but for that of me and your mother?'

Bertie burst into tears. When his father pushed the request, Bertie was unable to reply but nodded his head vigorously. The emotional 'chat' seemed to clear the air. Albert, in some pain, left Cambridge by train for London feeling worse physically but assured that the matter had been resolved.

Albert needed rest but was forced to confront a political problem. A mail ship, *Trent*, en route to England from the United States, had been seized by American government authorities. On board were Confederates aiming to reach England to raise funds and buy weapons. Palmerston, aware that the queen was in mourning and Albert was ill, had reverted to his former belligerence in a draft ultimatum to President Lincoln. Albert now had to intercede in a bellicose encounter that could lead to war. It added to the strain on him. It was his last act of conciliation as prince consort. He had contracted a serious lung problem that Dr Jenner, even more the optimist than the semi-retired Clark, diagnosed as pneumonia.

Clark returned to the court during the crisis, despite his own wife being near death. He believed that Albert probably had typhoid fever but complaints about severe pain in the stomach confused the diagnosis. Typhoid was the leading disease killer in an era in which one person in every three died of infection of some kind. The main reason was poor sanitation. Sewage went into the waterways, making the River Thames in particular a cesspool in the summer months. Parliament would rise early to avoid the stench. Victoria's keenness for Osborne and Balmoral was in large part because they were disease-free zones. The dreaded 'fever', which had plagued London since 1820—nearly all the time both Victoria and Albert had been alive—was not mentioned, especially to Victoria. She was desperate about her husband a few days after he returned from the Cambridge meeting. He went to bed but continued to decline. Albert insisted on telling Victoria all Bertie had said. It exhausted him further.

'He insisted that you would understand his behaviour,' Albert said in a whisper as Victoria sat beside his bed, holding his hand. Her face flushed.

'Do you know what he meant?' Albert asked.

'I have no idea whatever,' she said a little too quickly.

'He suggested that you could explain how you would know how he felt.'

'I have no idea what he is talking about. Has he gone mad? I would never condone his dalliance with such a person!'

Albert frowned. He seemed confused rather than suspicious as he lapsed into a deep sleep. She panicked and ordered the doctors to come quickly. They were concerned about her mental state and that the truth about Albert's condition would distress her too much. Victoria was in an emotional whirl over her husband that wavered between fear, false optimism and hysteria. She began to flail around for a reason, a scapegoat, for what had befallen Albert. She settled on Bertie and his behaviour that had so worried 'Papa'.

Albert had declined fast after the attempt at conciliation on the trip to Cambridge. Had their conversation destroyed Albert's will to live? It was bad enough for the highly moral, pious, and narrow-minded Albert to know that his first-born son had dallied with an Irish prostitute. Some fathers of that era (or any other) in any class may have been secretly relieved, even pleased that a son had 'broken his duck' in this manner. But not Albert, and not when he had lined up for his son a stunning, chaste young woman to be his wife and the future Queen of England. Certainly the father-and-son discussion had taken several hours outside in the cold winter's night air to avoid being overheard. Then Victoria reflected on Bertie's remark about her being 'understanding' of his behaviour. She wondered if this comment had sown some nasty seed of doubt in Albert's mind about her. Victoria fretted that it may have been enough to make Albert decline further.

On Friday 13 December, Albert took a turn for the worse. He died the next night. Victoria was grief-stricken as never before. She had lost her husband, closest friend, mentor, guide, in effect her *king*. It was Albert that had taken over the royal duties of attending to the toughest problems involving judgement, approval, disapproval and discussion over all affairs of state that needed the monarch's input, if only for a signature. He had created another deeper layer for royal involvement, weaving together the main themes of the era concerning government, science, religion, art, industry, capital, labour, personal endeavour and a sense of justice for all. In so doing, Albert had enriched, intellectually and aesthetically, the monarchy, all the institutions that counted, and society in general. That he was humourless, overly reserved, more religious than the archbishop, overbearing and apparently 'cold' was offset by his ideals, drive and sense of purpose. His legacy was a steady constitutional monarchy that had kept the nation stable in an era where all other European states were in turmoil. Had he not appeared at the British court, the monarchy may not have survived.

Victoria had lost people in her life—Melbourne, Wellington, Elphinstone and the Duchess of Kent among them—who were in their own way unable to be replaced. But Albert's closeness and her dependence on him would leave a chasm that would affect her private life and public duties in ways she had never contemplated. There was no-one to share the joys and damnations of parenthood; no partner to attend glittering events, or a quiet dinner over which almost every uncensored thought could be aired; no true love in the deeper sense beyond romance. Now that had vanished. Victoria was overwhelmed, as if trapped in some horrific, ethereal nightmare.

35

THE QUEEN HAS
GONE MISSING

It was as if the British empire had lost both Prince Albert *and* Victoria. A few days after her husband's death, she slipped into seclusion to mourn at Osborne for two months. She had lost the will to face her ministers, the public, her family, friends and life itself. Victoria did not believe she would live another year without her beloved. She returned to Windsor but remained out of sight. She slept with a cast of Albert's hand and clasped it through each night. She had the presence of mind, despite the blurred vision of her existence, to commission plenty of busts and statues of him. Everyone who met her in the first half of 1862 was struck by her melancholy and sadness. Some believed the death had this time truly driven her insane. Victoria indicated to Lord Clarendon that any major conflict in parliament might cause her to go mad. He let Lord Derby know that the opposition should go easy on the government until the summer recess.

Victoria ignored overtures to see anyone, including her Privy Councillors, something she had never done when in England since her first day as queen in 1837. Yet she did respond to her new clerk, who had the hopeful name of Arthur Helps. He suggested that she sit in one room while he and three councillors stood in another, with the door open between them. As each item on the agenda was read out, Helps looked to her for a response. If she nodded, he would say, 'approved'. Victoria began attempting to read the 'boxes'—the business of state that needed her royal assent and signature. She read things she did not understand either in part or completely. She had abrogated this responsibility among many to her husband soon after their marriage, which he hungrily and happily took over. Two decades on, she was lost, out of touch and at this moment uninterested in any affairs of state.

After a few months Victoria regained a vague connection to the family, making sure that Bertie was sent abroad—to Palestine—before the intended marriage to Princess Alexandra. She was carrying out Albert's fervent wishes. Yet Victoria refused to meet Bertie, believing more and more that his 'disgusting' behaviour at Curragh and specific remarks in the Cambridge chat had killed her husband.

'I never can, or shall, look at him without a shudder,' she wrote to Vicky. But Vicky leapt to her brother's defence, persuading her mother to reconsider. Victoria conceded that the affair may not have killed him but that it did break her husband's heart. She hardened towards the disappointing Bertie, insisting again that he was a 'caricature' of *herself*: she meant that he embodied her own worst features. Victoria poured out her feelings in letters to Vicky, who was nervous over her mother's comment about Bertie saying to Albert that Victoria would understand his behaviour. He had not said how, neither had he alluded to the Elphinstone affair, although it was a little worrying to Vicky that her brother had nearly, but not quite, divulged Victoria's biggest secret. She wrote to Bertie and reminded him never to even hint that he knew something. Bertie apologised in a letter, admitting that in a fit of pique over his father's demands he had said something he should not have.

Victoria was not so forgiving, although she dare not confront her son over what may have been said and why he had hinted at her 'understanding' of his behaviour with Nellie Clifden. The guilt of her own youthful years had come back, but things improved on Bertie's return from abroad. Victoria was impressed with his demeanour. When his governor (his supervisor, companion, guide and mentor), General

Bruce, died of a fever on the trip, she fretted over how the twenty-year-old would cope. He had lost both father and guide in a short time. Her concern was the first positive sign that she might be coming out of mourning although no-one close to her believed she would ever overcome her grief. Victoria's worry spilled into action. She sent Vicky as an envoy to the Danish royal court to explain Bertie's situation. She did not want him or his future partner railroaded into a marriage he and his intended bride would both regret. The fair-minded, sympathetic mother and mother-in-law re-emerged, if temporarily. But Victoria's level of interest in her family and offspring ran only in any depth to the immediate worries about Bertie's pending marriage. For the rest of her children, emotions, actions, even guidance were on hold at least until November 1862.

After that, Victoria began emerging ever so slowly from a void of gloom and mourning. It manifested by showing more concern for her family, which meant embroiling herself in everything from Bertie's marriage to Alexandra and who should take the throne of Greece to the battles between Prussia (and the Austrians) and the Danes. She reproached Vicky for siding with the Prussian attitude to that encounter, and argued with her over England not supporting the Prussians. She was involved, she was committed and she was effusive in her diary with endless references to Albert, mainly centred on asking: 'What would Albert do or say?' Or 'what was Albert's line or directive on this or that?' This was working through her grief in a positive way. But so far she had done nothing in public. Victoria had not gone out in an open carriage. She had not opened parliament. Press reaction, cautious at first, soon began to ask questions. Some even mentioned the possibility of abdication. Should she disappear into retirement and let Bertie run the show and 'the firm'? By the end of 1862, a year after the shock of Albert's permanent departure, she was thinking more clearly. There were no real thoughts about giving up, yet she was not yet committed to 'going on'. In part this was because she thought she should die. One 'friend,' the Duchess of Buccleuch, kept talking to her about the loss. She could not understand how her majesty could 'go on, or work or live'. It was not good commentary for Victoria's morale. But she was doing all three. It's likely that her inner strength was far greater than that of her friend.

Bertie's 1863 marriage to 'Alix' exacerbated some differences between him and his mother. When Alix's father inherited Denmark's throne in November 1863, the German Confederation (Prussia and Austria) took the opportunity to invade and annex the disputed territories of Schleswig and Holstein. Victoria sympathised with Prussia and Austria, where most of her relatives resided. Bertie sided with his wife, who was anti-Prussian, as was prime minister Palmerston and foreign secretary Russell. Bertie offended Victoria further in the same year by visiting Garibaldi when the Italian revolutionary leader came to England. Bertie's lead caused London society and the people to greet Garibaldi warmly in London, much to Victoria's fury. She rebuked Bertie, but he was 22 and maturing as his own man. He stood his ground. Victoria blamed his comptroller, General Knollys, who looked after his financial affairs, for arranging her son's meeting with Garibaldi. But Bertie took the responsibility for it: another sign that he was growing up. Victoria's general indifference in the wake of her losses allowed her son to go further on his own way, especially in his attraction to Paris, which was facilitated by Napoleon III and Empress Eugénie. Knowing of his early preference for prostitutes, they introduced him to the most sensual court courtesans, who were his for the choosing. And Bertie chose often, gaining a taste for the most erotic and exotic offerings of the flesh. Enchanted, Paris was set to become his favourite hedonistic centre.

Victoria still stayed away from her subjects who by late in 1864 were becoming disenchanted with her public shyness. Some were calling openly for her to make way for Bertie. Mrs M.A. Murray, a working-class 'fan', put her views to her beloved majesty and made her laugh, cry and think:

> My dear Queen,
> I earnestly hope you will excuse a poor subject
> writing to ask a great favour...it is to let your
> beloved son be Regent during the rest of your Life.
> Not that you have been an indolent Queen[;] a better
> could not exist and I am so afraid he will not live

long enough to be king. You know my dear Queen you will still be Queen Dowager and we will all regonize [sic] you just the same . . .

But it was not devotion, indifference or even detestation that was going to snap her out of her phantom life since Albert's death. Victoria reacted to all these attitudes, but it would take, if not the love of a man, then the close attention of someone she wanted near her. Ever since finding passionate love with Elphinstone, and then the best and most important relationship of her life with Albert, she had felt secure, loved, needed and adored. Since their deaths, no-one had filled the void. But, during the four years of her bereavement and relative seclusion, one man did emerge: John Brown, the Highlander.

Albert had seen his wife's warmth and attachment to Brown and had encouraged a close monarch–servant relationship. Brown had all the traits of the Scots that she loved: strength, compassion, obedience without subservience, courage without bravado, mental acuity without being over-educated, relaxed and in charge. He was a rough, handsome and intelligent *individual*. He was still in his thirties when their relationship was growing and had been in her life since he was nineteen. The blue-eyed Highlander was tall, with long, strong limbs. Victoria had always fallen for a certain type of good-looking male, especially one with chiselled features. He had a forceful chin and she adored this, mainly because she was lacking one herself, as were her sons. And what of Victoria's attraction for him? She was plump and no beauty in her mid-forties, yet her power and position added to a certain sex appeal for those close enough to her to appreciate it. Allied to this were her character, personality and sense of humour, which increased her allure.

Brown, seven years her junior, was never going to be the husband— although rumours circulated while she was out of public view—yet he was much more than a *servant*. On the surface, it was an odd coupling. On closer examination it was understandable. Victoria told her inquisitive courtiers that Brown combined the offices of groom, footman and page. He was also a sort of maid, handy in mending cloaks, shawls and other apparel. It was the way he did things that reassured her. He had no compunction about ordering her in his brusque manner to 'keep still!' while he pinned a cape on her or 'kep yura chun up', when he adjusted her bonnet. Brown was an alcoholic, keen on his whisky and so enchanted sometimes with it that he was not able to wait on her table at meal-time. His absence both amused and disappointed her. It was apparent to all by 1865 that Victoria was extra-fond of *her* Highlander, whom she referred to as 'fascinating Johnny Brown'. It appalled the more stiff-upper-lip–type of sycophants at the Royal Court that such a *servant*, such a wild *commoner* from north of the border, could be liked and admired by the queen. But what they could not see was that combination of fearlessness and gentleness, of strength and softness, of dedication yet independence that so galvanised her appreciation of him. Brown also carried a cloak of Celtic melancholy and fatalism, which he expressed through a deep love of Highland poetry. Victoria never tired of his quotes and brogue, which gave the great Scottish poets, such as Robert Burns and Sir Walter Scott, a growl of sincerity and authenticity. Even the words of the English bards he liked, such as Tennyson and Browning, were given a mellifluous ring. Victoria lamented that the English peasant had little or no interest in poetry, while the Scots were imbued with a passion for it.

Another attraction was Brown's capacity of 'second sight' or premonition, which was in vogue in the 1860s in Europe. He had a 'sixth sense' that Victoria revelled in. She didn't prompt it or demand any 'visionary' commentary but she listened whenever he uttered a remark of foreboding, which she noted in letters to her daughters. She had a spiritual side, although she could not be branded a 'spiritualist' as such. Victoria had even indulged in seances to 'contact' Albert. But again, rumours overplayed her interest in reaching those transported to the 'hereafter'. Such 'communication' was becoming a popular pursuit for those grieving on both sides of the Atlantic. Many of the better-off who could afford mediums sought solace in any words, hopefully of comfort, about the experiences of the departed in heaven or wherever they were believed to have found themselves.

Victoria often wrestled with the unexplained reason for Albert being 'taken from her' while so young. One explanation, which Brown had expressed, and her clergy confidants had expounded on, was that good people were often sent 'above' at their peak to carry on their grand work in that more enlightened environment. Victoria had so much wanted to believe this, yet every so often she expressed her doubts about there being anything beyond the grave at all, which was daring in its own way for the time.

Brown's appeal in a more mundane, pragmatic and useful way was magnified by him being a good man around horses. At one stage he stopped a runaway coach, thus avoiding an accident. And when Victoria's coachman drove her coach into a ditch at night, blackening a royal eye and injuring a regal thumb, it was Brown who rescued her. He was ever dutiful and Victoria needed him. She began to feel that John Brown was *made* for her after the recent trauma. She craved a sense of raw masculinity in her orbit but not the combat of emotions that accompanied her passions around a partner like Albert. Albert had been all about 'form', discipline and achievement. He had a grand sense of fun when with the children and her. Brown was about common sense, and sensibility, despite his gruff exterior. He had a subtle, dry, ever-present Scottish wit. It was crisp, irreverent and funny. Albert had had his tantrums but went to some lengths to avoid confrontation. He put his thoughts—angry, insulting and conciliatory—on paper. Victoria responded in kind. But sometimes she wanted to be taken and 'had' with passion—something that Albert would not countenance. Brown stood up to her in private and sometimes even in front of onlookers, addressed her without formality, calling her 'wumun!'—as in 'don't be so silly, wumun!' She was rarely affronted by him. It was what she wished to hear. Albert had put things on paper; Elphinstone had had more finesse, but Brown eyeballed her and told her what he was thinking. It was soothing: so refreshing, without being overbearing. Brown was everything to Victoria. At Balmoral, she and he had adjoining rooms a long way from the servants' quarters. He was often in her room at any hour. It all added up to them being lovers and in a de facto marriage relationship.

Victoria would never surmount the loss of Albert, but Brown was taking over as a consort of sorts while she avoided public life. He was everywhere with her in private, primarily in seclusion in Scotland and increasingly elsewhere. Brown seemed to provide comfort if not in words or deeds then simply with his presence, especially when she had to deal with 'loss'. Victoria was not fond of Lord Palmerston, but his death on 18 October 1865 marked a break with a link from the past, for which she longed. She wrote to King Leopold, whom she confided in again, and he could comfort her a little from a distance. But Brown was there looking after her, if not cleaning her shawls and coats, then driving her out from Balmoral. If, as biographer Strachey observed, Albert had been the wife and Victoria the husband, then Brown was servant, a kind of wife, a protector and a constant companion. Where Albert had led his own life by day, Brown was on call day and night. Where Elphinstone had been forced away to Madras for five years, and then chosen to leave her court for another decade travelling India and governing Bombay, Brown's circumstances made him less flexible and distracted. Even if he wished to leave, he would find it difficult. He was a drunk and would never find such pleasing employment elsewhere; nowhere else could he exert such influence over one so powerful. Victoria needed him even more emotionally when King Leopold himself died on 10 December 1865. (Vain to the end, he was buried wearing an elaborate black wig and with his skin rouged 'brilliantly'.) This placed her as head of the family. These permanent departures seemed to jolt her regularly. Apart from Albert, they were older influences, who had dominated her past. Brown was young and robust; a vibrant companion even if taken with the 'booze'.

Since Albert's death, Victoria had lamented her lack of conversation with people of her own 'rank'. She devoured talk with the Battenbergs (rulers of the Grand Duchy of Hesse) when they were in England, and received some intellectual rewards in correspondence, especially with her favourite child, Vicky, but other than this she fell back on her servants, and Brown in particular, for her mental nourishment.

36

THE QUEEN REVIVES: DISRAELI DAZZLES

After more than four years of widowhood and seclusion, Victoria summoned the courage to open parliament on 6 February 1866, but on her terms. She ignored the state coach and instead travelled to Westminster in a carriage with both windows down. Her subjects could see her snow-white, round face and drawn mouth, accentuating a dour look. Victoria did not want a fanfare. She banished the trumpets and refused to walk through the House of Lords, where she felt the stares of their lordships in the gallery were judgemental. Wearing a long, dark veil and dress, she donned a black cap like Mary, Queen of Scots, and discarded the crown. If she were going to go through the ordeal, she would do it her way.

Victoria draped herself on the throne and sat, po-faced, staring, not at the lord chancellor as he read her speech but at a spot on the floor. She neither nodded her approval at *her* words nor showed any expression. She was for the first time the zombie queen. It was all for 'show'. Inside she was ready to break down and cry. On the way home in the carriage she delivered a torrent of words to daughter Alice as adrenalin pumped through her veins and she reflected excitedly on the experience. Victoria's confidence in public was shaken. Attending such a focused-on, important public event was not like climbing back on a horse. It had been hell. If she ever had thought of abdicating, it would have been at this moment, but she never seemed ready to countenance this move. Deep down, she still enjoyed being the monarch, even if the pomp had lost its appeal and the circumstances were not ideal.

Victoria continued to shudder at the thought of Bertie taking over as monarch. Victoria thought he was drawn to a decadent life that was the opposite of what was required for a king. In June 1866, she wrote a letter to his comptroller, which she wanted shown to her son. Her reference to the London social set was a metaphor for Bertie. This 'elite' was 'so lax and bad' that he and his wife Alix had a duty to deny themselves amusement in order to keep up 'that [a certain] tone in society, which *used* to be the pride of England'. Bertie was to show his disapproval by 'not asking them to dinner, or going down to [his summer retreat] Sandringham and above all by not going to their houses'.

Lord Stanley (son of Lord Derby and an ally of Tory politician Benjamin Disraeli) noted in his diary that Victoria meddled in the lives of Bertie and Alix 'in every detail...They may not dine out, except in houses named by her; nor ask anyone to dine with them' unless approved by her. Victoria had spied on them at their home, Marlborough House, where the so-called 'fast set' assembled with him before launching into nightly excesses and 'deplorable' activities of gambling, smoking, drinking and 'associating with Americans and Jews'.

A daily report of these goings-on was sent to Victoria. This was carrying on Albert's distorted patronage. No matter what Bertie did he would never pass scrutiny in such a tyranny. Perhaps if he had been a replica of Albert—a model of propriety and piety—Victoria may have thought about giving up her monarchy for permanent privacy with John Brown. But Bertie was not in any way like her dear departed beloved. Her son was a born pleasure-seeker whom, she believed, preferred to wallow in his privilege rather than revere it.

Victoria's determination to deny Bertie the throne was the most fundamental reason for her staying on it, when otherwise her state of mind in the wake of Albert's death may well have seen her 'retire'. Instead of grooming Bertie to be king, Victoria was not giving him anything substantial to do. This was not assisting in diverting him from indolence and a hedonistic lifestyle, although at least he was following his father in one department—procreation. By September 1866, Alix was pregnant with her third child. But Bertie was not limiting his amorous pursuits to his lovely wife. He had never gotten over the erotic pleasures experienced with the lusty Nellie Clifden. Having been denied her, she had become his ideal fantasy. He was driven to find others like her, and this drew him into more promiscuous company. His never-ending push to make up for that unfulfilled relationship set tongues wagging at court. There were parodies in the press cartoons that displeased Victoria. But allusions to his nocturnal pursuits began to be replaced in London's scandal press with real reports of his alleged conquests of the boudoir. On a trip to Moscow and St Petersburg, he realised he could bed any woman he fancied. If he did not flirt with them, he indulged in flings. The tabloids heard the whisper about his behaviour and reported it. Victoria's ladies-in-waiting made sure that these reports were not seen by her.

In 1867, Victoria turned to her love of writing, which had been demonstrated in her copious letters and diary entries, into a gentle, cathartic exercise in composing a book: *Leaves From the Journal of our Lives in the Highlands*. She illustrated it herself and designed the cover of moss-green adorned with golden antlers. It sold an excellent 20,000 copies in 1868 in an initial burst, and promised many editions. Big sales brought a wave of jealousy from the literati, who sneered at Victoria for making author-like utterances about 'her book'. It was the unpretentious enunciation of a privileged life, which nevertheless brought its critics, not so much for its literary merit, but for its omissions *and* inclusions. *Punch* magazine thought it characterised a 'tea tray' sort of life, which ignored the whisky bottle that was equally prevalent. In other words, Victoria had written the tome wearing rose-coloured glasses.

She was also criticised by some in her own entourage who objected to biographical footnotes about footmen as if they were gentlemen. Lady Augusta Stanley punned unintentionally when she observed that such descriptions gave the dangerous impression 'that all were on the same footing'. Nevertheless enlightened courtiers could see the potential for tapping into Victoria's vast support among the middle and working classes, who would appreciate her more egalitarian, at times progressive, perspective on life. The publisher's offer for a quick, cheaper edition was taken up. It maintained Victoria's other (far briefer) 'career' as a best-selling author.

The experience lifted her and was coincident with 64-year-old Benjamin Disraeli becoming prime minister in February 1868. She had not always been enamoured with him. Her earlier diary entries reflected a negative attitude to this Tory dandy, whose vitriol against 'free trade' had been 'dreadfully bitter'. Victoria had thought him too reckless. He had seemed unprincipled in his attacks on her beloved Whigs, and she had regarded him as lacking respectability, yet she had been intrigued with his speeches in parliament, which had sometimes enchanted her, and occasionally caused revulsion. But it was his way with words directed at *her* that appealled most. Her natural instinct was to follow the near-universal prejudice against Jews, but a combination of her flexibility, fair-mindedness and lack of bigotry allowed her to keep her thoughts open when dealing with such an unusual figure. Decades earlier his looks had repulsed more than attracted. As she warmed to his manner over time, she gazed on his appearance with more benevolence than in previous assessments. The weak chin took on a character of its own. His outsize nose and dark eyes may well have had a certain sex appeal for her. His black ringlet hair curls became idiosyncratic rather than effete. His strength in her eyes was his verbal *expression*, which she had come to appreciate more as her reign stretched into a fourth decade. Victoria had been stunned by the graphic mind of her first prime minister, Melbourne. Disraeli's intellect was more rounded; his humour sharper; his mind quicker. And Disraeli was just as tough, but less of a snob, and less of an elitist. Victoria had been under Melbourne's spell when little more than a naive child of sixteen. More than three decades on she found it much harder to be entranced by anyone. She had seen much, perhaps *too* much to be less than judgemental from her lofty position in British life. This made the late advent of Disraeli all the more captivating. When she congratulated him on his success at ascending to the top political job, she observed that he had to be a most patient man (at his age).

'Ah, but a person should beware of endeavouring to be great in a hurry,' he replied. 'One attempt in ten thousand may succeed. These are fearful odds, ma'am.'

He was *different*, deliciously so for a queen who had thought she would never be entertained again by a leader in so many ways, mostly intellectually. He wrote with a flourish that opened up a spectrum of parliamentary observation, especially with pen sketches of characters and descriptions of speeches that he continued to send her. A colleague, Ward Hunt, was 'a giant...with the sagacity of an elephant, and the form.'

Commenting on another politician, Disraeli once remarked: 'He was distinguished for his ignorance; for he had only one idea, and that was wrong.'

Quite often his characterising of a speech was a metaphor for the speaker. They might be 'elaborate', 'exaggerated', 'lugubrious', even 'flat and flatulent'. Victoria loved puns, *bon mots*, a clever turn of phrase or a telling character summary, no matter how trite. When discussing his aim (later fulfilled) to create a precedent by removing Catholic rituals from the Anglican liturgy, Victoria said she fully supported the principle of short, simple services. Disraeli observed that 'a precedent embalms a principle, ma'am'. When she praised his fiction, and asked him to talk about his favourite books, he replied: 'An author who speaks about his own books is almost as bad as a mother who speaks about her own children.'

Victoria laughed. It was a reflection of the conversations she had every day about her offspring. When Victoria mentioned his critics and how well he seemed to handle them, he observed: 'How much easier it is to be critical, your majesty, than it is to be correct.'

This had resonance for her, especially over her tentative effort in book writing, which had taken the odd pillorying. Victoria loved the fact that he often peppered his remarks with, 'we authors, ma'am ...', even if she may have realised that he was overdoing the collegiate reference. Even with his long political career, Disraeli was prolific, producing eighteen fiction and eight non-fiction books.

Once she apologised for reminiscing too much about Albert's moral values and diligence.

'Never apologise for showing feeling, ma'am,' he told her gently, 'when you do so, you apologise for the truth.'

These kinds of aphorisms and adages tweaked her mind and caused her to admire him for his insight. In her maturity, people with insight, and those with 'second sight', captivated her as much as men with good looks and bodies. The 'colour' in Disraeli's character infused his use of the language. He carried it on in his florid novels, which Victoria lapped up. She could count on witticisms from him in person, which demonstrated his fertile, kaleidoscopic mind was not just evident when crafted on paper. Disraeli had personality. He used his considerable charm—part genuine, part contrived for his queen—to overcome her initial repugnance. Some viewed his manner as unctuous; others devious. But once the more mature Victoria had to deal with him as her prime minister her attitude changed.

A quarter of a century after being unsure about him, Victoria's benefit of the doubt was given. Misgivings were overtaken by an overwhelming personality. Disraeli *romanced* her just short of seduction. It began with their first meeting with him in the highest office. He humbly took her tubby fingers in his and, eyes down, mumbled, 'in loving loyalty and faith'. Some prime ministers genuflected to her, but none did it with such panache. His approach to her was charged sometimes with a near-operatic sweep or literary expositions that reflected popular histrionics of the era. No leader had touched her so much with such humility, and it seemed genuine. Victoria believed that he was sincere. It suited her own view of how she, as queen, should be treated. Those in service, including all elected officials, should be dutiful and devoted. Other prime ministers had been too mature, too intimidated, too *dignified*, too vain, too self-important or too conscious of their position vis-a-vis hers. But here was a very independent-minded, strong-willed, brilliant individual who took his role as her number-one minister so seriously that he bent his knee to the floor and kissed her hand with passion.

This meant much to her. It pushed aside the unwritten division of powers between the institution of parliament and the monarchy. His professed attitude placed the queen above everything. Disraeli's style was comforting. It restored her faith in the importance of her role. It seemed to stop, at least in her thinking, the slide of the monarchy to oblivion with the rise of democracy. His philosophy here was both cynical and two-faced.

'Everyone likes flattery,' he noted, 'and when it comes to royalty you should lay it on with a trowel.'

Disraeli's method was effective. When Victoria later expressed fear about a foreign venture to him, he observed that 'fear makes us feel our humanity, your majesty'. Little wonder he almost always left her with a warm inner glow. Having created the ambience they were experiencing, he then articulated *her* emotions by summarising their future relations as 'on her part, perfect confidence; on his part, perfect devotion'. He went on to compliment her unmatched experience, which surpassed 'all living princes and most living people'. Disraeli begged her 'not to withhold the benefit of her guidance'. He promised to submit all the grand issues of the day to her. He would look after the trivial matters to save her from the tedium. It was a cunning declaration, and he reversed it in action. Disraeli put only the less important matters to her and burdened himself with the big decisions and issues. But it was the *impression* that counted. Having been flattered by his expression of the importance of her role, she was happy to be ignored over the more contentious problems facing the empire. Victoria turned 49 in 1868 and had no inclination to work like her husband had on expanding the role of the monarchy.

Disraeli's stint in office was just ten months. He was replaced by the 59-year-old William Gladstone, with whom Victoria had always clashed when he was chancellor of the exchequer in the mid-1850s, and again from 1859 to 1866. First among her complaints about this accomplished orator was that he always addressed her 'as if I were a public meeting'. There was none of Disraeli's finesse, flattery or gentleness. The granite-faced Liberal statesman had had a half-century of political life and he never felt inclined to pay too much attention to his monarch. He had a nation to run. This approach displeased Victoria. To confront was one thing; to ignore her *importance* was a sin in her eyes. Disraeli tried to downgrade him by saying Gladstone was 'God's only mistake'. But such a trite put-down could not wipe away Gladstone's skills and their fierce rivalry. It had gone on for decades in parliament and outside it. Victoria was jealous of Gladstone. He was popular with the electorate and had been dubbed the 'people's William'. His portrait was in homes across the country alongside that of the monarch, or it replaced hers. Victoria was not amused by his style of campaigning, which she referred to as 'Royal Progresses'. She called his press reports 'Court Circulars', indicating her envy of him as an alternative 'monarch'. Their relationship was not helped by Gladstone's determination for reforms, including the extension of the voting franchise, elections by secret ballots and a reduction in the power of the House of Lords. Victoria opposed them all. Gladstone paid no attention to her protests, and pushed on with all these changes.

37

BOUNTIFUL BERTIE

ertie began to find his own way a decade after his father's death, despite his mother's strictures. Providence conspired in 1871 to generate a profile for public consumption. First, he opened the Thames Embankment, not a world-shattering event, but royalty had rarely given themselves so willingly for such 'use' at public events before. Then he fell ill with the ubiquitous killer typhoid when staying with other guests at a lodge in North Yorkshire. One of the guests, Lord Chesterfield, died. The nation became concerned. There was universal relief when the heir to the throne recovered. When his youngest son, John, died just a day after being born, the nation saw a side of the man that endeared him to it. He insisted on placing the tiny body in the coffin and cried when he did it. The press reported his emotion and grief. Suddenly there was the image of a public prince with a human face and feeling.

It allowed Bertie some 'credit' as the nation became aware of his 'good time' attitude to life, which he filled with frivolous attractions. He took regular trips to Paris when the Belle Époque era had established itself with the high-kicking girls in clubs on the stunning boulevards, Impressionist artists prevalent and cafe society at its peak. 'France is my mistress and England my wife,' he would say often, and at home he made country house parties his favourite pastime. Hosts had to provide everything, including large quantity of game needed for a big shoot. He had his own set of friends that his mother did not vet and would not have approved of. He was fast laying claim to being the nineteenth century's most impressive charmer. Bertie appreciated his luck in being born into an elevated social position and luxury. But instead of flagellating himself over this as his father had, Bertie accepted and enjoyed it. He reached out for those outside his privileged family and circle, regardless of background, although those he patronised all had to be high achievers and with wealth. Bertie surrounded himself with aristocrats and powerful businessmen, but his interest in people spread far and across class barriers. He met the Labour leader, Joseph Arch. He invited the working-class member of parliament Henry Broadhurst to stay at his country house at Sandringham in Norfolk. But there were borders of etiquette that Bertie would not cross. Broadhurst did not possess evening dress, and dinner was served to him in his room to save him from embarrassment.

Bertie's love affair with Paris and many of its more stunning inhabitants was well established in his thirtieth year in 1871. He was even-handed in his largesse. He became friendly with General Marquis de Gallifet, who had suppressed the Paris Commune in that year with executions of leftist rebels, but he also embraced the radical politician Leon Gambetta. He demonstrated an unusual public relations skill by persuading these sworn enemies to lunch with him at the Café Anglais. Bertie was in his element, using his fluent French, while working his kind of high-mileage diplomacy over a huge meal featuring roast beef and potatoes, horseradish sauce and Yorkshire pudding, and the most expensive champagne. Neither Frenchman had eaten such fare, which Bertie was turning into a staple British favourite, usually for Sunday lunch. The two Frenchmen were intrigued by something so quintessentially un-Gallic. They were captivated, if not with the food and each other, then with this *agréable anglais* and his attempts to solve *their* disagreement. Bertie told them he had a vested interest. He did not want civil war in France. It would interfere with his annual 'fun'. How could they be other than enchanted with someone so influential who enjoyed good times in their country even more than in his own?

His bonhomie and efforts like this to foster good relations with the French and other European countries earned him the sobriquet 'peacemaker'. His only failure was with his universally disliked, difficult nephew Wilhelm, of Germany, Vicky's son, a grandson of Victoria. Bertie had found him tricky. But he was not alone. Wilhelm cultivated as many enemies in Europe as his uncle won friends.

Bertie could not bear to be alone. It brought back memories of those dreadful days studying as a child and youth with just books to keep him company. Now he yearned often for male companionship and eschewed reading, while liking women more than either. He craved the attention of beautiful females, in complete contrast to his father, who had avoided the company of women. In this way Bertie was nearer in make-up to his mother, who commanded male companions who were not always her physical or generational match. But what Bertie lacked in pure handsomeness was more than made up for by his personality, style and elegance. He was a slavish creator of fashion rather than a follower of it. He made wearing tweed, Homburg hats and Norfolk jackets fashionable. He popularised black ties and dinner jackets. White ties and tails were out once Bertie left them in the royal closet. Fashion was one facet of society where he could lord it over others. Once he told off Prime Minister Lord Salisbury for wearing the wrong formal jacket-and-trouser combination. Salisbury had been deeply involved in an international crisis at the time.

'Forgive me, your royal highness,' Salisbury had responded, 'it was dark this morning and my mind must have been occupied by some subject of lesser importance.'

Bertie's fashion passion, plus his title, potential wealth (he would not be 'rich' until he was king) and reputation as a trendsetter who loved socialising, saw society's most accomplished beauties manoeuvring into his orbit in the hope of making a stellar attraction. Some of the most compelling and sensual women of the era in England and Continental Europe gravitated his way. Actress Hortense Schneider in Paris experienced his pull, and he felt hers, as did Sarah Bernhardt in London. The latter maintained her histrionics off stage by making love to Bertie in a silk-lined coffin that she kept in her room. His best-known courtesan paramour was a parson's daughter, Lillie Langtry. She loved press attention, especially when a London journalist wrote at the top of his gossip column that there was nothing whatsoever between the Prince of Wales and Lillie Langtry. The next week in the same space he wrote: 'Not even a sheet.'

Langtry lost favour when she became bored at a dinner party and tried to liven things up by pouring strawberry ice-cream down the back of Bertie's neck. Once ostracised from his set, she took her cue from namesake Lillie Clifden by becoming an actress to cash in on her notoriety.

Society stunners over the decades in France and England—including the Princess de Sagan, the Duchess of Mouchy, Lady Brooke (the future Countess of Warwick) and the Hon. Mrs Alice Keppel—were lured Bertie's way for fabulous holidays at Biarritz on the French coast. Keppel was a favourite; so was the demure, elegant French socialite Aline Caroline de Rothschild, who married his close friend Edward Sassoon. Lady Randolph Churchill (mother of Winston) and noblewoman Susan Pelham-Clinton were also not immune to his allure. Nor was the wealthy humanitarian Agnes Keyser able to gyrate away from him. Later Bertie remained serenely vulnerable to brilliant courtesans, such as the Spanish singer-dancer Cora 'La belle' Otera, who performed a magnificent dance for him while stripping to Spanish music. Then there was Guilia Barucci, who removed her gown as soon as she was introduced. Bertie didn't need a second invitation. Plymouth-born, Paris-based Cora Pearl went one better. She was served to him naked and smothered in cream on a huge silver platter, which appealed to his two favourite pursuits concurrently.

Bertie took his devotion to the search for his original excitement over Nellie Clifden to a new level by having his own special room at the Paris brothel La Chabanais tucked away in a side street (at 12 Rue Chabanais) near the Louvre in an attractive part of the old city between the Opera and the Palais Royal.

At his request, the coat of arms of the Prince of Wales was placed above the bed in the Chambre Hindoue—the Hindu Room. He even had his own 'love-chair' built to order; a curved and gilded wooden structure sculpted in Louis XVIII style. It was covered in green satin cushions. The lower level was a long mattress. The upper section, built on four strong legs, leant backwards with vertical arm-rests and its front had two gilded stirrups. There were foot-rests on the legs. This allowed him to make love to two, even three women at a time. Bertie also had his own silver-plated copper bath, built in the design of a half-woman, half-swan. It was filled with champagne for a wash after exotic love-play. If his affair with Nellie had not killed his father, knowledge of these extreme erotic endeavours surely would have finished off Prince Albert, especially as it was all done under a royal insignia.

An equally celestial accomplishment was to train his lovely wife, Alix, to turn a blind eye to all this playing. She remained faithful as long as some of his well-spread affections were sprinkled on their children, if not her. But her loyalty was tested. There were occasions when his indiscretions turned into scandal that Victoria, Bertie's household and the government could not contain. In 1870 the prince was subpoenaed to give evidence when Sir Charles Mordaunt, a member of parliament, brought a divorce petition against his wife, whom he claimed had committed adultery with two of Bertie's playboy friends. Lady Mordaunt signed a confession admitting her adultery, but threw in Bertie as a third co-respondent for good measure. The evidence maintained that he had visited the sensual lady on several occasions at her home, notably in the afternoon. This was the time in the day when all promiscuous gentlemen and gentlewomen of leisure were ready for another assignation, and all good parliamentarians were in the Commons or Lords. Bertie, looking resplendent in court and even princely in his innocence, denied the claim, which caused those in the know to smile. He made out that he just dropped around to hear Lady Mordaunt's piano recitals, while she was adamant that she entertained him more royally.

38

BROWN THE
BODYGUARD

By 1872, after a six-year close relationship, Victoria was beginning to venture out more with John Brown, which gave him a unique status in the history of the monarchy. He had begun as a humble servant but had advanced to being something much more important. When early in the year Victoria sat next to him in her carriage coming back to the palace from St Paul's, it was a sign to the world that he was surely her man, rather than man*servant*. Brown looked powerful, even indestructible, with his solid jaw, and his tree-trunk legs visible under his short kilt. Victoria had proved courageous in the numerous attempts to assassinate her or do her harm, but for the first time as queen she felt properly protected with Brown beside her. In this respect he was also her bodyguard and he took his role seriously. This was made clear when Victoria ventured out two days later to 'feel' the atmosphere in the streets as the republican push that had worried her for so long began to subside. The streets were crowded. There was clapping and cheering. Emotion, for that was the fickle barometer of popularity of the time, which very much influenced Victoria's moods, was sweeping her royalist way again. One indicator that was never measured, but which may have had much to do with her rise again in the public esteem, was the link with Brown. He had been ridiculed in the press and the upper classes but the far greater numbers in the working class of England and Scotland were impressed by her undemonstrative yet obvious loyalty to *one of them*. This showed the masses that she was, in a solid way, a queen and symbol for all the people, not just for her own class. Here was this tiny empress and queen riding closely with a man mountain who would not have been out of place in the popular bare-knuckle boxing rings of the day.

Just at the end of the ride as the carriage approached the entrance to Buckingham Palace, a youth pushed his way through the crowd and passed police to the carriage door. He lifted a pistol and pointed it at Victoria. Brown did not cower or pull back. He leapt straight at the would-be assassin and gripped his throat so hard that the youth's body went limp. Several policemen jumped to Brown's aid but they were superfluous. Their only service was to stop Brown from strangling the attacker, a seventeen-year-old Fenian, Arthur O'Connor. As they apprehended the young Irishman, Brown took the pistol, opened it and smashed it on the ground. O'Connor claimed that the weapon was inoperable and that all he wanted to do was to 'beg' the queen to support a petition for the release of Fenian prisoners. Victoria wanted him transported.

'Uch nay!' Brown told her. 'That will only bring the beggars at you again. Let the court sentence him as it sees fit.'

O'Connor was sentenced to a year's imprisonment and twenty strokes of the birch, which was not enough in Victoria's eyes. But the attack had benefits. Demonstrations of loyalty increased. Brown was billed as a hero by even the most scathing members of the press who had until then viewed him negatively. The two rode out a third time in week. Crowds surged to the carriage in every street. The queen waved and delivered a smile, albeit a wan one, while Brown sat unmoved watching the circling masses like an eagle looking for prey.

The queen was smitten by the Highlander more than ever. She established a gold 'Victoria Faithful Servant' medal for him, which was supposed from then on to be given for 'any very special act of devotion to the Sovereign'. Brown was the only person ever to receive one.

The relationship between Victoria and John Brown had progressed to an accepted thing to the public at large, although it would remain unacceptable to the royal court. Bertie detested the Highlander. Victoria, fearing a confrontation, made sure they were kept apart. The unofficial coupling of queen and servant brought reaction from many quarters. Fledgling republican movements pounced on the relationship. Anti-Brown propaganda mounted sporadically in the 1870s and referred to the queen's 'morganatic husband', which more than implied that Victoria and Brown had secretly married but without him having claims to any title. Rumours began about them having a child, then children. The foreign secretary, the Earl of Derby, recorded in his diary that the two slept in adjoining rooms contrary to etiquette and even decency. Rumours almost always surfaced as tittle-tattle, but not from the Highlanders who looked after Victoria at Balmoral or Loch Ordie, where she stayed on occasions; they were discreet to the point of open hostility to prying questions from the press. Victoria was enjoying sex again although Brown's performances were sporadic. They would sit by an open fire tippling with his favourite Begg's Best whisky, with Victoria gaining a taste for it. Then, depending on the level of Brown's drunkenness, they would retire to her bed for 'hochmagandy', as the queen too began to refer to their lovemaking.

Naming it as such gave it more credibility for her. She had become aware that the Scots, at least the Highlanders with whom she mixed, were not afraid of celebrating natural culminations in intimacy. They were discreet enough but still different from the English, she believed, who seemed to hide the subject of sex away as some squalid thing. She felt that the god-fearing, superstitious Irish filled the most natural of acts with unnecessary guilt. Perhaps only the French, along with the Scots, enjoyed her appreciation of intimacy, for which she still had as much passion as riding and music.

Brown's boozing was not the only block on more fun for Victoria. One night on a quick autumn holiday in 1874 at Loch Ordie, she was just in the act of settling on Brown with anticipated pleasure when she cried in pain and fell off him.

'Deary, what is wrong?' Brown asked as he held Victoria, who gasped for breath. She could not speak but instead pointed to her vagina. He fetched a glass of water.

When she had recovered she sat up on the bed.

'Lately I have had pain down there,' she said. 'It's just more difficult for some reason. The pain is awful.'

'What's the wee problem? Can you explain it better?'

She smiled and kissed him again, 'Has my favourite servant suddenly become a doctor?'

'I've always been a natural vet. I know when the wee mares are having trouble.'

'I am not a horse, Johnny Brown!'

'Them that have done much foaling have certain problems. You probably have the same trouble, dearie.'

'Such as?'

'Hernias. They damage the walls of the horse's abdomen and cause a slippage of the uterus. Ya canna let the stallions near them.'

Victoria was reflective. She knew of such animal problems and she always listened to Brown's common sense, which often cut to the core of a problem.

'I'll be all right in the morning.'

'Dearie, you should see a doctor.'

'What? And have some specialist from Harley Street probing me? Never!'

'Suit yourself, but it means less hochmagandy.'

Victoria reached for her whisky glass on the bedside dresser and indicated Brown should top it up.

'Not if I kill the pain,' she said coquettishly.

39

VICTORIA UP: BROWN DOWN

Disraeli, in his second stint as prime minister, kept his secret intention to involve Victoria with the less vital issues of state while making her believe they were of the highest importance. He pushed the *Royal Titles Act 1876* through parliament and on 1 May Victoria took the title 'Empress of India'. This 'acquisition' had much to do with her son's eight-month tour of the subcontinent, mainly India, which had just finished. It had been even more successful than his first tour, of the United States, when he was just a lad. Now 34, Bertie was proving more impressive to foreigners than to British subjects, although he had become an acceptable figure at home. He complained in a letter to some ministers that British officials in India were not showing the Indians respect: 'Because a man has a black face and a different religion than our own,' Bertie said, 'there is no reason why he should be treated [poorly].'

These were more direct extensions of his mother's sentiments. Victoria still carried some contempt for her son and his pleasure-seeking, which blinded her appreciation of his achievements, yet she was bemused to discover that he was becoming popular with the masses.

The Indian title thrilled Victoria but she was displeased over Disraeli's failure to act against Russia in the Russo-Turkish War. She threatened to abdicate over the issue five times between April 1877 and February 1878, but she was ignored or talked out of it. No-one close to Victoria really believed that she would hand the reins over to Bertie, who continued to be hell-bent on avoiding work and embracing leisure pursuits. He had not helped his cause by clashing with John Brown, whom he thought had an undue influence over his mother. Victoria supported and encouraged Disraeli's expansionist policies. They led to conflict, including the Anglo-Zulu War and the second Anglo-Afghan War. Victoria justified it all by saying that if Britain were to maintain its position as a first-rate power, it had to be prepared for attacks and wars at all times.

The British very much believed their own publicity about their racial and national superiority. Victoria had become the empire's standard-bearer. She expounded on the propaganda by professing that the acquisitions worldwide were civilising and benign. Native peoples were being 'protected' from more 'aggressive and cruel rulers', such as the Dutch, French and Germans. A case in point was Australia. The British had taken over the entire continent, an area bigger than China, dispossessing the many Aboriginal tribes, who had inhabited the land for 50,000 years or more. The Dutch, and the French in particular, had explored the huge island's west coast, but the British had taken over the lot and garrisoned it, making any part of it untenable for any other empire, unless they were prepared to go to war. Victoria claimed it was not Britain policy or custom to annex countries, unless obliged or forced to do so, yet she was well aware that obligation and retaliation were easy to arrange.

Victoria enjoyed this period of her reign more than any other with the agreeable empire-builder Disraeli at the helm for a six-year stretch. She became so confident and comfortable with him that his defeat at the polls in 1880 dismayed her. Worse, she had never had time for his successor, William Gladstone, who had already appalled her for six years as prime minister from 1868 to 1874.

In 1881, Victoria was devastated by the news that Disraeli was on his deathbed, and she wished to visit him. He told an aide: 'No, it is better not. She would only ask me to take a message to Albert.'

Disraeli died aged 77. Victoria was 'blinded' by 'fast-falling tears'. As was usual for those who had pleased her, he received a monument. A memorial tablet to Disraeli was created. The inscription said it had been 'placed by his grateful Sovereign and Friend, Victoria R.I.'

Once more she used the 'friend' label. This sobriquet bracketed Disraeli with Elphinstone and Melbourne. The classification continued to have a special significance in the royal court and within Victoria's most intimate circle.

Victoria's popularity had stabilised in the two decades since her post-Albert, prolonged mourning from late 1861 to early 1866. Even with Gladstone taking much of the limelight, by early 1882 the 62-year-old Victoria was a broadly acceptable figure. Talk of a republic had died away. Suggestions of abdication were muted. More than half the British population had been born after her accession. She was the only monarch they had known and, along with the older members of society, they were content with her reign. Still, the odd disgruntled individual emerged. On 2 March 1882, Roderick Maclean, a poet, was so upset that Victoria would not accept one of his poems that he took a shot at her as her carriage left Windsor railway station. Two Eton schoolboys, who knew their Tennyson but not Maclean's works, attacked him with their umbrellas until he was apprehended by the police. Maclean was charged with attempted murder and taken to court. There was outrage when he was found not guilty by reason of insanity. This was poetic *injustice* to many. Victoria was unhappy at this 'excuse' for his actions but took solace in the huge amount of positive mail she received. Most letters expressed sympathy for her and discontent that Maclean had not been hanged.

'It was worth being shot at,' Victoria said, 'to see how much one is loved.'

A year later, Victoria fell down stairs at Windsor and was hurt, but it was nothing like the pain she suffered ten days later when John Brown died from a severe skin complaint, erysipelas, on 27 March 1883, aged 56. They had been companions and lovers for more than twenty years, which was about the length of time she had been with Albert. It had been a more sedate relationship, but a more contented one than with the always preoccupied and busy prince consort. Victoria, 63, wrote to Viscount Cranbrook, saying that perhaps never in history had there been a stronger, truer, warmer or more loving friendship between 'the sovereign and servant'. Victoria went on to describe Brown's strength of character and power'. She mentioned his 'fearless uprightness, kindness, sense of justice, honesty, independence and unselfishness combined with a tender, warm heart'. This made him 'one of the most remarkable men'. Victoria felt she had been deprived 'of all' she needed for a 'second time'. The blow had 'fallen too heavily not to be very heavily felt'.

On 8 April, amidst a torrent of exchanges with Vicky, she wrote:

> He protected me so, was so powerful and strong—
> that I felt so safe! And now all, all is gone in this
> world and all seems unhinged again in thousands of
> ways!—I feel so discouraged that it requires a terrible
> effort to bear up at all against it. This forces me to
> revisit the loss of dear papa in 1861.

Vicky wrote back letters of sympathy and her own sadness did not help a heavy flu that forced her to hospital in Berlin with 'a neuralgia in my forehead and eye'. During her short stay, her son Willy came to see her. She was asleep when he arrived and Willy sat for a minute sipping tea. He noticed an envelope with Victoria's royal seal on it. Realising it was from his grandmother, he opened the letter and began to read it.

Vicky stirred and saw Willy quickly place the letter back in the envelope.

'You have no right to read my private correspondence!' she snapped, trying to sit up.

'Mama, it is from the queen and you know how much I love her!'

'No excuse!' Vicky said.

'But I have a right to know about her! The rumours about the stress she is under—'

'Of course she is under stress! She lost her mother, E and Albert all in a short time . . . and now the passing of her favourite manservant.'

Willy wanted to ask more but she waved a dismissive hand, turned over and went back to sleep. Willy was keen to ask her who 'E' was. He sat quietly finishing his tea, his eyes flicking from his mother to the letter. Was the answer in there, he wondered. He was even tempted to take it with him when he left but thought better of it. Instead, he wrote his mother a letter that she received a few weeks later at her home in Potsdam. He apologised for reading Victoria's letter in the hospital and asked about her reference to 'E'. Vicky was stunned. She wrote back a blistering missive, attacking her son for his 'prying, devious, suspicious ways'. But Willy persisted, saying that he would write and ask Victoria herself if his mother did not tell him what it meant. That 'blackmail' forced Vicky's response. She did not trust her son, but she did not want her mother to know that Willy knew 'the secret'. In the end, she composed herself and wrote to him, telling him in the barest detail of what Victoria had written to her of the Elphinstone affair. Willy was pleased to have the upper hand with his mother, yet he swore to her that he would never divulge the 'tale' of his beloved grandmother's 'adventure'.

Victoria, in her anxiety over Brown's demise, turned to writing, which in the past had helped salve grief. But her aim was distorted by her feelings. She began composing Brown's biography. It was a lengthy eulogy, which acted more like an emotional purging than an exercise to inform readers. Her private secretary, Sir Henry Ponsonby, and the Dean of Windsor, Randall Davidson, fretted over her desire to have the book published. They became alarmed when they read her first draft and others as she reworked and massaged passages like a professional. Disraeli had been her earlier consultant on how to create books and he had encouraged her to write a second tome. This was it. Ponsonby and Davidson thought the narrative was too revealing. They approached her, hand-wringing and with apologies, suggesting that the book would fuel the old and lingering rumours of a love affair with Brown. Victoria, still with a perspective distorted by her deep emotion, tried to edit through the changes. Ponsonby read them and delivered the bad news: her story was still too intimate. It had to be destroyed. Victoria was angry, frustrated and depressed. What was the point of being a queen if she could not even publish a memoir of a worthy servant? She salvaged a little of her intentions by publishing a sequel to her first work, calling it: *More Leaves from a Journal of a Life in the Highlands*, which she dedicated to her 'devoted personal attendant and faithful friend John Brown'. It was not nearly enough. Victoria's burst of commissioning statues, busts and memorials to him threatened to match that for Albert. It placed the Highlander alongside him, Melbourne, Disraeli and Elphinstone. Bertie was furious. He vowed to destroy them all when he became king. His anger that year saw him make some remarks that were indirectly aimed at his mother and her attitudes.

'Class can no longer stand apart from class,' he said in his capacity of founder of the Royal College of Music, which he opened in 1883, 'I claim...that music produces that union of feeling, which I desire to promote.' But if Bertie were true to his word, there were contradictions. Soon after this enlightened comment he ordered the clocks at Sandringham to run half-an-hour fast to create more time for shooting. He had some way to travel if he ever seriously intended to break down class barriers beyond music.

40

GLADSTONE OMNIPOTENT

Victoria's youngest child, Beatrice, planned to marry Prince Henry of Battenberg in April 1883, but Victoria objected. The thought of her last child departing distressed her. It was a sense that had haunted Victoria. As she aged, the emotion around losing family or friends had increased. Victoria never felt she was being selfish, believing her emotional needs as queen overrode the lives and sensitivities of others. Beatrice was denied her happiness for a year until a compromise was reached. In return for being allowed to marry, she would remain living at court and close to her mother. Henry may have been concerned with living so close to such a demanding and domineering mother-in-law, but he was willing to make the sacrifice, which was wise. Keeping Victoria happy would mean she would fight the government for a sizeable Civil List payment to keep him and his bride in the manner of the more salubrious members of the royal family.

Victoria was inconsolable at the death of Leopold, who was 30 when he died of haemophilia. He was the second of her children—Alice having died in 1878—to die young. Victoria told her diary that she was grateful for 'the good Lord' having given him three decades on earth.

Gladstone continued to undermine Victoria's regal powers, which was his constitutional and democratic right, aided by his unmatched popularity as leader. He was renowned for his scruples, which gave him a moral authority. In this way, he rivalled the authority of the Church and the monarchy. Gladstone could never grasp why he was so exalted by the public. It was in part to do with his inspirational speaking style, and not a little to do with his reputation as a principled individual. His reforms too, had endeared him to the masses. It all irritated Victoria, who craved public adulation and being loved more than anyone else in her empire. Gladstone was more secure, despite his appeal even at times unnerving him. He claimed not to have courted popularity, and that in fact he was disturbed by nightmares about halls of people waiting for him to address them.

Throughout history, people in any country yearned for a strong, believable leader they could trust. In England in the first half of the 1880s it was William Ewart Gladstone. Victoria remained discontented at being a distant second in her nation, as his influence spread through all the key institutions of politics, Church and army at the expense of the monarch's. He had an impact on the constitution; his word carried more weight than Victoria's in Ireland, Europe, Africa and even India. He stretched his prerogative and power over the entire empire at the expense of his queen who was powerless under the British system to diminish it. Perhaps if Albert had been alive there may have been more checks and balances to this creeping democratic development, but even he would have been required to bow to the growing democratisation of the nation. En route to this zenith of influence, Gladstone did not simply *refuse* to listen to what she said; he did not bother to even give her a hearing. Worse, he did not make time to tell her what his ministers were saying about issues. On occasions, they were under orders to withhold information.

Victoria was not yet an imitation of the country's leader, but Gladstone's strength and integrity had enhanced the office of prime minister to being far superior to that of the monarch.

'His [Gladstone's] first allegiance should have been to the Sovereign,' she remarked often to courtiers with a distinct bitterness borne of years of frustration with the prime minister and his cabinet. This first consistent and emphatic breaking of the nexus between a dominant monarch and a subservient government changed the arrangement of the constitutional monarchy in Britain forever. A new paradigm had emerged. In her hurt and frustration, Victoria cried wolf once more about abdication because she hated being, or being seen as, a rubber stamp. Again, no-one believed her. Since recovering from Albert's death, she had given the impression of being engaged to a point. But she could never match Gladstone, who was deeply involved with every aspect of running the nation and empire. There was much news of her grand production line of children and grandchildren; their comings and goings across Europe, the empire and the world; their good behaviour and bad; their births, deaths and marriages. This could not be compared to the important affairs of state, which Gladstone and his experienced cabinet were handling to the electorate's satisfaction. Victoria's disappointment at these developments was in some measure balanced by her own attitude. She was proud of being a constitutional monarch as opposed to most of her royal colleagues and family on the Continent, despite her thinking at times that she had power where she did not. There was little wonder that she rejoiced when Gladstone retired late in 1885 after his budget was defeated, saying his government was the worst she had ever had. Victoria blamed him for the death of General Gordon of Khartoum, reflecting a popular press cry. It was claimed that the government was responsible for abandoning the Sudan, and then for not acting quickly enough to send troops to Gordon's aid in a siege.

Once the 66-year-old Gladstone stepped down, Victoria demonstrated she still had certain powers by moving with alacrity and a sense of vengeance to replace him. She was motivated by the need to push the government on and also to prepare for her own spring vacation in Europe and the wedding of another grandchild. Victoria, pointedly, did not consult Gladstone about who should succeed him. Initially she chose Lord Rosebery from within the Liberals, when his 58-year-old rival, Sir William Harcourt, whom Victoria did not like, was judged by many to be better equipped for the job. But Rosebery's agenda seemed to her to be the same as Gladstone's, without his conviction. In the end she had to call for the conservative Lord Salisbury. His government lasted a few months only and Victoria was forced to ask Gladstone to take over as prime minister *again*. He attempted to pass a Bill granting Ireland home rule, but it was defeated in July 1886. Victoria was delighted, even if it meant more government games of musical chairs. There was an election. Salisbury took the prime ministership once more.

Victoria was engaged in her role with more concentration than ever before. Her popularity increased. In the three years since John Brown's death, instead of mourning him for a prolonged period, she had busied herself with work and attended to family matters, all the time taking pride in her expanding family, which was marrying into Royalty in several European countries. But Victoria missed constant male company, which she had had with few breaks since her first ever affair began with Elphinstone at the age of fifteen. Most people, especially women of that era, would have resigned themselves to a single life in their late sixties. But not this queen and empress. She was still restless for attractive male company. Victoria would not rule out finding a way to command it, mainly because, as queen, she could.

41

VICTORIA'S
NEW PASSION

In the summer of 1887, Victoria was enjoying her Jubilee celebrations, although she did not care to be reminded by her bedroom mirror that she was now 68 and very much a rotund, ageing monarch. Her years still did not stop her being enamoured with the company of attractive younger men. In keeping with her Elphinstone-generated lifelong infatuation with India and her role as empress, she was 'given' the first of her Indian servants to mark her milestone. They were supposed to wait on Indian princes attending the Jubilee. The two servants who caught her experienced eye were the 24-year-old Abdul Karim, who was tall, dark-bearded, dark-eyed, handsome and ingratiating, and the solid, pleasant Mohammed Bukhsh. Karim was the most attractive, 'beautiful' male she had met since Duleep Singh 34 years earlier in 1854, and before that, Albert in 1839. Singh had disappointed her by his relentless womanising in England. Worse he was now nothing like his statue in the Durbar Room at Osborne House. He had become a portly 50, and unappetising to Victoria. Karim, a clerk, who had worked in the gaol at Agra in Northern India, was her new piece of human exotica.

The Indians kissed her feet when they were introduced at Windsor. Victoria enjoyed it and looked forward to it every day. She had them stand behind her at breakfast, where, using a golden spoon, she ate her customary egg in a golden cup. They were told to wear 'dark blue dress', although she did not care what colour turban or sash they wore, as long as they did not clash with her yellow cutlery. Karim rose quickly from servant-waiter to secretary, then cook. He had only prepared simple curries for a week before his elevation to 'Munshi', meaning teacher. But he could hardly read or write English. Victoria overcame this by charging him with teaching her Hindustani. She asserted that learning this language would help her understand India and Indians because she had had little contact with them before. Victoria had less fortune in convincing her family, courtiers and onlookers, who could see that she was enchanted by this striking foreigner, with his alluring appearance and fawning obedience. He was a 'very strict master' she noted, although 'a perfect gentleman'. She told those around her how intelligent and quiet he was. She was helping him with his English. Victoria thought he would soon be able 'to *copy* a good deal' for her.

There was added concern from onlookers with some of the phrases she was learning by heart. 'You will miss the Munshi very much,' raised eyebrows. 'Hold me tight!' wrinkled observers' brows. Victoria was alone in the royal court and in the family in appreciating Abdul Karim. Everyone else found him pretentious and irritating. Victoria heard about these attitudes and put them down to the racism she abhorred. She gave him a comfortable bungalow at Windsor. The other courtiers, being strictly hierarchical, were annoyed to learn that he could enter the billiard room and have meals in the household dining area. Soon he was following her to Balmoral and Osborne. Smitten with his appearance, and at ease with his nature, she commissioned Austrian artist Rudolph Swoboda to paint his portrait, keeping a copy for herself. Victoria attempted to cover for her infatuation by suggesting to Karim that he might like his wife to come out from India, but no-one around her was fooled by this gesture. The Munshi was an Indian version of John Brown. Bertie, for one, was angst-ridden that yet another favoured male companion seemed more important to his mother than him. There was also concern that Hindus would be upset by Victoria favouring a

Muslim. Worse, the secretary of state for India, Lord George Hamilton, worried that the Munshi might be a security risk. He advised that he should not be allowed to read confidential papers. Karim was a close friend of a young lawyer, Rafiuddin Ahmed, who was linked to the Muslim Patriotic League. There was some evidence that state secrets were being sent to Afghanistan. Victoria's defence here was that the Munshi did not read English well enough to know which documents were important. As her Indian secretary he was 'handy' for drying the ink on her signatures. After some hesitation on Karim's part, Victoria finally organised for his wife to join him, a move that did a little to dissipate rumours that Victoria's relationship transcended the platonic. They were now given cottages on each of her estates so that Karim could always attend to Victoria. She became fond of Mrs Karim too. Letters to her were signed 'dearest mother' or 'your loving mother, Victoria R.I.' She became solicitous and helpful when she learnt that Karim and his wife were trying to have children. Victoria arranged that her doctor should assist and advise Mrs Karim.

Despite all the objections from her family, the court and snide press remarks, Victoria continued to develop a close relationship with her choice of 'partner'.

She would not let go of her past affiliations either. Apart from reminders of Albert everywhere, and of Brown here and there, in 1889 Victoria commissioned Gustav William Mullins to paint a copy of an 1859 photograph of Elphinstone for her Royal Collection.

In 1891, Bertie was kept in the public eye for all the wrong reasons when he was embroiled in two scandals reflecting the indolence and preoccupation of the upper class. First he was involved in a baccarat scandal when it was revealed he had been in an illegal game. Bertie had to appear in court for a second time when one player unsuccessfully sued another for calling him a cheat. The press made much of a storm in a thimble, which hardly threatened to break down public morality, especially when many of the population played cards for money. A second scandal was more in line with the public image of Bertie. A good friend, Lord Charles Beresford, threatened to reveal details of

Bertie's private life, including some facts about the 'special' chair in the French brothel, in a protest against him interfering with Beresford's affair with Daisy Greville, Countess of Warwick. Both incidents were likely to do only minor damage to the public perception of the future king. But they did not help his cause in being allowed to step up his responsibilities.

Victoria had faced many deaths of people close to her but in her old age she found the demise of her grandson Eddy, who would have followed his father, Bertie, as King of England, hard to take. Outliving her husband, two lovers (Elphinstone and Brown) and many favoured men of state was one thing, but attending the funeral of a grandson was one of her saddest moments. Eddy died of pneumonia in January 1892, aged 28. Alexandra was devastated. Bertie lamented to his mother that he would 'gladly have given' his life for Eddy, 'as I put no value on mine'. This self-deprecatory comment reflected Bertie's penance for his scandals in the previous year but it would have raised eyebrows. Eddy had never covered himself in glory, yet the nation spun into a mood of pathos as he was lauded in death in a way that could not have been done in life. Eddy was a more dissolute character than his father; one who did not inspire the nation. It was in mourning, but no-one other than the family cared. An accident of birth had destined him to be king. An accident of nature had saved the nation from him. Eddy had been about to marry the fair, straight-backed and elegant German Princess May, the daughter of the queen's cousin, the Duchess of Teck. Eddy's permanent departure spared her a probable life of misery. The royal family adored her so much that they lined her up for his brother George, who was now the next in line for the throne after Bertie. Demonstrating a remarkable matrimonial flexibility, Princess May paid her respects to the dead betrothed she hardly knew, and shifted her devotion to Prince George, whom she had never met before Eddy's funeral.

In August 1892, a change in government seemed imminent, as 82-year-old William Gladstone, now deaf and visually impaired, took over as prime minister after six years of Lord Salisbury. They had played 'tag' with the high office over a 34-year period, with only Disraeli interrupting their occupation between 1868 and 1874. Gladstone was now into his fourth 'term'. Victoria sniffed at the prospect of dealing with him yet again. As usual everyone dropped out of the running when they realised that Gladstone, despite his disabilities, felt the call of the nation and colleagues to take charge, surely, he hoped, for the last time. Victoria had to make do with a more amenable cabinet. Bertie, of late, had been trying to show he had his finger on the pulse of the nation's politics. He urged his mother to recommend Lord Rosebery as foreign minister, but Rosebery's wife had just died and he didn't want the job. Bertie wrote him a persuasive letter and changed his mind. Confident in his diplomatic skills, Bertie pushed for access to cabinet decisions. Victoria demurred. She noted that Salisbury had not given him the 'boxes' containing state papers, so Gladstone shouldn't either. Bertie was denied once more. He had first asked to see state papers soon after he married in 1863. After the Garibaldi incident in 1864, Victoria had thwarted further efforts by Bertie to meet foreign sovereigns and statesmen in attempts to solve international crises, although she could not prevent him penning the odd diplomatic letter. Gladstone delivered papers to him secretly. Later he was sent summaries of cabinet reports but he was stopped from seeing the detail. Bertie had been allowed to take state visits, starting with the United States when he was eighteen in 1860, and where he had been a big 'hit' at a moment when there was considerable anti-British feeling. He went to the subcontinent, primarily India, for eight months in 1875–76. Russia followed, then France, which he loved and subsequently visited almost every year. Victoria did not stop him opening bridges and public buildings.

This latest block over the 'boxes' didn't help his demeanour and only increased his controversial proclivities, especially regarding women and gambling. His mother was 73. She was going deaf. Her eyesight was failing. Her manner towards him made it clear that she would never abdicate but she could not go on much longer. He had been the most patient Prince Regent; waiting 33 years (so far) beyond the age he would have been eligible to become king. He reckoned she had a decade left at the outside, which gave him ample time to prepare for the job while still playing up as he had ever since his first dalliance as a nineteen-year-old. Bertie continued his lustful ways but his lifestyle in his early 50s had his doctors warning that he was a candidate for a stroke or a heart attack. Bertie the gourmand, or glutton—depending on the perspective—had a 1.22 metre waistline, which he maintained by mounting assaults on sometimes twelve courses at a sitting. He was famous for taking five meals a day, which would have out-devoured the King of Tonga, who was no slouch in the devastation of banquets. Then again, many of the aristocracy and his set lived this way because they could. At his age many were already dissipated after decades of a degenerate lifestyle. Bertie, as the pinnacle of British society, believed he had the right to do as he wished, especially as no major responsibilities had devolved to him, either by his mother's attitudes or his reputation with Church leaders, the guardians of the nation's morality. Bertie had become more reckless in his maturity but he was no fool. He was not prepared to give up his debauchery, but he did begin to make more of an effort to look like a capable king-in-waiting. He would never be regarded as a statesman, but he cultivated a middle-man, 'go-between' image. It was far too late to be seen as a man of letters but, as he showed in his turning of Rosebery's mind, he could compose a well-written letter for the good of the nation. And when he put his mind to it, he was a fair diplomat. Certainly no public servant could match him in bringing foreign leaders together in peace rather than war. In this respect, he used his power positively.

Bertie also exercised power for personal gain in the private confines of his select circle. He kept it exclusive for the very fact that this made outsiders pay him to get into this future monarch's elite 'sphere'. The rich on the fringe of a world that tantalised them found this Prince of Wales was an accommodating gatekeeper.

There were unwritten rules about how to gain entry. Outsiders had to entertain him and his titled and layabout cronies. They had to create avenues for Bertie and Co., including the more impecunious, to make money through insider investments. One of the first let into the top British 'club' was Hungarian Jewish banker Baron Maurice de Hirsch. He bought an introduction to Bertie in 1890 from Austria's Crown Prince Rudolf. In quick time he became Bertie's new best friend and unofficial adviser. When Hirsch died in 1896, this position was continued by another Jewish banker, Ernest Cassel (who converted to Catholicism). Bertie drew them into the circle with a smile. Other Jewish bankers entered the royal-backed 'club', including Edward Sassoon, the Liberal Unionist Party parliamentarian. There were also several of the mighty Rothschilds with already established riches on the Continent and in Britain. This brought objection and comments from the British elite about Bertie's 'philo-semitism', which was a euphemistic way of expressing the more harsh 'Jew-lover'. But this misjudged him. When a Royal Commission was proposed to impose 'stringent' control on Jewish immigration, Bertie was in favour of it. His affections were not towards Jews; they flowed to rich *bankers* who happened to be Jews. He gained diverse knowledge, inspired views and useful business tips from these more worldly, canny, sophisticated and broadminded figures. In an era when Jews were despised by the upper classes, Bertie ignored the bigotry and consorted with whom he wished. They helped him invest his money so that he had enough for socialising and an extravagant lifestyle. If he ran out of funds, they offered loans, which were often 'forgotten'. They would help to refinance mortgage loans on his properties when he borrowed against them. Victoria was concerned that Bertie would end up mortgaging the monarchy when and if he were king.

Irish-born diplomat and writer Shane Leslie observed: 'From the wisdom of businessmen and the wit of beautiful women, he learnt how to deal with men.'

Bertie was alert to the assessments of his more permanent and savvy mistresses, especially when it came to characters in politics, business and diplomacy.

42

PLAYBOY PRINCE

Bertie, 51, in 1893 was forgoing a few of his pleasure pursuits. One was to delay a spring visit to France to chair a London meeting over retirement funds for servants, when he would have preferred to take to a more elaborate chair in Paris. But there were really just minor distractions in his relentless pursuit of pleasure. A usual year included a round of visits to large country houses, with shooting, gambling and attendances at race meetings. This would be followed by weeks in London with parties and banquets. Then there would be his visits to Paris, the French Riviera and Marienbad in Bohemia. In public and private, he was hardly ever seen without a cigar or a cigarette in hand. In private, it was the same but with the most stunning, sensual women close by.

Victoria tried to disabuse him of his lifestyle in leading an 'immoral' strand of the aristocracy in flaunting its wealth and self-indulgence when so much of the country lived in poverty. She was aware there was a rich streak of hypocrisy in her censure of him.

In a rare meeting at Windsor Castle in the spring of 1893 Victoria told Bertie: 'Your behaviour sets a bad example and incites the working-class into radical and *democratic* thinking.'

'I don't agree. The aristocracy is an essential bulwark of society as long as its privileged members do their public duties, such as acting as lord lieutenants of the Counties.'

'But your excesses—your partying—are undermining everything you do!'

'We are entitled to our pleasures in private, surely?'

'You leave me in despair, Bertie! You really do. One day, when you are king, you might realise how out of touch your sentiment is! You will lose your popularity. And it is so difficult to retrieve. It is a fickle thing.'

'I believe I am accepted by all classes. The upper class does not shun me; on the contrary, they embrace me. The working class mimic me with my gambling. I am cheered when my horses win and they sympathise when I lose!'

'And the vast and growing middle class?'

'They aspire to be in a higher class. I represent that aspiration!'

'You delude yourself. Self-delusion is a dangerous thing.'

Without telling his mother, Bertie believed he could parlay popularity into a wide appeal when on the throne.

At Christmas 1895, Vicky visited London with her family. She loved to spend time with Victoria where she stepped out of the voluminous correspondence between them and into real conversation. In those chats with her and other members of the family, particularly Bertie, Vicky realised that she knew far more about the queen and her private thoughts than anyone else. The diaries allowed Victoria to let go some feelings, but the letter communication to her daughter was the positively cathartic place to vent all her emotions. They joked about being each other's 'High Priestess'. They had written about 150 letters a year to each other over 40 years, which added up to around 6000 pieces of correspondence.

Bertie was still loitering on the edge of significance in Britain's affairs as his long wait for the throne continued. Victoria and Salisbury would only throw him ceremonial tokens, such as on 14 May 1896, after nearly six decades, Victoria giving up the trooping of the colour at the Horse Guards Parade, and letting her son do it. Undaunted, he revelled in his own pursuits when one of his thirteen racehorses, Persimmon, won the Derby. The prince led his horse into the winner's enclosure to the biggest spontaneous ovation he had received to that point in his life. Many of the punters at this prime British race had backed Persimmon because it belonged to Bertie. This win took the prince's stake earnings to nearly £29,000 for the season, a few thousand short of what it cost for the upkeep of his stud. Victoria was one person not impressed. She had warned him he would not be able to compete financially with the Rothschilds at *anything*. But Bertie wasn't listening to his mother on such matters anymore, regarding her as a 'killjoy' when it came to his fun-seeking.

Bertie was allowed to plan the Diamond Jubilee to celebrate his mother's sixtieth anniversary of her ascending to the throne in 1897. He insisted on a bit of austerity, royal-style, by not inviting the crowned heads from other countries. His nephew, Kaiser Wilhelm, at all costs was to be kept away. Bertie told all the major dignitaries involved that any surplus monies raised for the occasion would go to the 'Metropolitan hospitals and Convalescent Institutions'. That done, he turned to the challenge of riding a bike. Cycling had become the great new fad of the mid-1890s. His weight and age made it a tough mission, but after several falls he succeeded, causing *Punch* to dub him 'The Prince of Wheels.'

On Saturday 20 June 1897, the queen and her seven surviving children attended a service at St George's Chapel, Windsor, and then visited Albert's tomb, with its Matthew Noble-sculpted sarcophagus of a recumbent prince. (It was more than similar to Noble's Elphinstone memorial lying in the quiet surrounds of St Peter's, Limpsfield, in Surrey.) Monday 22 June was declared a bank holiday for the much grander public celebration and thanks at St Paul's in London. Huge crowds attended. London's population had tripled to just under four million since Victoria's coronation, and at least a quarter of them were out and about hoping to get a glimpse of her and the Prince of Wales. Bertie was prominent, riding a horse on one side of the grand state landau drawn by eight horses that departed Buckingham Palace to much fanfare at 11.15 a.m. Elphinstone's close friend, the old Duke of Cambridge, rode on the other side. The queen sat alone in the large carriage with the Princess of Wales (Alix) and Princess Helena (Lenchen) placed opposite her with their backs to the horses. Prince Arthur, Duke of Connaught, now a field marshal, followed. Protocol dictated that Vicky, an empress dowager, precede the landau in a smaller carriage. Alfred, as his father had ordained, was now a sovereign after inheriting the duchy of Coburg and Gotha. He, too, had to ride separately.

There were as many tears as cheers for the procession. All onlookers were aware that the ailing grandmotherly sovereign was 78 and probably attending her last grand public ceremony. Royal supporters and rebels alike acknowledged that she had been a significant presence and dominant image for almost all onlookers for all their lives. They had known no-one else as the symbol of British life, in an era that had long been named after her. Victoria's legacy was in place even though she was doing less and less in public.

Bertie had to step up his involvement in ceremonial activities, which he enjoyed more than his mother. He was lively and ingratiating and always gave the impression of being captivated by those he met. This contrasted to solemn Victoria, who could not hide her fatigue and lack of interest. She was winding down while the only thing that Bertie seemed to be slowing up on was his extra-marital affairs. His obesity had led to impotence and attendant medical problems, including arteriosclerosis and diabetes. Aline Sassoon was seen less and less. His number one mistress in the late 1890s, Daisy Greville (Lady Warwick), was keeping herself out of his grasp by attaching herself to eccentric causes. She also returned fitfully to her husband to allow him conjugal rights after a thirteen-year denial. She became pregnant and kept apart from Bertie's set as he looked more and more like a neutered king-in-waiting. The tall, blue-eyed, bosomy Alice Keppel was becoming his female accessory of choice as his lusty days as a royal stud faded.

Granulated rhinoceros horn, special Chinese herbs, imported oysters and 'natural' sex drugs from India could bring him to attention but it was often a struggle. His diminished sex drive made him grumpy and Keppel was the woman to keep up his spirits, if not his pecker.

Bertie would still find ways to have his erotic pleasures, but he needed a full-time occupation to balance his need for his brothel whores, society women, horses and gambling mates. Being king would do.

Victoria's strange, unconventional relationship with Abdul Karim had been maintained for a decade after the Jubilee events and the family, the royal court and the press were becoming concerned. Without Victoria's knowledge or direction, her private secretary, Sir Henry Ponsonby, sent British spies to check on Karim and discovered he had misrepresented his father's profession in claiming he was a 'surgeon-general'. In fact he was a pharmacist working at the Agra gaol where Karim had been a clerk. When Ponsonby informed her, she refused to believe it, saying that he must have the wrong man. Ponsonby's diligent intelligence-gathering displeased Victoria so much that she did not invite him to dinner for a year, which he understood was punishment.

Several of Victoria's children tried to talk her out of having the Munshi so close, but to no avail. They were troubled that she wrote so much to him, sometimes several letters a day. Courtiers' fears had some substance. Karim's English had improved and as he diligently dried her majesty's moniker, he saw every letter that she sent. Victoria turned to him to discuss India's sectarian problems between Muslims and Hindus, and she, in turn, passed on advice to India's bemused viceroy. Her solutions, it was noted, always favoured Muslims. The worry for courtiers and family came to a head when Victoria spent the night with him in the isolated Scottish cottage at Loch Ordie that she had once shared with Brown. After this intimate encounter, Karim was emboldened enough to ask for a knighthood, saying it would bring him and his family enormous prestige. Victoria consulted a few trusted courtiers, who delicately advised against it.

Bertie was monitoring all these developments and was in constant letter communication with Vicky over it. She responded that Victoria had always done what she wanted when it came to affairs of the heart. After losing Elphinstone, for instance, she had eventually won the battle to have him restored to the royal court. Vicky observed that she had always loved the company of attractive men. Bertie wrote back that he could condone her relationships if they were not having such extraordinary ramifications for affairs of state. The situation was so serious, Bertie informed Vicky, that he said he would tell Victoria to stop pushing for Karim's knighthood. He thought it would endanger the monarchy. But Bertie could not summon the courage to confront her, which he told Vicky would be the hardest thing he would ever have to do. He shirked the issue, even though he had the ammunition to fire at his mother concerning the Elphinstone affair. He was in fear of her. But there was also the moral high ground. He could hardly take it himself given his private life, which had now spanned four decades. Instead, he used her personal physician, Sir James Reid, to handle it. He was an Aberdeen Scot and not in the habit of mincing his words. Victoria usually appreciated this, but on this occasion she found it most unpalatable. Reid met her in private and consulted her about her health. Then he raised the issue of the Munshi.

'It is not doing your mental state any good,' he said bluntly, 'and it seems to me you are thinking too much of his feelings. But this is of infinitesimal importance compared with the gravity of the situation as regards your majesty.'

Victoria stiffened as she sat opposite on a chair in the drawing room. Reid fiddled with his satchel, putting his notes and medicine away. He was not nervous, yet his fidgeting was a sign of agitation. She knew his manner well and braced herself for some contentious advice.

'People in high places are saying that your majesty is not sane,' he added, 'and they are saying that the time will come when, to save your memory and reputation, it will be necessary for me to come forward and say so.'

'Say what?' Victoria asked firmly.

'That you are not well; that you are indeed not sane.'

'You are insane to suggest it!' she shouted.

'I spoke to the Prince of Wales yesterday,' Reid responded, standing his ground, 'and he spoke to me very seriously on the subject.'

'Coward! He has not the stomach to see me about it!'

'That is not true, your majesty. He says he has quite made up his mind to come forward if necessary.'

'He sends you to do his dirty work.'

'With respect, no, your majesty. Quite apart from all the consequences to you, it affects him most vitally.'

'Why?'

'Because it affects the throne.'

This comment only caused Victoria to be even more stubborn. Not frightened by the doctor's sharp message, or her son's behind-the-scenes threats, she went on the offensive, concluding that the royal household was being racist.

'Bertie,' she wrote to Vicky, 'is being his usual selfish and mean self.'

Victoria called Reid to another meeting and raged at him. Reid did not fold and this caused her to break down. He had to comfort her and settle her down with a sedative. Even this hardy Scot had had enough, at least in confronting his queen. Realising the predicament in which he had placed the much-respected doctor, Bertie told him he had his full support. Reid then confronted the Munshi, who had to put up with tirades, abuse and intimidation. The Indian's only real supporter of any weight was Victoria herself. The older she became and the longer he remained close, the worse it became for him and his family. In the end, Victoria did not urge for Karim's knighthood anymore but instead pushed harder for his privileges and defended him at every turn. Ponsonby reflected the general frustration from all around her about this strange relationship with an unlikely individual who had embedded himself into the monarch's affections. Ponsonby saw her attachment to the Indian as one of strong emotion. He likened the Munshi to a pet, similar to a horse or dog that she could not willingly give up.

Karim became sick with a carbuncle on his neck. Victoria visited him twice a day and examined him just as she had seen the doctor do. She fussed about him, stroked his hand and made sure he was comfortable. When his pain subsided, he resumed giving her Hindustani lessons, in his room. He had access to her in much the way Brown had done. Victoria wanted the close, *private* attention of a handsome male and she was prepared to appear eccentric to ensure it. She upbraided anyone who challenged her choice. The Duke of Connaught complained to Ponsonby that Karim was allowed to move among the gentry at the Highland Braemer Games. Ponsonby explained that he was there under the orders of the queen, who understood Indian etiquette. If he (the duke) had a problem, it might be better if he brought it up with her.

Ponsonby wrote that this caused the duke to shut up. The private secretary was amused by Victoria's behaviour, the Munshi himself and the reaction to him by the aristocracy. It also demonstrated that the plump little old monarch instilled more fear into pompous members of the establishment than ever before. That look of disapproval, perfected over half a century, had self-important men and women trembling, even from a distance. Instead of rejoicing in the old queen's pleasure at having attractive young male company, they incurred her displeasure at what she perceived as snobbishness, racism and even jealousy. Some called her defence 'odd'; others continued to suggest her behaviour was a sign of 'madness'. The comparison with George III, especially in his later years, emerged as it had before. But Victoria would not let Karim go. She would never forget how, as a young princess, she had been bluffed, lied to and connived against over her desire for Elphinstone. It was one thing for her Lord to take away Albert; but mere mortals had not been able to banish John Brown. She was determined that they would only remove Karim 'over her dead body', which was likely: he was 44 years younger.

Vicky became ill in the summer of 1899 and made a trip to Balmoral for a medical examination at Victoria's suggestion. The queen mustered the best specialists to attend and they concluded she had inoperable cancer. It was a distressing time for all, particularly Victoria, who expressed her despair at the thought of outliving her favourite child, but was nevertheless stoic in front of her daughter. Yet Vicky did not feel sorry for herself and insisted on walking in the hills with Bertie, who had come to see her after the doctors' verdict.

He could not keep up and had to sit halfway up a hill catching his breath.

'I'm glad we could be alone,' she said. 'I wanted to talk to you about the letters.'

'What?' Bertie said.

'Between me and Mama. I made sure that once she had read them they were sent back to me. I have most of them. Well, the contentious ones at least.'

'I am not clear what you are getting at.'

'I have put my thoughts on paper about Willy becoming kaiser,' she said sadly. 'I know it is awful to talk about one's own son like this, but he would be dangerous. He wants to expand his empire. I have heard his private boasts. My physician tells me in private that Willy is a kind of megalomaniac. He wants power to compensate for his weaknesses, which are legion.'

'Poor Vicky,' Bertie said, patting her arm, 'you have been through much.'

'The doctors say my illness has been brought on by my concerns.'

Bertie nodded sympathetically.

'I don't think you understand,' she said locking her drawn, sad eyes on him. 'Willy could be mad. He will want to prove himself through his country's actions, even unto war with Russia and the United Kingdom.'

'I must say, I have never liked him, sorry.'

'No-one loves Willy. He is cold, arrogant, jingoistic and over-ambitious.'

'Surely he would not move against England?'

'Not while Mama is alive. He would never dare. But when she passes over...'

Vicky gripped his hand. 'You must get Ponsonby to come to Friedrichshof [Castle, Kronberg, her family home] and collect the letters,' she said earnestly. 'They must never, ever be read by Willy. I really fear his reaction for everyone if he ever read them.'

The thoughts distressed her. Bertie kissed her forehead. 'Don't worry, my sweet sister. I'll attend to it.'

'There is something else,' she whispered, her eyes welling up in tears. 'Willy knows about Lord E.'

'E?'

'Elphinstone!' Vicky dabbed her eyes.

'Did Mama tell him?! I can't believe—'

'No, no, never! I was ill in hospital in Berlin about the time Brown died. Mama wrote a most impassioned letter. Willy visited me in hospital and while I was asleep he began reading it. I awoke and admonished him. In explaining Mama's comments I mentioned 'E.' Later in correspondence he forced me—at the threat of writing to Mama—to say who 'E' was.'

Vicky cried more. Bertie put his arm around her.

'There, there. He won't dare say anything.'

'You can never know with Willy! It's now all there in a letter! I feel terrible about writing it, but I had no choice. It was blackmail!'

'We'll have to get that letter back somehow.'

'Apart from that one letter from me to Willy, you do realise that the entire file at Friedrichshof contains all Mama's secrets, most of mine, and thoughts about everyone, including you. There is detailed, intimate comment by her about Elphinstone, Papa, Brown and Karim, not to mention her sometimes scathing commentary about every prime minister, foreign head of state and just about everyone in British and royal society! It is explosive!'

'Don't concern yourself,' Bertie consoled her. 'I shall make sure we get back all potentially damaging material.'

43

SYMBOLISM OVER INVALIDISM

Victoria battled on as queen long beyond her used-by date. Early in 1900 she was concerned about the news from the Second War in South Africa against the Boers and world reaction to it. The conflict had dragged on and British troops had incurred high casualties, distressing Victoria. There were stories of gross incompetence at the highest levels, which led her to believe that making her son Arthur army commander might turn things around. She met him and Bertie at Balmoral to plot a strategy and a royal succession in the armed forces that might make a difference.

'Mama, I am not sure I am qualified for the role,' Arthur confessed.

'Poppycock! You are royal. You are qualified from birth!'

'It may put some generals' noses out of joint, Mama,' Bertie remarked.

Victoria was miffed.

'I don't understand either of you,' she said with a frown. 'If you are concerned about qualification, then I suggest that some of my grandchildren join the Horse Guards and create a career path to higher command later.'

Neither man responded, indicating they were lukewarm to the idea.

'The thirteenth Lord Elphinstone began that way,' Victoria went on, 'and his performance in India suggests he would have been an admirable commander-in-chief.'

Bertie blinked. He was astonished that his mother would refer to her one-time lover.

'Mama, it's a different era,' Arthur began bravely. 'You can't expect your grandchildren to follow the paths of those leaders of half a century ago.'

'There are many more enticing and rewarding things to do now,' Bertie said with a supportive nod for his younger brother, 'especially in things like property investment, business and diplomacy.'

There was a chilly silence before Victoria said: 'You both disappoint me. Arthur, I shall write to Salisbury and express my desire that you be head of the army in my lifetime.'

A few days later, Prime Minister Salisbury received the letter and mumbled to his secretary: 'Bloody nepotism! When will the old girl stop? I believe I can sit out this particular royal directive. She can't have that long to go, can she?'

Victoria's fortitude was evident in March when she took a trip to Ireland, her first in 40 years. En route from Windsor to Woolwich she detoured via London. Perhaps this was for one last cheer from her subjects, or just to demonstrate that while now mainly wheelchair bound, she was still in charge, if not of an empire, then herself at 80. Victoria received a rapturous and positive response in the capital, verifying she was still the member of the royal family who counted most in the land. Biographer Stanley Weintraub said she had chosen 'symbolism over invalidism'. It was also a triumph of her will over her woes. On the way to Woolwich she stopped at a military hospital, a naval school for boys and a crippled children's home. It was obvious to all onlookers that this near-deaf, near-blind diminutive octogenarian was struggling but she showed concern for others at every stop. Her determination was an inspiration to all she met.

Courage, it seemed, was genetic. Bertie was in Brussels on his way with his wife to her family in Copenhagen. At 5.30 p.m. on 4 April 1900, just as his mother stepped foot in Ireland, he was on a train leaving Brussels. He and Alix looked out the train window as it began moving. A figure was on the footboard a few paces away aiming a gun at them through the window. The train jolted just as he fired. Two bullets flew between the royal couple's heads instead of into them. The would-be assassin took aim again but was pulled from the footboard and set upon by brave Belgian travellers. Sixteen-year-old apprentice tinsmith Jean-Baptiste Sipido was arrested. Alix was upset; Bertie was stoic. He had the presence of mind to telegraph Alice Keppel, his number-one paramour, letting her know he and Alix were unharmed before the news hit London in the morning papers. Relieved to be alive, Bertie was magnanimous. He asked Belgian authorities to be lenient with the youth, whom he assumed was mentally unstable. Whatever the youth's level of sanity, Bertie wrote to his sister Louise saying that the assailant was fortunately a very bad shot.

Victoria was informed. She mused on her own near-assassination misses and may well have believed there had been divine intervention for her family's sake yet again. Other than that, the attackers were all poor marksmen.

Sipido's Belgian trial was a farce. The accused was sorry he missed, blaming Bertie for the deaths of thousands of Boers in South Africa. His juvenile response had resonance in Europe where the British were criticised for their conduct of the war. It was enough for a Belgian jury to find him 'not guilty'. He admitted he tried to kill two people. At best this was attempted murder, but the anti-British mood and emotion held sway over any rational response. Sipido was set free and this sent shock waves through the palaces. The royal family worried they would now be targets for more political fringe-dwellers with grievances, real and imagined. Soon after the incident, the kaiser expressed his sympathy to Bertie over Belgian indifference. Bertie doubted his nephew's sincerity, especially when in Copenhagen he read in a French paper that the Germans were plotting with the French and Russians to join a coalition against the British. The rewards for a joint action would be colonial acquisitions in Egypt and India.

Bertie avoided Paris, a rare thing for him, where Anglophobia had peaked. On arriving in London at Charing Cross Station, he was greeted by cheering crowds. Thousands more demonstrated their support and approval as he took his carriage home to Marlborough House. Nothing, it seemed, lifted a public figure's popularity like an assassination attempt. In British minds, justice had not been done over the would-be killer and support for Bertie was enhanced.

Vicky's cancer spread and by the autumn of 1900 had reached her spine. She was given six months to live. Mother and daughter continued their correspondence, which became frenetic and impassioned in the knowledge that they were both too ill to travel; they would never see each other again. As ever, their correspondence gave each other strength. Vicky did not mention the 'problem' she saw arising over their many boxes of letters neatly marked and sitting in the attic of her home at Friedrichshof. She did not wish to worry her mother but, in a letter, she again urged Bertie to act before her own death, reminding him that Willy must never be allowed to get his hands on the correspondence. She worried that, because Willy deluded himself he was Victoria's favourite, there was no telling what his reaction would be if he knew that she despised him, as everyone else did.

Bertie wrote back promising once more to visit her and have the letters removed for safekeeping back to Windsor Castle.

In the last months of 1900, at Osborne, Victoria struggled to do her duties as she had done for most of her more than 63 years as monarch: reading the 'boxes', signing papers, dictating letters and writing her journal. She had trouble keeping up her own entries or scribbling, partly from blindness, mainly from the effort. It was easier to mumble sentences to her secretary. Dramas within her mighty family seemed to multiply. Earlier, in July 1900, she had been inconsolable over the death from throat cancer of her 56-year-old son Alfred, Duke of Coburg, and six months later she was worrying daily about Vicky's condition. Sad information would depress her. Sicknesses, divorce threats, scandal and any other alarms did not now reach Victoria. These omissions, or 'edits', concerning her relatives' lives did not fool her, but she was too listless to make enquiries. It wasn't that she did not care. Over the decades her diaries had demonstrated a constant worry and concern over her children and grandchildren, and all her in-laws. The weather on the Isle of Wight caused enough grey moments without augmentation from the pressures of her all-encompassing life, as mother, queen, emperor, friend, symbol of an empire and human being.

Victoria was fading away, although she was not prepared to accept it. She would ask her doctor, 'Am I getting better?' The response would always be positive. She wanted to live. Dr Reid knew this and did not wish to discourage her passion for her life and grand position. Victoria loved being queen and empress. In the last few years she could always make excuses for not letting Bertie have important responsibilities, but they were never the point. Victoria had known no other life since she was eighteen. She could never contemplate abdicating to be dumped in a castle or house to see out her final years, out of sight, perhaps even out of the public mind. Victoria knew that her son was popular and capable, despite his deficiencies, in her eyes, of doubtful company and extravagant lifestyle. He would be a king to fit more profligate, perhaps frivolous times when so much rapid change, mainly technological, was upon the world. Victoria never seriously considered anything but going on to the end and dying in 'office'. That way she knew the world, and not just her extended family, would focus on her to her last breath and beyond to a grand funeral she had planned to the last musical and written note. But remaining monarch when she was not fit for the role took a huge toll as 'the 'horrible year' of 1900 stormed to an end of wind and rain. Victoria blamed the weather for not being able to see. It was dark and grey every day; Reid told her that she may have been right but it was her way of denying her diminishing senses. She went to bed earlier and was too fatigued to rise before noon. Any work distressed her. The new year began and for the first time in her life of keeping a diary, she did not start with a resolution.

Victoria told her diary that she entered 1901 feeling weak and unwell and that this made her sad, yet she was as stoic as ever, telling her daughter that she expected her health to soon 'improve'. But her deep care for life was missing. So was a diary entry on 14 January. Victoria had been most attentive to her writing since 1832 when she was twelve years old. Since then the only serious gap had been the three weeks in October 1835 when she was very ill under the most traumatic conditions.

Lord Roberts, British commander-in-chief in South Africa, was the last soldier she saw. Joseph Chamberlain was the last minister. On 15 January 1901, she was put in her pony-chaise, hoping for a ride with Marie of Coburg, her widowed daughter-in-law. But the rain was incessant. She never had that final ride. On 16 January there was a last order, showing her faculties were still with her, despite her now perpetual fatigue. Victoria had her ambassador in Berlin informed that he should not accept an honour from the kaiser, her least liked grandson, Wilhelm II.

On 17 January, Dr Reid knew she was in trouble. She found it difficult to express herself and had experienced minor strokes. It made her fret. She was confused. Reid summoned a heart specialist. The next day the Duke of Connaught, in Berlin, was informed of her condition. The kaiser heard about it too and invited himself to England to be with his grandmother at the expected end. On 19 January, Bertie rolled into Osborne. He hated the place, finding it bleak, boring and without the night-life he craved. Seeing his entourage arriving, locals knew that something serious was afoot. He ordered a bulletin of understatement, saying that the queen had not been in her usual health due to the 'great strain' on her powers over the past year. In the next 48 hours she would rally, slip and rally again. Bertie left. Gloom was an emotion he avoided. The kaiser came and stayed. He wanted to demonstrate something: perhaps loyalty, maybe a strange showmanship. But he was there and he had every right to be. He loved his grandmama and she was the most powerful figure in his life. But Victoria, when she was conscious, called not to him or Bertie or one of her daughters; she asked for her little Pomeranian dog, Turi. It was placed on her bed. Victoria noticed it and then lapsed into semi-consciousness. Turi disliked the lack of attention or elevation and jumped off.

Bertie returned. He went into his mother's room. She recognised him and opened her arms to him, uttering her last word as they hugged: 'Bertie!'

She once blamed Albert's death on him, but that was forgotten. Bertie, a sentimental fellow, was touched. The Bishop of Winchester and the Vicar of Whittingham hovered in the room; the kaiser waited outside. For once, Wilhelm showed humility. It surprised everyone so much that he was granted a place at the deathbed. Again, for once, he seemed concerned about someone else other than himself. For the first and last time, he had all the family's respect. The two clergymen tacitly now took charge. Death, or as they preferred, the transition of a life to somewhere else, was their business. They prayed aloud. Victoria lay unmoved through verses of many prayers. The bishop recited alone; then the vicar tried. They chanted together. There was not a flicker from the dying queen. Perhaps her mind had already departed. Then the bishop recalled John Henry Newman's hymn 'Lead, Kindly Light', which had been Victoria's favourite. She had first sung it as a fourteen-year-old in 1833 in the church at St James's Palace about the time she first befriended Elphinstone. The bishop leaned over her, not reciting, not really singing, but chanting. He lightened his tone to almost song. There was still not even a twitch from the sunken cheeks of the 81-year-old Victoria. By the time he reached the last two lines of the third verse of four his voice was lilting. The bishop noticed that she seemed alert, listening: 'And with the morn those angel faces smile/Which I have loved long since, and lost awhile!'

Encouraged, he carried on through the last verse, which Victoria had said for most of her life were the most beautiful words of faith she had ever heard. As a vibrant young girl, she just liked the sound of them. As a dying octogenarian, she understood them:

> Meantime, along the narrow, rugged path,
> Thyself hast trod,
> Lead, Saviour, lead me home in childlike faith,
> To rest forever after earthly strife
> In the calm light of everlasting life

Satisfied that he had reached her before the end of her 'earthly strife', the bishop moved aside with the vicar. It was 4 p.m. on 22 January

1901. Outside, darkness was falling along with a light drizzle. A bulletin, sounding much like a shipping report, went out to the world: 'The Queen is slowly sinking.'

A member of the royal household leaned close to Bertie and wondered if the queen would be happy in heaven. He didn't have any idea, but on reflection said that Victoria would have to walk behind the angels. Bertie didn't think she would appreciate that.

Dr Reid and Wilhelm moved to either side of her and, sitting on the bed, supported her so that she did not slide below the pillows. They stayed there for another two-and-a-half hours, Wilhelm testing his one good arm in an awkward position. Her breath came quicker and shallower. Her face took on more the look of a death mask. The room shrunk as her children (with Vicky among the living missing) and many of her 37 grandchildren filled it. Then, in a bizarre ritual to hold her back from the brink, they began calling their names, perhaps in the hope that she would be teased into staying with her huge brood a little longer. But, if anything, it may have quickened her final bow and leave-taking. She hated death-bed scenes like this. Victoria had let Vicky know it eighteen years earlier when commenting on what she had been told about the end of 82-year-old Prince Charles of Prussia. 'I think it very dreadful that everyone was there,' she had written with indignation. 'I shall insist it is never the case if I am dying. It is awful!'

But Victoria was not in a position to insist on anything ever again. At 6 p.m. her offspring stopped calling to her. At 6.30 p.m. the bishop, fittingly and usefully, claimed there was a 'great change of look, and complete calmness'.

Victoria was dead.

44

FUNERAL FOR A CONNOISSEUR

Victoria had had a passion, even macabre obsession with death and funerals. She had had almost manic concern for the way those close to her, including a favourite dog, made their exit. She had enjoyed the melancholia surrounding burials and, if the departure was of someone important, the sheer pomp and show of it. The more operatic a funeral the better. Not surprisingly, this fascination had led to fastidious planning for her own end. She had wished it to be the best she ever attended, beginning with what was to go on the one-way journey with her inside the coffin. Once the room had been cleared of her weeping relatives, it was Dr Reid's turn to take over from the clergy in organising her after-life as much as was possible. On instructions, her dressers moved in with a prepared list of items to be placed in the coffin with her. They included Albert's dressing gown and one of his cloaks that had been embroidered by Princess Alice. There was also the plaster cast of his hand that Victoria had clasped in bed for most of four decades. Photos were placed neatly in several positions. Her lace wedding veil was put around her. A photo of John Brown was inserted between the fingers of her left hand, along with a lock of his hair. Finally she was adorned with rings, chains, bracelets and lockets. Each one had a story, including several relating to Elphinstone and Abdul Karim, from India, the country she never saw. The artefacts from them were not to be seen by the family. Reid, obeying this dictum, placed a bunch of flowers over the hand holding Brown's photograph and other items. The doctor cut locks from Victoria's hair for those among the family who wanted them. He then invited the mourners back into the room.

Bertie, now king and showing grace through metaphorically gritted teeth, asked Karim, now a portly 36-year-old, to enter so that he could pay his last respects, which was part of her direction in her last show on a grand stage. Once Karim had stepped away, Bertie signalled for the coffin lid to be closed and it was then draped in a white satin pall. An honour guard of sailors marched in and carried it, festooned with flowers, to the dining room where it would be protected for a week by four of her Grenadier guardsmen. Victoria's diamond-studded crown sat on a velvet cushion on the coffin. A big Union Jack hung from the ceiling and huge candles flickered. The kaiser seemed overwhelmed by the exquisite scene and he wanted something to remind him of the occasion. He asked for the flag. Bertie, in a generous mood with another person he despised, agreed he could have it.

A great weight had been lifted from Bertie now he was king. It had been a long wait and he must have wondered, with his own diminishing health, if his mother might outlive him. He loved her and did not wish her gone. But now that she was, he would experience a fresh surge in his existence that he hoped would pay for his patience.

A strange atmosphere enveloped London that night. People scurried through the streets and disappeared into their homes to avoid the bitter cold, which added to the pall of sadness that lowered over the city. American-born novelist Henry James, who had lived in London for the last 39 years, was in the Reform Club on Pall Mall when the news of Victoria's death reached him. Even though he was a British subject, he held the concept of royalty in contempt, especially in light of the progress of the United States to a successful republic. But when he left the club and pulled up his coat collar against the freezing night, he noticed the reaction of the public. People spoke in hushed tones as if frightened. James was surprised by his own emotional reaction. It was after all, he said, 'a simple running down of the old used-up watch. Just the death of an old widow who had thrown her good fat weight into the scales of general decency.'

Later, more feelings tumbled surprisingly from James. On reflection he wrote of the demise of the 'brave old woman' with her 'holding-together virtue'. Searching for the source of his own reaction he decided that Victoria had been a 'sustaining symbol'. He mourned the 'safe and motherly old middle-class Queen, who held the nation warm under the fold of her big, hideous Scotch-plaid shawl'. Her reign had been 'so extraordinarily convenient and beneficent'. It had 'prevented all sorts of accidents'.

James could sense that the Victorian era, with all its faults and virtues, was already fading away. On dredging his own sentiments his reflective words fell into the mood that he noticed had pervaded the streets. There was uncertainty about what the future held with Bertie at the helm. For the moment, 'hope' was the only thing to hold on to.

The coffin was transferred across the Solent to Portsmouth on 1 February and the following day it was taken to Victoria Station. People were in black beside the track. In London, the crowd on the pavement strained to see the coffin, which was on a gun-carriage drawn by men of the horse artillery. Once glimpsed, many spectators bowed their heads, only to look up again to see four monarchs following the coffin on horseback: Edward VII, Kaiser Wilhelm, King George I of the Hellenes and King Carlos of Portugal. Crown princes of Germany, Romania. Greece, Denmark, Norway, Sweden and Siam (Thailand) were in train. The Emperor of Austria, the Tsar of Russia and the King of Italy were also well represented.

At Paddington the coffin was taken by train to Windsor, where thousands withstood the icy cold winds of early February to take in the moment marking the end of the longest rule by a monarch in British history.

Sailors replaced the artillery men in dragging the carriage through Windsor streets, and up to the castle's Long Walk towards St George's Chapel, which was not Victoria's favourite. A short service took place, while cannon fired a salute of 81 guns, one for each year of her life. On 4 February, the artillery men were back in harness pulling the carriage to her final resting place next to Albert in the mausoleum at Frogmore. After her husband's death, she had had the mausoleum built with the Latin inscription above the door: '*Vale desideratissime.* Farewell most beloved. Here at length I shall rest, with thee in Christ I shall rise again.'

Victoria had instructed that the two white marble statues of Albert and her created by Turin-born, Paris-raised London resident Carlo Marochetti were to be placed side by side on the sarcophagus of Aberdeen granite. But there had been a problem. Her own statue had been sealed into a cavity in a Windsor Castle wall. One old worker from the 1860s was located and he recalled its location. It was retrieved and placed next to Albert. His effigy stared straight ahead, like a Greek god's gaze fixed on eternity. But, by direction, Marochetti had portrayed Victoria with a more human look, inclined towards Albert in a white, pristine environment.

The mausoleum's gas lamps were left burning eerily as the family members filed outside. As if by design, sleet floated down on the grass, soon covering it in white too. Victoria had planned the end so well that even the weather bowed to her wishes.

45

EDWARD VII—
PAYBACK TIME

Victoria had gone but the secrets of her life lived on in the Victoria–Vicky correspondence. The revelations in them could damage, even ruin, the monarchy and revive images of decadence, which had been with the institution before Victoria. In the early 1900s, this would not be acceptable and Bertie and the other members of the royal family knew it. But because he was preoccupied with other issues, including attempts to rid the world of evidence of his mother's relationships with Brown and Karim, Bertie put it down the list of his immediate concerns.

Meanwhile, witnesses to the Victorian era and her secret life began to pass on. Just two weeks after Victoria's death, Dr Husna De Crepeney died in a Paris hospital with a close friend, Céleste Vernard, in attendance. Husna had been born in 1814, making her 48 when she was finally allowed to graduate as a doctor in Sweden in 1862. After sitting further exams in France, De Crepeny practised for the next four decades. Her interests were varied and she was influenced by Vernard, the long-time companion she had first met at the Paris Hippodrome in the 1840s. Vernard had married an impoverished count—Lionel de Chabrillan, the first French consul to Australia. When he died and was buried in Melbourne in 1858, Vernard returned to Paris and established herself as an outstanding writer and impresario in literature, opera and theatre. She renewed her friendship with Husna, who inherited a fortune when her father died in 1869. Some of the money was used to fund Vernard's many creative ventures, particularly the Mogador theatre in the working-class area of North Paris. Husna's last request was to ask Vernard to hang a portrait of Elphinstone in the foyer of the theatre, telling her: 'You spoke of your many loves, but you always said there was one above the others—your husband, the Count. I had but one, the thirteenth Lord Elphinstone, and because he was so special I did not seek another, apart from the "man" I married, who was someone I could never love...Lord E was the only true, true love in my heart.'

(The painting remained there another forty years until World War II, when it disappeared during the German occupation of Paris, 1940 to 1944.)

Winston Churchill, 26 years old and a cocky young celebrated war correspondent, was in Canada lecturing on the Boer War when he heard about Victoria's death. He was intrigued to see how Bertie, whom he had advised by private communiqués about the South African conflict, would perform as king.

'Will it entirely revolutionise his way of life?' Churchill later asked his Brooklyn-born mother, Lady Randolph Churchill. It was a question on many lips. 'Will he sell his horses and scatter his Jews or will Reuben Sassoon be enshrined among the crown jewels and other regalia?'

'No,' she replied, 'he will remain true to all of them, including his horses and mistresses.'

'Including you?'

'I was speaking generally.'

'Will the Keppel be made Lady of the Bedchamber?'

'I would think so.'

'I am glad he has got his innings at last, and am most interested to watch how he plays it.'

Bertie's turn at the wicket got off to a bright start. After the closed-off nature of Victoria's court for 40 years, Bertie came across as accessible, friendly and frank. He seemed decisive without being imperious, dignified without being stubborn. Bertie was free from constraint after a lifetime of being conscious of parental 'control', even though he had rebelled with his licentious ways. Mother's disapproving look was not there to hound or haunt him anymore. His first act was to be known as King Edward VII, not the King Albert Edward that his mother had wished. He would say that he could not match his father in name or performance but in reality he did not wish to be in his shadow. There would be no confusion in the annals of history about who was who.

Personal matters concerning Victoria were attended to first. Abdul Karim, his family and other Indians were told to leave the royal court, the palaces and the country. Letters and diaries became the new king's chief concern. Bertie sent Princess Beatrice, his wife (now Queen Alexandra), and some guards to Frogmore Cottage where they demanded all the letters written by Victoria to the Munshi. While the Munshi and his wife wept inside, the correspondence of the heartfelt union and photographs warmly signed by Victoria were put in a pile outside the cottage and set alight. Bertie was attempting to wipe the memory of what he saw as his mother's indiscretions.

Shrabani Basu wrote in her book *Victoria and Abdul*: 'The new King did not want to see any more turbans or smell the curries from the royal kitchens.'

Memorabilia of John Brown, including statues, was also discarded, either destroyed or dumped somewhere. This was posthumous revenge for his mother's perceived 'infidelities'. Bertie wanted no reminder of these philanderings, which he believed had retarded his own progress with Victoria. He hated Osborne House and wanted to sell it. He ordered Windsor to be 'uncluttered', which meant he wanted most of his mother's things to be taken away or at least stored out of his sight. He did away with paintings, statues and heirlooms that she held dear.

Three weeks after his mother's funeral, Bertie visited Paris and made an unscheduled detour into Germany to see Vicky in the last week of

February 1901. He took with him Ponsonby and an armed bodyguard for a secret mission. Vicky had reminded him several times to take possession of all her letters to Victoria, which had been so damning of Willy. Bertie's mission was a tricky one. Ponsonby, with three soldiers, would take the boxed letters from the Friedrichshof attic, load them in a truck and head for the border with France. Once over the border the boxes would be put on a train with the armed guard and taken to England and stored at Windsor. But it had to be done quickly. Once Wilhelm II knew that his uncle was visiting his mother, he was expected to make the journey himself. Willy was a perennial paranoid. He suspected the English and the French were always conspiring against him. In this case, he was correct, at least about the English.

Ponsonby and his guard arrived on 23 February 1901 and left the next day with all Vicky's letters. Bertie stayed on for four days, knowing this would most likely be the last time he saw his beloved sister alive. He had always regarded her as more a surrogate mother than an elder sister, for Vicky had always given him sound advocacy and had his interests at heart.

As the others predicted, Willy came to the castle with a full entourage. He had always been afraid of his imperious, strong-willed uncle. Despite Willy's differences with Vicky, he always sought her approval and part of his bombast, she always suspected, was an effort to impress her. He had his staff ask questions of his mother's courtiers and discovered Ponsonby's mission. Willy was furious. He tried to arrange a private audience with his mother but she would only see him with Bertie present. The three discussed the letter issue at the long dinner table on 25 February after a six-course meal attended to by twenty staff.

'Those letters belong to me, the kaiser, your son!'

'She has left them to the British crown, Willy,' Bertie said, chomping on a cigar.

'They are letters from my mother to my grandmother.'

'And my sister to my mother,' Bertie said, keeping calm.

Willy asked his mother, 'Why do you betray me so?'

'It is not betrayal,' Bertie interjected, 'It is what your mother wants. The argument should end there.'

'But why, Mother?' Willy implored her.

'I felt that all my correspondence with Mama should be in England. I own them, remember, and can do what I wish with them. With respect, Willy, they are more for my dear mama's memory. They have nothing to do with you.'

'But when you . . .'

'Pass over? It changes nothing. They reside in England. The letters are owned by your uncle now.'

'But the copyright surely is with your estate?'

'And I am willing them to England.'

'Your brother over your son!'

'No, you are avoiding the point. I believe that because the correspondence between me and Mama is connected to the British throne, not the German, then they should be in England.'

Willy fiddled with the glove to his withered arm. He looked like he might cry.

'Why the sudden interest in your mother's correspondence?' Bertie asked. 'Have you ever asked to see or have it before?'

Willy blinked, got up and left the table in a huff, saying nothing.

One of his staff followed him up the long, winding staircase as he headed to his room. Willy stopped beneath a portrait of Victoria.

'Your majesty,' the courtier said, 'I could not help overhearing the discussion.'

'Yes?' Willy said impatiently.

'I just wished to tell you, majesty, that I have been to the attic with our informant. He showed me a huge cache of letters. They were written by Victoria to your mother.'

'Have you read them? How many are there?'

'No, we would not presume to read them, your majesty. There are several thousand of them.'

Willy thought for a moment and shook his head.

'If they were left by my uncle they must be of no interest, no value,' he said dismissively and continued on his way to his bedroom miffed and preoccupied by his relatives' actions behind his back.

★★★

Vicky did not have long to live when she wrote again to Bertie mid-summer in 1901 to tell him that the cache of letters from Victoria to her was still in the attic. She suggested that they should also be taken back to England.

'I thought they had gone with my letters until recently I was told that mama's were still there in a separate part of the attic. Remember that they contain information about the Elphinstone affair, Papa, Brown and Karim, among many others. They should reside at Windsor, or even be destroyed.'

Bertie wrote back reassuring her that he would arrange for Victoria's letters to be returned, but with all the other issues of kingship on his plate, it slipped his mind. He had business and pleasure of higher concern to concentrate on. Then on 5 August 1901, Vicky died. Bertie and Alix attended the funeral but did not visit Friedrichshof. Victoria's voluminous correspondence remained in two large boxes under sheets gathering dust in the castle's attic.

46

THE EDWARDIAN ERA

In 1904 Bertie achieved his much-desired Entente Cordiale with the French, after a decade of frosty relations, in which he had even seen scurrilous, near-obscene articles and cartoons about him in French magazines. The agreement delineated British and French colonies in North Africa, and ruled out future wars between the two countries. It marked the end of centuries of Anglo-French rivalry and Britain's isolation from Continental affairs. Although nothing was said publically, the agreement was also an attempt to counterbalance the growing dominance of the German Empire and its ally, Austria–Hungary.

Bertie's demeanour, proficiency in the French language and genuine love of most things across the Channel caused him again to become as popular there as at home. It also gave him renewed access to his beloved Paris brothels. He had become an icon for madams wishing to encourage business, and prostitutes desiring generous payment for services. The latter had to be more inventive than ever, given his majesty's limited capacities as he wandered riskily, but happily into his sixties. Despite doctors' exhortations, his wife's concern and his mistresses' warnings,

Bertie did not curtail his daily consumption of twelve fat cigars and twenty cigarettes, champagne and whisky, and copious amounts of rich food. His kingly position provided the opportunity for more of everything. He did not hold back. Bertie's constitution was amazing, but obesity, heart disease and now worsening asthma began to trouble him.

But by 1906 there was little evidence he was slowing down apart from with his sexual indulgences. Even then he would not give up visiting high-class bordellos, especially his favourite, La Chabanais. In early June 1906 he decided to take his son George, next in line for the throne, to Paris to celebrate George's forty-first birthday. They stayed at Le Meurice Hotel, met briefly with the French president and prime minister at the Élysée, and visited the Louvre. At 6 p.m. the king told George he had a 'private meeting' and that he would be back at 9 p.m. to dine with his son at Les Innocents, an exclusive club restaurant.

Bertie's undisclosed rendezvous place was La Chabanais where he and three royal bodyguards were met by the brothel manager, who had shut the establishment for three hours for the king's visit. The courtiers were offered drinks at a dimly lit bar while the king waddled off to his private Hindu Room with his former coat-of-arms above the ornate, four-poster canopied bed. He sat on his love-chair, and loosened his shoes while the manager paraded six young women for his selection. There were three French, two from Africa and one from Siam (Thailand). Bertie chose three. The rejected three fussed about, filling the bath with champagne and lighting Bertie's cigar, while the 'selections', all scantily clad, removed some outer garments and helped Bertie undress. They were soon drinking with him, kissing and caressing everywhere. After about 30 minutes of contortions and cavorting on the love chair, he was so out of breath that he signalled he had had enough. He was helped from the chair by the women, soaped down, and taken to his copper bath. He invited the three other girls to join him in the bath.

After another fifteen minutes and consumption of much champagne, Bertie seemed to choke on the drink. He couldn't stop coughing. His head slumped below the liquid level. Thinking he was dead, the girls screamed. Gathering their wits, they pulled his head up so that he would not drown, but found it too difficult to lift his limp frame from the bath. One ran out to the manager who rushed to the room with the three bodyguards. They revived Bertie, who moaned and clutched his chest. 'I think heart...heart...fetch my doctor and my son...at Le Meurice...'

A concerned George and the doctor who travelled abroad with Bertie arrived at the brothel 35 minutes later. They found him dressed and sitting in a lounge, sipping a whisky.

'I am fine,' he said, 'fine!'

The doctor examined him. Bertie's pulse was erratic and running faster than normal. His face was still flushed.

'I suggest, your majesty, that you go straight to bed,' the doctor said, putting away a stethoscope. 'You may have had a mild heart attack. Er...too much exertion, I suspect.'

'Nonsense,' Bertie said, getting to his feet unsteadily, 'my son and I have a dinner appointment. I shall take it easy. Had those damned pains many times before.'

'Yes, your majesty, you recover from these turns remarkably well, but rest would help.'

Ignoring his doctor's advice, as he often did, he and George sat down at Les Innocents, attended by a dozen waiters and staff. The petite dark-haired manager, Martine, greeted the king with a measured familiarity. When he made a joke, she responded with an accompanying light comment, showing the right balance, from Bertie's perspective, of respect and fun.

'Such a nice change from the grovelling at home,' he said quietly to George as they were seated. 'Don't you think?'

They paused to consider the menu with help from a bevy of waiters. Bertie loved the process of ordering copious amounts of food and drink, where George hated this kind of excess, and his silence said much until his father commented, with a trace of cynicism: 'I know you'd rather be shooting on the moors or playing with your stamp albums but I prefer living. You never know when your time is up. I would rather go out with a perfect, real black woman by the name of Penelope astride me than looking for perfect Penny Blacks—if you'll pardon the pun.' He chortled. 'Do you know that your grandmama banned the reference to "Blacks" while that Indian was at court?'

George did not respond. He sampled the wine and nodded his approval.

'Sorry to have worried you tonight, my son.'

'I don't know why you jeopardise so much by—'

'What? Visits to a bordello?'

'What about Mama? What about the gutter press?'

'No one saw me go into the place. No one saw me come out. It was for my private use for three hours, or however long I wished. Total privacy and discretion.'

Cold consommé was served as a first course.

'Given the little scare tonight,' Bertie said, dropping his voice a fraction, 'it is a good time to tell you a few secrets, before my time really is up.' While the next three courses were served and devoured mainly by Bertie, he discussed money, property and some family secrets. A few of them left George gaping. Other revelations saw him shaking his head or blinking furiously. During the fifth course, a superbly garnished salmon, Bertie said: 'That's about it.' Then as an afterthought he added, 'There is one other thing you should know about your grandmama. She had an affair with a well-bred Scot.'

George frowned. 'Well bred? Brown was a servant.'

'I am not referring to her gillie. She had a relationship with the thirteenth Lord Elphinstone.'

'I know the current sixteenth—'

'The thirteenth died in 1860.'

'But—'

'The affair happened, or at least began, before she married.'

George looked stunned.

'Believe me, it's true,' Bertie said, pushing away his fish and suppressing a belch. 'She told your aunt Vicky all about it in letters.' He paused to sample the wine and signalled to a waiter to bring another bottle. 'And the letters are still in an attic at Kronberg.'

'What should I do?'

'Wait for an appropriate moment. Steal 'em back and have 'em burnt.'

'No. They should be preserved at Windsor, and guarded for the family.'

'I'd burn 'em. Every single page.' Bertie grunted. 'We burnt all that Indian bastard's letters, ya know.'

Bertie's continuing improvement of relations with France made his nephew the kaiser suspicious. Apart from Bertie's habitual tours of Paris, he trotted off to Athens, Oslo, Berlin and Stockholm. He met another nephew, Tsar Nicholas II, on their yachts in the Russian Baltic port of Reval (Tallin) in 1908. This fuelled Willy's fears into a state of paranoia about his philandering yet felicitous and universally popular uncle. Was he surrounding Germany with enemies? Was it all a British plot to subsume German interests and eventually the nation itself? Bertie's political flirtation with his Russian nephew created problems at home too. Socialists and radicals hated the tsar, who had a planned campaign of persecution against Jews. He also courted trouble in increasingly democratic-minded Britain and the international community by banishing political opponents to Siberia. The tsar used the oppressive secret police—the Cheka—for nefarious purposes to maintain his control of Russia. Its dissident elements were becoming more restless observing France, the United States and the UK with their burgeoning democratic institutions. Three Liberal and Labor parliamentarians rose in the House of Commons and criticised Bertie's overtures to the tsar. He retaliated by not inviting them to his annual garden party for members of parliament at Buckingham Palace. None of the ostracised was too miffed.

Their actions did not seem to dent Bertie's popularity. If there had been an international peace prize at the time, he would have won it. His reputation had shifted from Edward the Caresser to Edward the Peacemaker, except in Germany where he was attacked in the press at the kaiser's behest. But it was believed everywhere that while Bertie ruled, there would be no war in Europe. He had his nephew bluffed.

Early in May 1910 the past caught up with Bertie and his heart began to register a serious protest. His asthma worsened. On the morning of 6 May, at Buckingham Palace, Bertie insisted on leaving his bed and sitting in an armchair to ease his breathing problem. 'I will not give in,' he told his doctors. At 11.30 p.m. he was carried to his bed, where he died fifteen minutes later. Bertie was 69 and had been king for nine years. The timing pleased the royal courtiers, as it had concerning his father's death. Edward VII's demise made news in the morning broadsheets. Most papers acknowledged that he had done much, perhaps more than anyone else, to keep Europe at peace before and after taking the crown.

One decree in his will had executors baffled. It referred to the royal correspondence in Germany over which he had procrastinated throughout his reign, although he had briefed his son a second time, reminding him that the Victoria–Vicky letters were a potential time-bomb sitting in the German attic. Edward VII had bequeathed the problem to his son. When George V read it, he was reminded of an unwanted responsibility over the family secrets, which in their own way had more potency than the family jewels.

47

THE FORGOTTEN LETTERS

In matters of health, George V took more after his father than his grandmother. After 24 years on the throne, he was, by 1934, an ailing 69-year old. He had reigned during World War I in which he had seen Germany defeated, his cousin Wilhelm deposed and cousin Nicky assassinated by Bolshevik revolutionaries. George V had ruled through tough depression years in the early 1930s and now he was exhausted with lung and arterial problems. The fascist Adolf Hitler, leader of the Nazi Party, had come to power as chancellor in Germany. George let German ambassadors know his thoughts about him but they could do nothing. Hitler was an uncompromising dictator who had come to power by murder and thuggery and was not going to change his ways, causing a dark mood to envelope Europe. War, which had caused untold devastation sixteen years earlier, was looming again.

To make matters worse, more constant in George V's mind for years had been his concern about his son successor, David. David was forty and with an insouciant, careless disregard for his position and future. He had been a compulsive, unfettered womaniser through the 1920s and 1930s.

George V had done so much to maintain and improve the monarchy that he fretted daily about how David would destroy it. Those close to David said he had never developed mentally beyond adolescence; the king hated his dalliances with married women. It reminded him of his own father's utter disregard for decorum and the sanctity of marriage. But at least Edward VII had taken a wife and created a family. George V did not want David to inherit the throne and he had far more respect for second son Bertie, who was next in line after David. George V overlooked his stutter and insecurity and saw a man with the potential to rise above his weaknesses, especially with his diminutive yet dynamic wife, Elizabeth, by his side.

After a string of inappropriate dalliances, David became closely involved with American socialite Wallis Simpson. She had divorced her first husband in 1927 and then married Ernest Simpson, an Anglo-American businessman. She seemed to have some hold over the future king. Some said it was her sexual expertise, allegedly gained in China, which somehow gave her undescribed erotic skills. Others claimed it was her bossiness in handling the immature David, who had never grown up. Her grip on the future king was most likely a combination of both, and he may well have felt 'safer' with married women.

George V and Queen Mary met Mrs Simpson at Buckingham Palace in 1935. They were most unimpressed and refused to receive her again. This further estranged father and son. George could not believe his son's attitude, and that he did not want the responsibilities that went with his birthright. Yet he seemed to want the accoutrements of royalty, including funds from the Civil List, which allowed him to continue 'playing'.

George V had battled ill health for years, starting with septicaemia in November 1928. He was a heavy smoker and this exacerbated his breathing problems. In this respect alone, he followed his father in continuing a bad habit even though he and his doctors knew it was slowly killing him. Chronic ill health associated with his lungs and pleurisy forced him into semi-retirement for a few months in 1929 at the seaside resort of Bognor, Sussex (which became Bognor Regis after his forced sojourn there). George V never fully recovered and he often returned to the resort in summer months. In 1934 he began the intermittent use of oxygen.

At this time George was estranged from David and closer to his second son Bertie, who visited him at Bognor mid-summer. He and wife Elizabeth found him sitting on a balcony overlooking the sea with an oxygen mask over his face reading *The Times*. George V was brightened by their arrival. He had a special affection for his daughter-in-law.

'Time for you to know the family secrets,' the king said, beckoning them to sit on wicker chairs with him. Elizabeth stood up to leave.

'B–b–b—,' Bertie stammered, 'but shouldn't D–David be told ra–ra–rather than me?'

'I don't trust him. Mark my words. He will do something foolish and either bring down the monarchy, or himself. One of the two. If it is himself, you two will be king and queen. If I am wrong, you can pass on to David what I have to say, at your time of choosing.' In between gulps of oxygen and a few seconds silence to steady himself, George V proceeded to outline some of the family secrets. He came finally to Victoria's letters and her confessions about the Elphinstone affair, of which they knew nothing. They were both surprised.

'The letters have been in that attic for about 40 years,' George V said. 'After Willy's abdication and exile to the Netherlands the letters seemed less of a threat. I admit I did nothing just as my father did not bother about them until he was…ill…a few years before he died. Now I am as guilty as him, as far as inaction is concerned.'

'What do you want done with them?' Elizabeth asked.

'If there is an opportunity, they should be carried secretly back to Windsor and stored there under lock and key, not to be seen by anyone unless the monarch decrees they can be viewed.' He paused for more oxygen and added, 'I think with this current German chancellor it may not be the time to attempt to secure them. I am told that the borders are getting impossible to cross. But when he is deposed, which I believe will happen soon, you should see to it.'

'Did you see any of the letters?' Elizabeth asked.

'No, alas I did not. But my father told me that Vicky was very, very concerned about them.' He paused to take in more oxygen. Then he explained what he knew of the relationship between Victoria and the thirteenth lord. Every sentence was an effort for the king. 'It's the sort of thing that spoils . . . the reputation of our House.' He struggled for breath again.

George V slumped back as if he intended to sleep. Then he sat up, startled, played with the oxygen mask and said, 'Oh, and there is another thing. Willy knows about the Elphinstone affair. He tricked and blackmailed his dear mama Vicky into her telling him about it. Unfortunately, it's all in writing. The letters concerned will be in his exile hole in the Netherlands. Even harder to get hold off with him still around. Still he might drop off the perch, but not before I do, I should expect. When that miserable sod does go, you should direct someone to raid his home and retake the "incriminating" correspondence. All right, Bertie?'

Bertie blew out nervously and nodded his head.

George V coughed long and hard, then tore the mask from his face. He pulled a fat cigar and matches from his coat pocket.

On 15 January 1936, George V went to bed with a cold, deteriorated and began drifting in and out of consciousness. At one point he enquired: 'How is the empire?'

It was an odd question, but his secretary answered dutifully: 'All is well, sir, with the empire.'

The king lapsed into unconsciousness. On 20 January, his physicians, led by Lord Dawson, assembled to discuss how to word a bulletin for a waiting empire and world. They wanted to say: 'The king is nearly dead' or 'The king is dying'. They settled for a more soothing euphemism: 'The king's life is moving peacefully towards its close'. Dawson decided it would be better if he were to die that night, which would mean that *The Times* would again have the 'scoop' on a monarch's death, being the first to announce it on the morning of 21 January 1936. The respected broadsheet was considered more fitting to carry such news than 'less appropriate evening journals'.

Just before midnight on 20 January 1936 the nurse in attendance administered a lethal dose of cocaine and morphine. George V, aware vaguely what was being done, mumbled his last words: 'God damn you!' which were not quite as symbolic as those uttered by his father. But George V had had a much tougher, longer reign.

George V's four surviving sons—David (now King Edward VIII), Bertie, Henry and George—mounted the guard (the vigil of the princes) at the catafalque on the night before the funeral. The dead king was interred at St George's Chapel, Windsor Castle, on 28 January 1936.

There was promise that the 41-year-old, unmarried Edward VIII would do more than his predecessors to reach out to his subjects and the new monarch seemed aware of the need to 'democratise' the institution. But only months into his reign he caused a constitutional crisis by proposing to marry Wallis Simpson, who was seeking a divorce from her second husband. Prime Minister Stanley Baldwin and those from the dominions opposed the marriage. It was supposed that the peoples of the empire would not accept a twice-divorced American as wife of the king, and possibly his queen. Edward's response when told that the Australians did not want him to marry Mrs Simpson was to say there were 'not many people in Australia'. There were then more than six million. Their opinion did not matter.

The Church of England also opposed the union, which created a tricky conflict of interest given that the king was head of the Church. Baldwin lifted the stakes by saying he would resign if the marriage went ahead. Such an act would have brought the issue into the political sphere if a general election followed Baldwin's departure. Edward VIII realised that such a situation could damage the monarchy. He now had a choice: abdicate and marry Simpson or stay king and end his relationship. In a dramatic radio broadcast to the nation he announced his abdication in order 'to marry the woman I love'. He had reigned for 326 days and was never crowned. His successor gave him the title Duke of Windsor.

Edward VIII had 'ruined' himself a year into the reign, and in so doing delivered the late king his fervent wish: that his second son, Bertie, would now be king and, after him, George's beloved grandchild 'Lilibet', who would be queen. To keep the continuity with his father, Bertie wished to be known as George VI. The whole business of his father's death and his brother's short tenure was an ordeal. Bertie never wanted the monarchy and now it had been thrust upon him. He dreaded public speaking more than ever, although his impediment had been improved by his Australian therapist, Lionel Logue, who had reduced Bertie's problem from a stutter or no words coming out at all to an acceptable hesitancy and occasional stumble. Logue was on hand again now that his former patient had been called to the highest 'office' where pressure would mount, especially with the prospect of war increasing.

48

THE PROBLEM
WITH DAVID

The main problem for George VI was not a dreaded reoccurrence of his speech problem, the sudden burden of high office or any unpalatable kingly duties. It was his troublesome brother, now the Duke of Windsor and again just plain 'David' to family and friends. He had to be exiled, at least for a time. There would be no joy for anyone if the high-profile, society-oriented meddlesome duke were wandering England and Scotland like a disconsolate royal ghost. He was given a job with the military mission in France. It didn't work. His known Nazi sympathies upset the French, the British royal family and the British government.

The duke married Wallis Simpson in a private ceremony on 3 June 1937 at Chateau de Cande, near Tours, France. In October 1937, David and Wallis visited Germany against the advice of the British government and the king. George VI was chain-smoking more than ever and his brother's behaviour was not helping his health. Like his father and grandfather, George VI was susceptible to lung and heart problems.

The duke created further concern in the royal family when he visited Chancellor Hitler at his Obersalzberg retreat. The German media captured the meeting, particularly the moments when the duke gave his version of the stiff-armed Nazi salute. The former king justified his unofficial diplomacy by quietly endorsing German fascism as a bulwark against communism. He favoured a German alliance with the UK. His views were influenced by his German heritage, which he held more dear than his British heritage. He also hated and feared Communists after the assassination of his uncle Nicky in Russia in 1918. The duke spoke of the need for appeasement; anything in his mind that would avoid the calamity of another war and 'the never ending scenes of horror'.

Hitler believed that the duke was well disposed towards him and the Nazis, and the German chancellor had been irritated by the abdication, believing that Edward VIII would have been good for Anglo-German relations. 'His abdication was a severe loss to us,' Hitler told fellow Nazi Albert Speer. He wanted to reinstate the duke as a regent, if not king of England, in a fascist Britain.

But Hitler's plans for Britain were still a little way off. First, he had plans in Europe, and in 1939, Germany invaded Poland, sparking World War II.

Aware of the Nazi sympathies of David and his wife, the British government installed him as Governor of the Bahamas. This move depressed him in a similar way to when he was sent from gay Paris to corroded Cairo in 1916 to be on the staff of the Australian General John Monash. The duke did not help his cause by describing the Bahamas as a 'third-rate British colony'. Neither did he distinguish himself with his anti-black and anti-Jewish observations, which demonstrated a susceptibility to Nazi propaganda.

Through this period, the duke and Wallis Simpson continued to be in correspondence with Nazis, especially with German royalty associated with the fascist movement in the early war years.

★★★

Soon England was in Hitler's sights. George VI and wife Elizabeth stayed in London during some of the German bombing raids. The first, on 7 September 1940, killed more than 1000 civilians, mostly in London's East End. On 13 September, the Luftwaffe struck again. Two bombs exploded in a courtyard at Buckingham Palace and narrowly missed the king and queen. This drew out Elizabeth's strength.

'I am glad we have been bombed,' she said. 'We can look the East End in the face.' Her remark and defiance marked a moment in the nation's morale at the most difficult time in its history. The royal family took the solidarity with the most oppressed a step further by making it known they were receiving no special favours with rations, heating at the palace or restrictions in the use of bathwater.

In May 1940, Churchill replaced Neville Chamberlain as prime minister when George VI preferred Lord Halifax. The king was dismayed when Churchill appointed Max Aitken (Lord Beaverbrook), the influential Anglo-Canadian media mogul, to his war cabinet but that was as far as their differences went. George VI soon fell under the spell of the determined Churchill who believed he was fulfilling a destiny at this critical time. The two met for lunch every Tuesday from September 1940 and grew to respect and like each other as they discussed war issues in secret.

On 3 June 1941, Kaiser Wilhelm II died of a pulmonary embolism in Doorn, in the Netherlands. He was 82. German soldiers had been guarding his estate, which annoyed Hitler, but his political expediency and feverish clinging to symbols overrode his animosity. He wanted to give Willy a state funeral to take advantage of the kaiser's image, which had been strong in the mind of the German nation for most of World War I. But Willy had made sure he would have a small military funeral in the Netherlands. He wanted nothing to do with Hitler and the Nazis, whom he hated for their ignoring his claims to a rejuvenated monarchy, but he could not stop German occupying authorities making sure that Nazi swastikas and other regalia were on display when he was buried.

Willy's family decided to preserve his Netherlands home as a temporary shrine of sorts. Tucked away in a large safe were a cupboard full of letters. Scores were from Victoria and the rest were from his mother, Vicky.

Throughout the war, George VI and Elizabeth visited bomb sites, munitions factories, hospitals for the wounded and British military forces at home and abroad. Their courage, grace, humility, dedication and warmth built support for the monarchy to an all-time high. No royal couple in a thousand years had endeared themselves more to a galvanised public in need of national symbols. Churchill's leadership, determination and riveting speeches were vital, yet a set-upon nation needed a balance of pure humanity from those at the pinnacle of society and the royal couple provided it. Forgotten were reminders of the first family's German heritage and the houses of Hanover and Saxe-Coburg Gotha. The Windsors appeared the epitome of the best of the British and they provided continuity when prime ministers came and went.

Allied victory over fascist forces (primarily Germany and Italy) in May 1945 after an exhausting war left Britain as an impoverished nation further in need of morale-boosting and continuity. The high-profile images of the king and queen had been associated with national resistance nearly as much as the prime minister. They were cheered by a huge crowd on the balcony of Buckingham Palace during Victory Day celebrations and were hailed again when they invited Churchill to be with them. This erased the 'error of judgement' in inviting Chamberlain onto the balcony when he returned to England in 1938 after apparently drawing from Hitler a promise not to go to war with the UK.

It seemed that nothing could go wrong for the image of royalty after the monarchy's existence had been threatened less than a decade earlier by the antics of Edward VIII.

A few days after the capitulation of Germany and the end of the war, Queen Mary and Queen Elizabeth met for tea in the well-manicured gardens of Buckingham Palace.

The two women sat quietly sipping their drinks before Mary spoke of her concerns about the letters in the attic at the castle in Kronberg.

'Oh, you mean the Victoria–Vicky letters?' Elizabeth asked, 'King George told us about them. There are those also with Willy in the

Netherlands.' Apparently he tricked his mother into divulging the Elphinstone affair.'

'Not just *those* letters,' Mary said archly. 'I also wrote much to my relatives. In my teen years I made many trips to the Hesse castles near Frankfurt.' She shuddered and added grim-faced: 'The whole area is now an American-occupied zone. I worry all the time that the letters could fall into unscrupulous hands. There may well also be incriminating correspondence between David and that woman, and the Nazis.'

'Perish the thought!'

'Yes. You must ask George to do something, before it's too late.'

'What do you suggest?'

'I know where most of the letters are to be found. They're not all at Friedrichshof.'

'Then you should tell him.'

'I could brief Morshead [the Windsor Librarian] but he is not *expert* in how to go about such a difficult mission.'

'Then Anthony Blunt should go with him.'

'Blunt, the picture expert?'

'Oh, he is alright.'

'A Marxist at Cambridge, wasn't he?'

'Weren't they all? He taught French. Did his graduate research in French art history.' Elizabeth paused and added, 'He is a very nice person. Bit lost. He has no family to go home to. Hence he is always willing to play games with us. Anthony does a wonderful elephant when we do charades.'

'But why send him?'

'Didn't you know? He's an intelligence officer. Very, very good at his job too, I'm told.'

'Good. No time to waste. Suggest to your husband that he sends them off on a letter-finding mission as soon as possible.'

49

BLUNT'S MISSION

A week later, in June 1945, George VI called a secret meeting in the library of Windsor Castle. Present were Sir Owen Morshead, 55, the royal librarian, and Anthony Blunt, 38, art historian and adviser to the king. The tall, lean and lugubrious-looking Blunt, with steel-grey eyes, was believed to be distantly related to George VI, who favoured him. He also was an espionage agent working for MI5 and, secretly, a traitor controlled by Soviet intelligence, the KGB. The king wanted the courtiers to travel to Kronberg, where his German relatives lived.

'It is v–v–vital that all these let–letters are retrieved,' George VI said. The return of his stutter, which he mostly had under control in recent years, revealed deep concern.

'If there were trouble on this mission, majesty,' Blunt said, 'what would be the priority amongst all the correspondence?'

George VI glanced at Morshead before answering: 'The letters from Victoria to Vicky.'

Blunt nodded.

'B–but you must endeavour to obtain them all,' George VI said gaining confidence. 'It will be no less embarrassing if any of my brother's communications with Hitler are taken by the Americans.

If their press got hold of anything, I sh-shudder to think of what would happen.'

George VI detailed what they should look for concerning Edward VIII: 'Any letters and memoranda of conversations between him and Hitler and top Nazis. Transcripts of telephone calls made by David while he was in Germany in 1937 are also of further interest.' He paused after putting his stutter aside for a sentence and added firmly: 'I repeat that it is essential these sensitive communications do not fall into American hands. It may be a difficult mission. They now c-c-control a militarised zone that includes the area you visit. Take whatever guard you need.'

Blunt and Morshead handpicked four British soldiers to accompany them first on the flight to Frankfurt in late July 1945. They then drove a two-tonne army truck to Kronberg, where they found the US occupying forces using the nineteenth-century palace as an army camp. The British party drove past it about 3 kilometres to the dark tower of Schloss Friedrichshof, which seemed to hang over the wooded slopes of Taurus Mountains. The castle's stone portico entrance was emblazoned with Tudor roses. Blunt left the truck and entered the large entrance hall. He was struck with how similar the castle, built by Vicky, was to Queen Victoria's beloved Balmoral Castle. It was wooden-beamed in Scottish baronial style and its entrance and corridors were cluttered with paintings of Vicky's royal relatives.

Blunt was greeted by Captain Kathleen Nash of the US Women's Army Corps. She was in command of the rest camp. Blunt asked where he could find the Hesse family, the king's German relatives. Nash redirected him to a townhouse in the grounds of the old Kronberg Castle. The Hesse family was a bit taken aback when Blunt produced a letter signed by George VI and carrying the royal seal. It requested permission to remove the royal letters and 'other communications' to England for 'safekeeping'. The problem for the Hesses was that they were technically leaderless. The titular head, Prince Philip, had been a senior Nazi. His twin brother, Wolfgang, explained that Philip had fallen from favour with Hitler and was in Dachau concentration camp.

'Are you not the head of the family in your brother's absence?' Blunt asked. 'We need permission to take the documents.'

The family asked Blunt to wait while its members conferred. They emerged after an hour with a letter from the mother of Wolfgang and Philip, the 72-year-old Princess Margaret, who was Victoria's granddaughter and Vicky's youngest child. She gave her permission for the removal of the more than 5000 documents in question. They were marked in packing cases.

'They're stored in the attic of Schloss Friedrichshof,' Wolfgang confirmed to Blunt.

In the evening, the British party drove back up the winding road through the Hesse estate to the castle. The six men entered and were again greeted by Nash. Blunt accompanied her down a passage to an office. He produced the two letters from George VI and Princess Margaret. Nash asked Blunt to sit in a chair while she read the letters.

'What papers are you wanting?' she asked.

'They are private letters between the Windsors and Hesse family.'

'Windsors?'

'Yes, the royal family. The British royal family.'

Nash shook her head. 'I don't have the authority to relinquish control over any papers.'

Blunt nodded at the letters. 'That is all the authority you need.'

'What?'

'The king—the head of the UK, empire and dominions—has signed that letter.'

'Major, anything here is the property of the US army.'

'Not royal correspondence.'

'Everything. I have orders.'

Nash was intractable.

'I would appreciate you calling US Army headquarters in Frankfurt,' Blunt said, remaining his glacial self.

'Why?'

'So that I can speak to your superior.'

'Look, major, I am in charge of this camp. I have my orders.'

There was stalemate. Blunt stood, excused himself and moved to the door. 'I must consult with my colleague,' he said. He hurried to the entrance hall where the other five were waiting. Blunt was aware of Ponsonby's action in February 1901 in using a truck to remove all Vicky's letters from the same attic.

'She's refusing to let us take them,' Blunt told Morshead. He glanced at the stairs. 'Take the men to the attic, find the papers, and load them on the truck. I'll stall her.'

Blunt returned to the office. Nash had lit herself a cigarette.

'You're wasting your time, major,' she said.

'I really do think it would be in your interest to phone HQ,' Blunt persisted. He then uttered the British name that Nash would recognise. 'Churchill himself supports our mission.'

Nash stared at him. She knew nothing about the royal family or Windsors. But she was alerted with the mention of Churchill. She did not know if Blunt were bluffing. She had met a variety of types from both sides in the war, ranging from the imprisoned German paratrooper commandos to the toughest American leaders, including General George Patton. But this languid, ice-cool British officer with the long face and cutaway mouth was a different animal altogether. He was polite, yet remote. He behaved as if he had real, if obscure, authority. She remained firm, yet inside she was a fraction insecure. What if Churchill was behind it? His name was not on the letters. But would she be reprimanded by her commanding officer in Frankfurt if she did not acquiesce to Blunt's wishes? The argument continued. Blunt put his case more forcefully, saying his acquisition of the documents was of paramount importance. Nash relented and phoned Frankfurt, asking Blunt to leave the office. He hastened to the entrance just as Morshead and the soldiers came down the stairs with two packing cases. The party hurried to the truck, loaded it and drove off.

Nash could not reach her commanding officer. She stepped out of the office and walked to the front entrance in time to see the truck disappearing down the winding road and into the night.

Two days later, the Hesse family entertained Blunt and Morshead at a small castle at nearby Wolfsgarten. The twenty present dined in style with a sumptuous six-course meal served by liveried footmen behind every chair. A different wine accompanied each course. Just before midnight, Blunt retired to a room in the castle's guest quarters. He had placed the cases of documents and letters in the room with a guard outside, on the off chance that the Americans should dare to steal them back. Blunt removed the lids and began to sift through the letters, most of which were unsealed. He was thrilled to find one from Karl Marx, who had been called upon by a German court official in 1847, but the correspondence that riveted Blunt was between Victoria and her daughter. He soon understood why George VI was so nervous about retrieving their letters. Blunt found himself sitting and reading all night. He discovered that Victoria had used her beloved and trusted daughter as the person in whom she confided her deepest feelings about Elphinstone, her attitude to her husband and to her mother, her disappointment about Bertie (Edward VII), her scathing comments about Wilhelm and her thoughts about all the intimates in her life.

Blunt was stunned to also find there were the messages between Edward VIII (when prince and later king), his youngest brother, the Duke of Kent, and their German cousins, Philip of Hesse and Karl Eduard, Duke of Saxe-Coburg-Gotha. The letters showed that David and the Duke of Kent had been keen to ingratiate themselves with Hitler when he became German Chancellor and with the Nazi regime. Philip had been the link with David before, during and after he was king (January to December 1936). More damning was strong evidence that Edward VIII had collaborated with the Nazis during the war. In effect, the documents and letters demonstrated that the former King of England and Wallis Simpson had passed information secretly to Hitler from at least 1934 to 1943. This meant, whether they perceived their intentions as good or not, that they were technically traitors from 1939 to 1943 when Britain was at war with Germany.

Blunt now fully realised King George's anxiety about all the material. The KGB double agent was astonished at the extent of Edward VIII's links. There was clear evidence that he had been preparing to be placed back on the throne as prince regent if the Nazis took power. It would have been a pay-off for his support and a reward from Hitler for heading the so-called 'international *peace* movement' on behalf of the Nazis, which assisted Hitler's plan for taking Europe, piece by piece. Blunt reckoned that if these letters were revealed publicly it would mean the end of the house of Windsor. The British, not to mention the empire, had just been through a horrific war against fascism in Europe, Asia and the Pacific, which had taken an enormous toll on people and lives. If the king's tens of millions of subjects were now informed that his brother—the former king—and his wife had been Nazi collaborators it would never be tolerated. The huge goodwill that George VI and Queen Elizabeth had built up over nearly eight years would be wiped out in a series of press headlines.

Over the next few nights and on the return trip to London, Blunt sorted the most important letters. Then he microfilmed them and prepared to pass it all onto his KGB Control, Ivan Milovsorov. A couple that intrigued him were copied out in longhand. Morshead took all the correspondence to Windsor and began sorting them while Blunt had an audience with the king.

'We are all rather pleased with the success of your mission,' George VI, said beaming. 'I might tell you that m-my . . .mother and wife are quite relieved that the correspondence is . . .safe.'

'It was an honour, your majesty,' Blunt said, genuinely touched by his reaction. In the confused world of the double agent, serving conflicting masters was part of the unwritten job specification. Blunt loathed the ancient concept of the monarchy, which did not fit with Marxist principles, yet he had respect for the people in the institution, especially George VI.

'Would you like to be k-keeper of the king's pictures? We'd be delighted to have you on board full-time instead of your current honorary role.'

'Again, it would be an honour, majesty, thank you,' Blunt said without reflection. He was more than pleased and considered this could be his way out of the espionage maze. The KGB had information with which to blackmail him whenever it wished. His homosexuality, if made public, would ruin his career. And he had spied and recruited for the Soviet Union since the early 1930s. This would keep Blunt obligated to and working for the Soviets whenever and for how long they wished. His job as a double agent for MI5 and his ultimate masters in Moscow had exhausted him. He had worked long hours, keeping up the deception without faltering. But now, with the Nazis defeated, he wanted to leave MI5. He considered himself, in spy vernacular, 'a burnt-out case' even if the Soviets had yet to label him as such. And they were far from doing that. He had few peers in his efficiency as a stealer and pilferer of information and was one of the best half-dozen spies the KGB ever had. It wanted him to stay 'in place' inside MI5. Blunt wanted 'out' and the less dangerous role as a palace courtier. He would have no direct access to major British government military, political or espionage information. He had contacts and would learn things but it would be second-hand, at a distance from Whitehall.

Blunt contacted Milovzorov at the Soviet Embassy and they met, as they usually did, in a London East End pub at night. They were an odd couple. Thin and angular Blunt seemed out of place, with his neat suit and tie and upper-class mien. He normally would dine at a St James club near MI5 offices in the West End. Yet he dared not be seen anywhere near that area or clientele, with this short, portly, bull-necked foreigner, whose low brow often sweated. They drank and chatted. The Russian had fallen out from time to time with a few of his agents. Milovsorov tended to be heavy-handed and brusque. He was a slack spymaster whose reputation had been maintained by the quality of information he was receiving from a handful of top spies. Blunt told him of the king's offer.

'I am leaving MI5,' he said. The Russian was confused as Blunt added: 'My work at the palace will be just as useful. I will have the ear of the King of Empire.'

'No, no,' Milovzorov said, 'I will obtain a ruling from Moscow before letting you move.'

'You have seen the quality of material I have already supplied [by this connection]. This is because of the position at the palace.'

'It is more important for us that you remain inside [MI5].'

Blunt was not the type to lose his temper. But his expression clouded.

'You could, if you wished,' he said, looking around and lowering his voice, 'have unparalleled influence over the king with what I have already supplied. Now that I shall be at court, that influence could increase.'

'I still must consult Moscow.'

The thick-set Control seemed intractable and not that bright. He was cunning and tough, more instinctive than reflective. Blunt felt he would not read the microfilm material, which was in two canisters in a rolled-up copy of *The Times* that Blunt clutched in his hand. The implications of the material would have to be spelled out to him. Blunt took two pages from his jacket pocket and handed them to him.

'That's an example of what I have brought you,' Blunt said. 'Could you please take a minute to read it.'

'But you have written this!' Milovzorov frowned.

'Yes, Ivan,' Blunt said with barely contained contempt, 'I have copied two letters that would greatly embarrass the king and the government.'

The Control ran his fingers over the lines, mouthing the words and occasionally whispering a sentence. He looked up and said, 'This is from Queen Victoria in 1860!'

'It is. It's not something the current royals or government would ever wish to see made public.'

Milovzorov read on, mumbling, 'I am telling you that your not so chaste mama was not a virgin when she married your papa.' The Russian tossed the letter on the table, leant back in his chair and rubbed his eyes. Blunt explained its import. The Russian's mind cranked up a little as he sought to understand how the information could be used.

'In the final analysis, this sort of communication could bring down the monarchy, even the government,' Blunt said, attempting a bluff. He took the second letter and indicated he should read that too.

Milovzorov grimaced. Reading, at least in English, was a word by word effort. After a few seconds he looked up again. 'Ah, this one is to the German Chancellor from the king's brother . . . '

'Yes, Herr Hitler.'

Milovzorov read on: ' . . . would be honored to serve your government as prince regent of the United Kingdom . . .' He stopped and glanced at Blunt. 'Explain please.'

'King Edward wanted to be Hitler's royal puppet in the UK.'

'Shrewd and clever of him!'

'More shrewd of Hitler in attempting to tame a conquered and subservient British populous.'

'So Edward VIII was a traitor?!' the Russian said, raising his voice enough for two drinkers at a table next to them to look around. Blunt glared at Milovzorov, who realized his mistake. The drinkers went back to their vacant conversation and beer sipping. The Russian leant back in his seat once more and guffawed. Blunt remained stony-faced.

'You British,' he said, 'so arcane, so primitive!'

'You must understand, Ivan, I am close to the king and queen,' Blunt said, exaggerating. 'Royal courtiers learn much about government, the cabinet and the leaders of British society.' Milovsorov seemed unmoved. Blunt added: 'I don't think you understand. The king wants to send me on further important espionage missions. These will have top priority. I must collect much more about the links between Edward VIII and Hitler.'

'That is history now,' the Russian grumbled.

'Yes, but it gives you more influence to have the information.'

Blunt was the best 'middleman'—link between fellow British agents and the KGB—and was often used as a conduit for information, even equipment being passed to the Soviet Embassy for dispatch to Moscow. Milovzorov was anxious to know if Blunt would continue in this role. Blunt knew he had to say 'yes', otherwise the Russians might block his move to the palace.

'I would be prepared to carry on this work,' Blunt added, 'under certain circumstances.'

'What would they be?'

'Ivan, I shall be terribly busy in the new position.'

'But you would be available in 'emergencies'?'

Blunt nodded.

Milovzorov was disgruntled but satisfied that he had enough to justify to his bosses in Moscow Blunt's move out of the heart of British Intelligence. He said he would let Blunt know his decision as soon as possible. He got up to leave the pub, taking with him the rolled-up copy of *The Times* that Blunt had left on the table. They parted. Blunt was relieved that he had initiated the break. But he worried that he might never be free of KGB control and influence. He had been just too brilliant at his work to be given up.

50

POSTWAR WINDS
OF CHANGE

In July 1945 Churchill, to the surprise of England and the world, was dumped as prime minister after having done more than any other individual to defeat Hitler and the Nazis. The electorate's judgement was that he had been perfect for wartime command but not peacetime rebuilding and reform. The public's 'sacking' of Churchill in favour of Labour's Clement Atlee demonstrated a fundamental value that had been fought for and won: the democratic right of a nation to change a government. Churchill's temporary disappearance from power still left continuity at the nation's apex with the king and queen. Their frugal, mannerly, graceful demeanours, laced with an indefatigable determination, were right for the lean postwar period.

Queen Mary spent months reading Victoria's letters to Vicky at Windsor Castle library with the guidance of Morshead, who catalogued and classified them. She expressed a growing fear that Victoria may have told her grandson Willy some things that should never be made public. She also told Elizabeth, who had George VI's ear, of her concerns.

'They represent amazing history,' Mary said to Elizabeth over dinner at Buckingham Palace early in 1947. 'But I do wonder what Victoria wrote to Willy.'

'Oh, he is well dead, dear.'

'Yes, and how many letters did she write to him and where are they?'

'Preserved in his Dutch home, I should imagine.'

'They should be collected too, for safety and posterity.'

'Are you really concerned?'

'Oh, very. We must be thorough in retrieving as much of the correspondence as possible.'

'Oh, dear,' Elizabeth said then signalled to a courtier to bring them brandy.

'There were a few letters in the cache from Willy to his mother that somehow were put in the wrong file,' Mary said squinting into the distance. 'I believe that Vicky aroused Willy's commercial instincts and interest. He was always under the wrong impression that we in England had more than the German family.'

'If only it were true,' Elizabeth smiled. She raised her brandy glass in salute. She sipped her drink reflectively and added. 'It means another wee mission for Anthony.'

In August 1947, Morshead and Blunt were sent on one final trip to the Haus Doorn Holland home of the king's uncle, where he had died six years earlier.

The sizeable manor house was modest compared to Willy's earlier habitation in luxurious palaces. It had been seized by the Dutch government in 1947 and preserved under instructions from the Dutch royal family, who had family ties to the former kaiser through Queen Wilhelmina.

This was a less stressful project for Blunt and Morshead. At the king's behest the British government had been in touch with the Dutch, who agreed to let them take back correspondence but no other items. While examining the several hundred letters discovered, Blunt was tempted to 'souvenir' some of the artefacts, including paintings by

German courtiers, porcelains and silver. He spent time lingering over snuffboxes and watches that belonged to Frederick the Great. Marquetry commodes and tapestries also caught his attention.

This was an espionage 'clean-up' operation to find anything that linked the kaiser and the Duke of Windsor to the Nazis. It was discovered that the kaiser's son, Frederick William, and his wife, Cecile, had both been emissaries for Hitler in his dealings with the duke and Wallis Simpson. A second objective was to search for old letters from the prolific Victoria, just in case, as Mary feared, Victoria had mentioned her affair with Elphinstone or anything else of a private nature concerning other relationships with Albert, Brown and Karim. In the end, only a handful of innocuous copies of Victoria's correspondence were found. More intriguing were six letters written by Willy, which had somehow found their way back to him. They showed he had more than a passing interest in Victoria's affair with Elphinstone. Again, when alone, Blunt microfilmed every piece of correspondence that he thought might be of interest to Moscow.

Blunt and Morshead delivered the letters to George VI, who was once more grateful to both of them, particularly Blunt who was the experienced spy in the mission. The king's attitude to him caused Blunt to believe that he had an insurance policy of sorts should his traitorous activity for the Soviet Union before, during and well into the Cold-War period be discovered. These king's missions added up to immunity from prosecution for double agent Blunt. The king (and any future monarch) could not afford to see the art curator quizzed about his 'special projects' and what he discovered. Both the Windsor–Nazi connection and any letters that revealed Victoria's secret affairs could threaten the monarchy in the first decade after the war. Blunt believed he had protected himself, first, by carrying out this mission to Holland and the others he had embarked on for George VI; and, second, by him passing on everything to his ultimate KGB masters.

In March 1948, on a bitterly cold day he delivered the microfilm to a new Russian Control, Yuri Ivanovitch Modin, who was far more to the liking of all the double agents' than the heavy-handed Milovzorov. Instead of the grumpy-faced, ignorant Milovzorov, Blunt met the tall, intelligent-looking 24 year-old Modin, who was the new man running

Blunt and other contacts from Cambridge University days, including Guy Burgess, Donald Maclean, Kim Philby, Victor Rothschild and John Cairncross. Modin was more fastidious than his predecessor and went to some trouble to make their first meeting untraceable. He preferred circuitous routes to obscure parks and commons well clear of London's central area. There would be no more lazy meetings in Hammersmith or East End pubs that sluggish, overweight Milovzorov liked, although it was agreed that in emergencies they might have to risk a rendezvous or two somewhere closer to the capital's centre. This time the Blunt-Modin meeting took place at Wandsworth Common after several tube rides for both of them. Blunt was impressed by the new Control's thoroughness. Losing people who might follow you—'shadows' or 'tails'—was a Blunt specialty. He wrote the handbook on the subject for MI5, which, like everything else, was passed to the KGB.

Blunt arrived at the common at dusk and found Modin—wearing hat, overcoat and tartan scarf—standing near a bench on the path through the common. They sat next to each other on the bench, Blunt placing his rolled-up copy of *The Times* between them. At first Blunt was put off by Modin's youth. The British spy had been recruited at Cambridge in 1933 by someone twice his age. It was a quaint reminder that he had to wriggle away from the espionage world. He was too old for it. Nevertheless, Blunt was pleasantly surprised to learn that Modin had read much of the royal correspondence that he had snared for the Moscow Centre. The new man was also able to discuss its contents.

'I found it all very intriguing,' Modin said. 'Some wonderful work by you to obtain it.'

Blunt had not heard that sort of praise before in twelve years dealing with four Soviet spymasters. He did not respond at first.

'I mean what I say,' Modin said, filling the gap. 'You furnish us with amazing amounts of good material.'

'It's not all from me,' Blunt said, wishing to give credit to others.

'I know, I know. Mr Burgess and the Rothschilds supply much of it. But so do you. We are most grateful.'

'Really?' he said, 'You found it all useful? The royal correspondence too?'

'Oh, yes,' Modin grinned, 'very, very useful.'

'In what way?'

'My general education,' Modin replied. 'I want to know, the, how you say, 'machinery' of how your system works.'

As the conversation continued Blunt realised that young Modin, so polite and full of praise, was genuinely effusive about the Ring. He had unbounded respect for all of them. This was such a contrast to the past where cajolery or praise or even flattery were not part of the KGB Controls' ways. Encouragement was rare, especially with Modin's immediate predecessor.

After a harmonious meeting in which the attitude of the cool, sceptical Blunt thawed somewhat, Modin picked up *The Times* with its microfilm canisters and asked: 'What have you for us today?'

'More royal correspondence from my latest trip for the king.'

'Anything I should find interesting?'

'You've read the other letters. This new batch shows the kaiser's interest in the considerable property in the crown estates,' Blunt paused, his eyes flicking to the Russian for a split second. 'I see the kaiser's family is also upset by *your* property acquisitions in Germany recently.'

'Ah, yes,' Modin chuckled, 'we did "acquire" much property formerly owned by the kaiser and his family. I look forward very much to reading this new material.'

They shook hands. Modin said warmly: 'I'll be in touch, when we may need your assistance.'

It was not what Blunt wished to hear yet Modin's manner had made the thought of doing more espionage work for the KGB somehow less forbidding. Modin wrote in his memoirs that he used Blunt as a key middleman, through whom other agents, particularly Burgess and Victor Rothschild, would continue to pass espionage material as they always had, especially in the war years. Now, in the Cold War, experienced British agents were just as important to the Russians, with Stalin the most appreciative recipient of all in Moscow. According to Modin, the Soviet dictator knew the code names of all his key British spies. Before he was assigned to the Soviet Embassy in London, Modin would take their material personally to Stalin at the Kremlin. All this had built an enormous respect and awe for the British agents. Modin met Blunt, Burgess, Mclean and Cairncross regularly from then on, while rarely catching up with Philby and Rothschild. These two would give their espionage information to Blunt for passing on, although Rothschild, being the ubiquitous lord, would occasionally accept official invitations to Soviet Embassy functions. His cover was his importance at the centre of the British establishment.

Modin, in his memoirs, found Blunt 'haughty' yet still 'a most agreeable companion'. The young Russian spymaster said that Blunt's 'words matched his deeds'. He 'had a knack of looking at men in the same way he looked at pictures. He taught me, by example, that one can learn to understand people by noticing the fleeting expressions on their faces, and by contemplating their work.' This must have been quite a difficult method of analysis for Blunt because, as Modin noted, he had 'one curious defect: he hated to be looked directly in the eye. If one ventured to do this, he would look away.' Years of carrying out illegal practices and hiding his true identity as a spy and homosexual led to his furtiveness.

George VI's reign saw a further eroding of the monarch's power and an acceleration of the British Empire's dissolution. After World War II it was in decline. The end result was a long way from being the biggest, most powerful empire on earth, which the British could lay claim to its having been for several centuries. Two world wars had reduced the empire to a voluntary association of independent states, which became known as the Commonwealth and which owed almost everything to diplomacy and little to real power. Postwar British Labour Prime Minister Clement Atlee had no lust for empire building. He supported India and Pakistan becoming two independent states in 1947. Nevertheless, the myth of a great empire was maintained by developing the charisma of all matters royal. Princess Elizabeth, 21, married a third cousin (and descendent of Queen Victoria). This was Prince Philip of Greece, also a second cousin to Princess Elizabeth through King Christian IX of Denmark. He became the Duke of Edinburgh.

The princess loved him but her mother was under-impressed, especially with his three sisters marrying German noblemen, all of whom had Nazi connections. She called him 'Philip the Hun'. It would have been better in his mother-in-law's view if he had had money, but at least he had been born in Britain and had no Nazi links. The latter concern was a sensitivity concerning the king's German family. In the atmosphere of postwar Britain, where the nation had to mourn its dead, clean up the Luftwaffe bombing and other mess created by the Nazis, the queen would have preferred a suitable Scot or Englishman. But Princess Elizabeth was besotted with the phlegmatic young and impoverished prince. She had been writing to him since she was thirteen. In her mind, mature for her years, he was the male partner she wanted. Unlike Victoria, who had also been smitten as an early teenager, Princess Elizabeth was determined to be successful in marrying her first love no matter what the opposition. After all, she was destined to be queen. He had to be a suitable partner and consort for life.

The invitees to the wedding reflected the nation's mood. Philip's German relatives, including his three sisters, were not asked. The Duke of Windsor was ignored also. Philip took the name Mountbatten, the surname of his mother's British family but the Queen and Winston Churchill preferred that Windsor be retained.

'I am the only man in the country not allowed to give his name to his children,' Philip complained. But he did not appear too upset. Their first child, Charles, was born on 14 November 1948, thus creating a male heir to carry on the lineage of the royal house, whatever they labelled it.

In a move unimaginable in Victoria's reign, George VI sensibly relinquished the title of Emperor of India, which had so titillated his great-grandmother. He remained King of Pakistan, but gave up that title when India became a republic in 1950. Transjordan (Jordan) in 1946, Burma in January 1948, Palestine (divided between Israel and the Arab States) in May 1948 and Ireland in 1949 opted out of the Commonwealth.

51

BLUNT ACQUISITIONS

George VI's awareness of his great-grandmother's affair with the thirteenth Lord Elphinstone caused him to reflect that he may have been railroaded into a marriage to Elizabeth (however happily in the end), which linked him with the Elphinstone family via Elizabeth's sister's husband, the sixteenth Lord Elphinstone. This would help ensure that the original relationship remained hushed up. There was no need for George VI to pass on this family secret to his daughter. He happily left that to his wife, who said she would oblige if and when the need arose. By 1950, with all the apparent letter evidence placed in the library, heavily edited or destroyed, there was not the concern that there had been in previous decades. Although there would have been more concern than ever if the royal family learned that their *loyal* art curator Anthony Blunt had passed the letters, in their original form, to Soviet intelligence. But his traitorous activities were only suspected by a select few in British Intelligence and not yet confirmed. Therefore Queen Elizabeth and Queen Mary did not think it necessary to inform the future queen of Victoria's liaison, taking a 'what she doesn't know can't hurt her' attitude.

The queen and Queen Mary did let the princess know that Blunt had done her father special favours involving trips to Germany to retrieve important royal correspondence. The young Elizabeth inherited a loyalty to Blunt.

When questions were asked about the royal art historian, it was always said that he was a favourite of King George's wife. 'Anthony' was always available for parlour games at the palace and his work there was his life, along with his teaching activity at London's Courtauld Institute of Art—and his continued secret postwar espionage work for the KGB.

There was a further layer of importance that endeared him to the royal family: no-one had a better eye for the value of art. Blunt advised the palace on drawings and paintings that should be bought, whether for the institution or the aggrandisement of individual members of the family. He played his part in creating a dazzling array of royal treasures, which were 'of an unparalleled magnificence and variety', according to the British historian J.H. Plumb, who had access to them. The wonderful trove included almost every great master of painting . . . 'One of the finest of all Vermeers, magnificent Rembrandts, Rubens of spectacular quality. Portraits from Holbein to Winterhalter . . . hundreds of drawings by Leonardo da Vinci, exquisite examples of Michelangelo and Raphael; in paint or in pencil there is masterpiece after masterpiece.'

Blunt also had a say in what was acquired from the decorative arts in furniture, bronze, china, glass and jewels. Plumb believed that only Paris's Louvre, the Metropolitan Museum in New York, London's National Gallery and the Victorian and Albert Museum could better the royals' collection 'in quality and range. If the monarch's collection were placed in one building, it would take its place as one of the most outstanding museums in the world.'

Not only had Blunt helped the Windsor dynasty and the institution of the monarchy, survive, he had done much to make the moderately wealthy Windsor members asset-rich. But his cosy, safe set-up evaporated on 25 May 1951, when two members of Modin's British network— Guy Burgess and Donald Maclean—defected to Moscow. The rest of them and others under suspicion of working for Soviet intelligence, were interrogated by MI5 investigations in what became a hysterical witch-hunt. Blunt was a suspect. He was known to be close to Burgess.

MI5 pulled him in for questioning. Both he and Modin realised that MI5 had no solid evidence against him beyond his friendship with Burgess. Yes, he had written some art reviews through a 'Marxist' prism in the 1930s, but no, he had never been a member of the Communist Party while at Cambridge. The defections meant that Modin's network had to break up. Blunt stood up well to the initial questioning by MI5. His method was to shrug and say he did not 'have a clue why or how any of this happened'.

This stalled MI5 but Modin knew its operatives would come hard after Blunt. Moscow Centre gave Modin orders to persuade Blunt to defect. Spy-master and spy met in an emergency meeting in Normand Park, a small square in West London. Modin put a defection plan to him and painted a rosy picture of life in Moscow.

'No doubt you can also guarantee me total access to the Louvre and the Chateau de Versailles whenever I need to go there for my work,' Blunt said cynically.

It was his way of saying he would never defect. But after his opening remark, he became *blunt*. He said he couldn't possibly live in the Soviet Union.

'I know perfectly well how your people live,' Blunt said, recalling his own trip there in 1936. He assured Modin 'it would be very hard, almost unbearable for me to do likewise.'

Blunt went on to explain that he would never denounce Burgess. He was living in the hope that Burgess, his former lover and closest of friends, would return to England because there was no proof of him being a Soviet agent. In the meantime Blunt planned to withstand questioning.

'Burgess is the reason I refuse categorically to leave,' he told Modin.

George VI was informed about the interrogation of Blunt. As there was no proof against him, he was left in his job and nothing was said. But George VI told an equerry in touch with MI5: 'Under no circumstance is he to be asked about some special missions he made for me after the war. This work had nothing to do with security matters. It was private family business.'

The king was not about to discuss any of that 'family business' or the Victoria–Vicky and Edward VIII letters that had caused so much concern.

George VI's health had been impaired by the war and was always under stress. He smoked heavily to relieve it and had fallen into the trap that had helped to kill his grandfather and father. His smoking led to lung cancer and arteriosclerosis. Doctors for all three were aware of medical problems associated with nicotine yet the usual prescription in the era was to cut down on pipes, cigars and cigarettes, usually when it was too late to save a patient. George VI had a lung removed in September 1951 after a malignant tumour was found. The king's speech for the state opening of parliament was read for him by the lord chancellor, Lord Simonds. George VI's 1951 Christmas broadcast was read in sections and then edited together. His daughter, the capable Princess Elizabeth, who had blossomed into an attractive young woman, was being eased into his duties. She set out with her husband of four years for a tour of Australia via Kenya on 31 January 1952. Against doctors' orders, George VI insisted on going to the airport to see her off, perhaps sensing that it might be the last time he would see her.

On 6 February, he died in his sleep at Sandringham House after a fifteen-year reign. He was 56. His daughter flew back from Kenya as Queen Elizabeth II. His funeral took place at St George's Chapel, Windsor Castle, on 15 February 1952. Queen Elizabeth II's grandfather had been granted, posthumously, his wish to see her on the throne. After a run of four successive males (three of them ailing)—the debauched Edward VII; the competent, uninspiring George V; the selfish, hedonist Edward VIII; and the courageous, low-key George VI—the 25-year-old Elizabeth brought a breath of fresh air to the monarchy that had been lacking for 115 years, since Victoria became queen at age eighteen. Elizabeth had been educated privately. She received tuition from home in constitutional history from Henry Marten, Vice-Provost of Eton College, and was taught French by several governesses.

In 1955, Queen Elizabeth's Uncle Sidney, the sixteenth Lord Elphinstone, died aged 86. He had lived a good and long life without extending himself beyond what was expected from a wealthy Scottish nobleman. In his later years, he had revelled in the knowledge that he was the uncle to the reigning monarch. His successor was the 41-year-old John

Alexander Elphinstone, the seventeenth lord, who returned to the early family experience of the thirteenth lord and his forbears and relatives as a member of the British armed forces. He fought in World War II against the Germans and became a POW on 12 June 1940. John Alexander spent 1944 and 1945 as one of the 'Prominente' prisoners (including officers and those of the nobility) at Germany's Colditz prison. This was a POW camp in Colditz Castle on a cliff overlooking the town of the same name in Saxony. The thousand-year-old fortress was in the heart of Hitler's Reich, about 640 kilometres from any frontier not under Nazi control in the war. In mid-April 1945, American soldiers scaled its thick walls and liberated John Alexander along with hundreds of other prominent POWs.

In 1956, Anthony Blunt was knighted. After his several interrogations by British Intelligence, the award was an endorsement from the palace, and an indication that he would be protected because of his special letter-collecting missions for George VI.

5 2

STRAIGHT LIES

In January 1963, Kim Philby, a key member of British double agents under Modin's control, left Beirut for Moscow, and became the third defection of the so-called 'Cambridge Ring' recruited by the KGB in the 1930s. It was kept secret by the intelligence services and the British government but the ramifications for the Soviet Union's brilliant group of spies were huge. The witch-hunt of the 1950s now had a new intensity as MI5 'spy-catchers' cast their net far and wide in search of Philby's connections. But there was not yet concern at the palace about Blunt's link to him or the Russians. More problematic for the royal family was the health of Blunt's lover, Guy Burgess, who was dying of alcoholism in Moscow. All the spy agencies on both sides were nervous about his condition and what would be the consequences of his death.

In June 1963, Michael Adeane, the queen's private secretary, met Blunt in the basement at Buckingham Palace where he was examining some painting restorations. They had known each other since they had both attended Cambridge 30 years earlier.

'Her majesty would like you to do her a little favour,' Adeane said. Blunt put down a frame he had been inspecting as the secretary explained a problem over a set of drawings of the Duke of Edinburgh made by osteopath and surgeon Stephen Ward. Ward was a key witness in a sex and spy scandal. He had supplied prostitutes for parliamentarians, including British Minister for War John Profumo. It was potentially more than embarrassing for the royals if the sketches were known widely to the public, and media attention would have caused this.

'It would be most useful if you could acquire the drawings,' Adeane said.

'I think we would have to purchase more than Ward's sketches,' Blunt reflected.

'Why?'

'I would have to go to the gallery where they're on display and not make my intentions too obvious.'

Adeane understood. Blunt was given instructions to buy up the entire display, including the works by six other artists.

Burgess died on 30 August 1963. Blunt was devastated that his ex-lover had gone. He was now vulnerable to the renewed intense questioning coming from MI5's self-styled 'Gestapo' unit after Kim Philby's defection seven months earlier. Meanwhile Michael Whitney Straight, the only American member of the Cambridge Ring, also felt the pressure to keep quiet was off with Burgess's death. Burgess and Blunt in tandem had seduced and recruited Straight at Cambridge in 1936 and he had spied on American government departments and the White House for nearly three decades. Straight was bisexual and this had been held over him by the KGB as a useful blackmail tool. If he did not do what was required by his Moscow masters, he would be 'outed', to his public shame, on two counts, his sexuality and his spying, which was also the pressure point for Blunt to keep him in place.

With the West's Intelligence net tightening on both sides of the Atlantic, Modin worked out a fall-back strategy, which was passed to all agents. If Blunt should confess, or admit to being recruited in the 1930s at Cambridge, the 'line' from all the KGB recruits would be that they had sent 'information' to the Soviet Union during the war to help in the fight against fascism. They were to say they had not spied for the KGB after the end of World War II; that is, 1945. The other element of their combined misinformation was that they would all lead Western

Intelligence interrogators up wrong alleys. They were to hint at Western spies who were innocent, and to take investigators away from actual agents. Philby had started the deception in his 'confessions' to MI5 before he defected. Now Blunt, who was named by Straight as having recruited him, settled himself in for a long journey of denial and deception.

Peter Wright, the main MI5 spy-hunter, was aware that Blunt was his biggest potential 'catch' so far and he was keen to force a confession from him after years of detective work. Wright's deputy, Arthur Martin, flew to Washington DC to question Straight, the scion of the rich Whitney family, who'd had no trouble dancing around the interrogation by the US's Federal Bureau of Investigation. The FBI had no idea of the UK culture of espionage and Straight had few sleepless nights meeting the bureau's demands as its probed him. But Martin was different. He grilled Straight and managed to squeeze out of him an admittance of his recruitment to the KGB by Blunt. Martin asked Straight what he knew of Blunt's spying after the war.

'He was a palace courtier by then,' Straight said dismissively while playing the KGB line. 'Even his special missions for the King after the war had nothing to do with the Russians, except that Moscow would have received, I presume, whatever information he retrieved for his majesty.'

'What missions were these?' Martin asked, his tape recorder running.

'He had to bring back from Germany any correspondence that implicated Edward VIII's connection to Hitler.' As an afterthought he added. 'There were other letters, correspondence between Queen Victoria and the princess royal.'

'You say Moscow received it all?'

'Oh, yes, Anthony was very good at photography,' Straight said with a laugh.

Martin and Wright in London then queried Blunt on Straight's limited 'confessions'. Blunt agreed to 'confess' in exchange for a written guarantee of immunity from prosecution. But it was a stalling tactic in which he would give MI5 effectively nothing and instead lead them on false trails.

'The government will grant you immunity from prosecution in return for a full confession,' Wright told Blunt, with barely contained contempt for the double agent. 'Personally, I'd prefer you were charged and hopefully executed. But we must do what the Masters of the Universe [their intelligence bosses] tell us to do.'

Blunt would not make eye contact with his tormentor as they sat opposite each other on thread-bare couches and he did not respond.

'You are most fortunate, Sir Anthony,' Martin said. 'The Palace is clearly protecting you. But if you don't confess everything you know . . .' 'We are talking about your fellow traitors,' Wright butted in eagerly, 'and their KGB Controllers.'

'That's right, Sir Anthony,' Martin continued. 'There will be no deal if you don't give us the lot.'

Blunt kept his eyes on the thin carpet of the main room of the interrogation safe-house. Then he glanced up, making fleeting eye contact with Martin.

'I want this immunity in writing, please,' he said.

'And we want your agreement to spill everything in writing,' Wright said with vehemence, 'otherwise we'll have you charged with espionage.'

'I doubt that,' Blunt said softly.

'Oh, you do, do you?' Wright said, leaning forward and barely containing his rage. Blunt looked up, his cool mien intact.

'I doubt that you will *need* to do that,' Blunt said correcting himself. 'I shall keep my side of the bargain.'

'That would be wise, Sir Anthony,' Martin said.

He stuck with presenting the image of a wartime anti-fascist rather than a fully-fledged KGB operative. Wright asked about his missions for the king from 1945 to 1947.

'That was not a state espionage exercise,' Blunt said, remaining ice-cool even during his admissions. 'It was a private operation for King George VI. I am not at liberty to discuss it. I can only do that if you receive permission from the palace.'

This gave Wright and Martin pause. They wrote to Adeane. He consulted Elizabeth II, who in turn had a discussion with her mother over breakfast at the palace.

'Sir Anthony has confessed to spying for the Russians, mummy,' Elizabeth II said. 'It's serious. MI5 interrogators have been asking him about his special mission to secure royal correspondence.'

'He mustn't say anything about that or the letters' contents.'

'What on earth could be of interest to the Russians in Queen Victoria's letters?'

'Nothing dear, nothing.'

'Then what's all the fuss about?' Elizabeth II asked.

'Much to do about nothing, dear. Tell Adeane to let them know that any discussion about the king's missions is off limits.'

'I would like to know what's in the letters.' Tea and toast was served by servants, who bowed and departed. 'I think I should know.'

'Dear, May [Queen Mary] was the only one of the family who bothered to read them, and she didn't say much except that we should retrieve as much as we could from Germany. But we knew David and that woman [Wallis Simpson] had cosied up to Hitler. The fools!'

Elizabeth II sipped her tea and frowned.

'I take it Blunt knows what's in them?'

'Presumably he would have been briefed. Along with Morshead.'

'You don't think ...' the queen began and then broke off as she took a half-interest in the *Daily Mail* among the several papers on the breakfast table.

'What dear?'

'If Blunt was still spying for the Russians post-war ...'

'We're told he says he wasn't.'

'Mummy, he is a spy; he would say that.'

The queen mother picked up the *Daily Telegraph* as if the discussion should end there, but Elizabeth II persisted.

'Just imagine he passed the Russians copies of all the correspondence between Victoria and Vicky, and Uncle David and the Nazis.'

'Good God! There were thousands of letters. Would be impossible!'

'Not at all. Spies use tiny little cameras to photograph things.'

They both went on reading in silence. Philip, in dressing gown and pyjamas, entered the breakfast room carrying *The Times*.

'Hear the news?' the queen said.

'What?' Philip asked.

'We have a Russian spy at the Palace.'

'So I'm told. What's to be done with him?'

'Oh, he will be kept on,' the queen mother proffered.

'Why?'

'Sacking him might bring press attention. And, in any case, Anthony knows too many secrets.'

'Better to keep him inside the tent?' Philip asked.

'I think so,' the queen mother said. 'Besides I really like him. Delightful fellow.'

Philip and Elizabeth II remained silent.

Wright in particular was keen to know about Blunt's assignments for King George VI. He pushed Blunt, who began drinking heavily with the nagging, pressing MI5 methods that promised to go on for years. The pressures were getting to him as never before. At one point he turned up at the interrogation safe-house in Mayfair, London and said: 'If I show you a certain piece of royal correspondence, you must promise not to ever disclose it.'

'You can't bargain with us—' Wright began aggressively. Martin put up a hand.

'If it is not to do with national security you have our word,' he said, and then glancing at Wright added, 'right, Peter?'

Wright thought for a moment and then nodded sharply. He hated Blunt attempting to dictate terms.

'What have you got for us?' Wright asked sharply. Blunt handed him Queen Victoria's letter to Vicky dated 25 July 1860, which spoke of her relationship with Elphinstone. Wright sat in a chair and put on glasses. As ever a tape recorder was sitting on a table between them. When Wright and Martin had finished reading, Blunt said: 'That's the sort of information in the letters. Hardly anything that would interest the Moscow Centre, is it?'

'But you did give microfilmed copies to your Control,' Martin probed.

'I told you before,' Blunt said, rubbing his face, which was unshaven, 'I wanted to leave them after the war. My work for them was over. I had to make out that my new position at the palace was just as important as at MI5. I built up the king's assignments as something important, to show, you know, my proximity to the king.'

Martin glanced at Wright.

'So you admit passing them copies of the royal letters after the war?' Wright asked, staring at Blunt.

'It was not espionage,' Blunt said.

'You are a true traitor, Sir Anthony,' Wright said, 'no better than Lord Haw Haw.'

When Blunt had left, Wright and Martin mulled over the implications of what had been divulged.

'He could blackmail the queen with that sort of stuff,' Wright said, 'or at least the KGB could.'

'Would they do that?' Martin asked.

'Probably not. But fearing it was possible would be enough to keep Blunt his job at the palace.'

Two days later Adeane met with Wright and Martin in a cafe off St James Street in the West End and told them: 'Please do not pursue Blunt on the matter of his assignment on behalf of the palace. Strictly speaking, it is not relevant to considerations of national security.'

'Did he complain to you?' Martin asked.

'It doesn't matter,' Adeane said. 'Please do not pursue it.'

He left abruptly after the short 'chat'.

'We need to know everything,' Wright said to Martin. 'Must have the broader picture.'

'Peter, you heard the man. He is the palace spokesman.'

'What are they afraid of?'

'It's obvious, isn't it? You read that Queen Victoria letter.'

Wright grunted but said nothing.

'In any case, we can't grill him any more on his special royal missions,' Martin added with a sigh. 'The Masters of the Universe will take us off our "project" if we pursue it.'

53

CLIMATE OF TREASON

Richard Crossman, 60, a minister in Harold Wilson's government, visited Balmoral in October 1967. In a discussion with Elizabeth II, he brought up the London *Sunday Times*' revelations by its Insight team about Kim Philby, the MI5 spy who had defected to Moscow in January 1963.

'Your majesty,' Crossman said, 'have you read the story?'

'No,' Elizabeth replied frostily, 'I don't read that kind of thing.'

Her manner cut Crossman short. It was not a subject she wished to discuss. But, despite her comment, it was a story that she devoured. Elizabeth's fear was that Blunt might be connected to Philby, especially with all the tabloid talk about there being a Cambridge University ring of spies controlled by the KGB. Philby and Blunt had been at Cambridge at the time Blunt was a tutor. The press was touting the spectre of a 'ring of five' without telling the public that the KGB itself had first mentioned this figure. 'Five' was a simple odd number. It also diverted British intelligence and the pliant media from the idea that there might be more than 30 top British spies recruited at Cambridge,

Oxford and other top British educational institutions. The tabloids became hysterical about the number 'five', which their editors, with their more numerate readers in mind, could count on the toes of one foot. Burgess and Maclean were one and two. Philby was number three. Who were numbers four and five? Had they defected? Were they *still among us* like feared aliens from another planet?

This espionage revelation made Elizabeth II edgy. She had no idea of where her art curator and purchaser fitted into the nomenclature of the KGB and collaborative British media. But she had used Adeane to warn Wright and Martin *not* to interrogate Blunt about his special missions for her father. Elizabeth II did not want the Blunt connection and his missions being unravelled for public consumption. Too many other secrets could be laid bare.

Just before Christmas 1977, Arthur Martin sat down with Scottish radio journalist Andrew Boyle, 58, in a drab pub off the Strand, London. It was 4 p.m. and one other patron, in a hat and overcoat, drank alone in a corner while reading a paper. The two had known each other since the war when they both worked in military intelligence. Martin had left MI5 in 1970 to work in a more sedate job as a member of the Clerks Department in the House of Commons.

He took a thick folder from a briefcase, glanced around at the other patron and handed it to Boyle.

'It's just about all there,' Martin said in a near-whisper. Boyle placed it in his own briefcase.

'Remember, Andrew, you have not met me since late in 1945.'

'Of course not.'

'Under no circumstances are you to even hint at the source.'

'I gave you my word, Arthur.'

'I know, but it is very sensitive. Blunt has the support of the palace and the government.'

'I can't mention Blunt by name?'

'No. Use false names for all the key players.'

Boyle sipped his pint of Guinness.

'Can you remind me of your motive for this?' he asked.

'It's simple. Peter Wright and I worked to the point of dropping and these shits got away with the most traitorous activity in British history.'

Boyle nodded his agreement.

'We just want a bit of justice,' Martin said, his face determined.

Boyle's book, *The Climate of Treason,* was published in 1979. The author did not name Anthony Blunt but instead drew a pen-sketch of the fictitious homosexual 'Maurice,' *The Fourth Man.* The satirical London magazine *Private Eye* jumped on the book and named Blunt as the hidden spy. No other story in peacetime in British history caused as much media frenzy, especially with the many papers on Fleet Street.

Perhaps only the Jack the Ripper tale of 90 years earlier created as much fuss, but where the Ripper was never discovered, Blunt had been named. The similarity was that the press could become intertwined in the revelations by uncovering more and more angles. Packs of Fleet Street hacks went on the trail of both and the Blunt story had more 'meat' and intrigue. His connections included co-spies, the royals, former employers at the palace, the KGB, MI5, the Courtauld Institute, and his many former and current friends and associates at Cambridge. It could not be more 'juicy' for hungry reporters ready to trample on anything or anyone to grab a different line on the story. Editors moved to wring every last drop from it. Book publishers whirled into action commissioning a run of mostly fatuous, uninspiring tomes that created an industry. Many of Blunt's connections were concerned with what now might be revealed by his 'outing'. Would he 'sing'? Would he say anything that might incriminate others? A few saw the funny side of the media's endeavours that waxed between earnest and vicious. In Rome, art historian and Blunt friend Eric Hebborn had his home invaded. Undaunted, he answered the door to a gaggle of journalists and photographers. Seeing them he gasped. Slamming the door, he shouted: 'Quick Anthony, it's them! Get upstairs!'

Former MI5 spies Tess and Victor Rothschild, both very close friends of Blunt, sweated. Tess worked hard in support of Blunt, hoping that this would avoid him mentioning the Rothschilds' own secrets. Straight was worried. Like the Rothschilds, he had been interrogated many times by British Intelligence officers. The royal family was nervous. How many questions would now be asked about Blunt's special assignments for George VI from 1945 to 1947? Elizabeth II was concerned that not even the royal connections were safe from unwanted prying.

At breakfast at Buckingham Palace, the discussion soon after the revelations was about Blunt.

'Will he be prosecuted?' Elizabeth II asked.

'Never!' the queen mother said, flicking open the *Daily Express*. 'What's he done that hundreds didn't do at university?'

'Oh, mummy, it seems more serious than university exuberance.'

'He was a very loyal servant of your father, remember that!'

'Phillip,' Elizabeth II said, 'what do you think?'

'I think he's a bloody traitor.'

'Oh, Philip!' the queen mother protested, 'we are not at war with Russia!'

'He passed state secrets to the enemy,' Philip said. 'Used to be a hanging offence.'

'But that was all during the war. The Russians were not the enemy.'

'We don't know for certain that his "activities" were restricted to the war period, mummy,' Elizabeth II said.

'It's what the government will say,' Philip remarked.

'Will he be punished, Philip?' Elizabeth asked.

'No. They'd never put 'im in the dock. It'd open a can of worms. Can't do it.'

'Then what?'

'Take away his knighthood,' Philip said, opening *The Financial Times*. 'That will show your disdain for the bugger.'

'I shall discuss it with my staff, who will no doubt be contacted by Thatcher's staff.'

At 10 Downing Street, Prime Minister Thatcher met in her office with her key advisers, who gave a briefing on the background to Boyle's book, Blunt's immunity from prosecution, and the palace's reaction.

'The palace is comfortable with Blunt being relieved of his knighthood,' one staffer informed her.

'That's all very well,' Thatcher said, sitting up in her chair as the six advisers stood in front of her desk, 'but I had no idea about this immunity business. Why on earth was it granted?'

'We are informed by the service that it was in exchange for him divulging certain detail about other fellow traitors.'

'And you say he has always had the palace's support?'

'Yes, Prime Minister. Apparently he went on special assignments for King George VI just after the war.'

'What special assignments?'

'It's a very sensitive issue, Prime Minister, but we believe that there were certain royal family letters that the king did not wish to fall into American or German hands.'

Thatcher's eyebrows arched.

Another adviser added: 'The palace would prefer that Blunt's er...involvement...was not made public—'

'Oh, would it?' Thatcher interrupted. 'Well, it's too late for that. There are already questions in the Commons about who the characters are in Boyle's book.'

'Secrecy is *preferred* by the palace, Prime Minister. But it understands that this is impossible and that he could not be relieved of his knighthood without public mention of it.'

'Quite,' Thatcher snapped. She reflected for a moment. 'I take it that Blunt's immunity from prosecution does not include a guarantee to him of secrecy?'

'No, prime minister,' two advisers replied, almost in chorus.

'Then we shall publicly strip him of his honours.'

In Moscow, Blunt's former KGB 'Control', Modin, looked on with interest. He knew many of the royal secrets that had been passed to him by Blunt. He chuckled at the claim by Thatcher in the House of Commons that Blunt had stopped spying for the Soviet Union as soon as World War II was over in 1945. Modin had engineered that angle himself. 'Funny that,' he commented later. 'I had "run" Blunt from 1947 to 1958.' Modin was an exceptional psychologist. He was Control for some of the best, brightest and most complex men and women at Cambridge and Oxford.

He passed word to Blunt for him to write his memoirs, which the KGB would see first and censor. Modin had persuaded Philby in Moscow in 1967 to write *My Silent War*, and Straight to compose his *After Long Silence*. Modin had even suggested the titles, both with 'silence' in them. Blunt began writing, but became stranded halfway through. Unlike Philby and Straight he could not extend the lie of his existence, which had been laid so bare, so publicly. Modin believed in justifying their traitorous trade through books and he knew that half the Western public would accept the excuses put forward. Publishers were seduced into gullibility by the prospect of big book sales. False confessions had worked well for Philby, Straight, Blunt and many others before. Modin's approach was to intellectualise lies thematically in fat tomes, which caused much longer distractions than defensive newspaper articles planted by Western journalists who were in the KGB's pay—so-called 'Agents of Influence'. The books never contained footnotes or clues of how to check authenticity but instead were memoirs of the most unreliable kind. Literary criticism of these books could always be countered by spurious and specious arguments. Spies such as Philby, Straight and Blunt secured Masters degrees and PhDs in deception. Modin preferred the literary route to the KGB's other form of 'silence', which came with a poisonous umbrella jab or a dose of Strontium 90 slipped into the food of an unsuspecting victim.

Blunt did not have the stomach for finishing his memoir. It lay in his London apartment like a half-eaten sandwich turning stale and inedible. Those concerned about Blunt spilling what he knew need not have worried. Modin would make sure it was misleading propaganda designed to upset Western intelligence and send its agents scurrying down back-alleys that led to a maze or a dead-end. There would be no revelations about Victoria's affair with Elphinstone or Edward VIII's Nazi connections, although there would be self-serving, well-worn justifications for spying for both the Soviets and the British against the Nazis in World War II. There would be no mention of the Cambridge Ring's continued enforced espionage for the KGB long after the war.

In December 1979, members of the royal household braced themselves when newspapers disclosed elements of Blunt's royal mission to postwar Germany. The articles were sketchy, more fishing than fact. No details were given. No reporter could reveal anything substantial about what Blunt and Morshead had retrieved. Modin could have written the script for the response from the royal family. It would once more have had 'silence' in the title. Being royal it was 'dignified'. Elizabeth II did not have to tell anyone to shut up. Only her mother knew more than her daughter and she was not about to blab.

The queen mother's attitude was on display at a London Christmas lunch in mid-December 1979 at the home of Lady Perth. One member of the party had the courage to ask the queen mother what she thought about this alleged special postwar letter-collecting 'project' directed by her late husband.

'Lovely day, isn't it?' she replied with her trademark tilt of the head and smile, which charmed, deflected and warned off further queries. She later indicated that she was fond of Blunt.

'She liked homosexuals,' her friend intellectual Isaiah Berlin said 'She liked pansies—queers...'

The queen mother had told him: 'Oh, well, one can't blame them [the Cambridge spies] all. A lot of people made terrible mistakes—one shouldn't really go on persecuting them.'

It was a sweet sentiment, typical of her caring nature, tolerance and glass half-full approach to life, which sustained her past 100 years. But it was also a hard-nosed cover-up and defence of Blunt, who betrayed the nation before, during and after World War II. Her attitude was very much to put her family's interests ahead of that of her nation. It was a human and humane attitude that would cause writers and artists and playwrights to salivate over dramatising what comes first: family and friends or country.

Blunt made many people sigh with relief when he died of a heart attack at his apartment. He was 75. The press hounded him with questions until the day before he died. Several journalists were disappointed they would never receive first-hand answers from him again, even if his objective was to deceive at every turn. But they were in the minority. Many more interested parties were pleased with his passing.

In the US, Michael Straight, one of Blunt's star recruits for the KGB, celebrated. So did Tess and Victor Rothschild as rumours circulated in England that they, together, formed the identity of the fifth entity in the Soviet Ring along with Burgess, Maclean, Philby and Blunt. (In 1986, Thatcher was forced to make a frosty and unconvincing one-paragraph denial in the Commons in which she claimed that MI5 had no information that Victor Rothschild was *The Fifth Man*.) In Moscow, Modin, now retired, held a quiet wake with other operatives, who appreciated Blunt's considerable espionage work for them. At the palace, Elizabeth II and the queen mother breathed easier too. The issue over Blunt's missions for George VI was not buried, but it was less likely to cause concern now that the main participant, whom Elizabeth II loathed and her mother liked, was dead. However, the royals remained aware that the complete and unedited archive of royal letters lay in a vault at KGB headquarters in Moscow.

Postscript

Exposé

Modin, in his seventies in the early 1990s, was suddenly a pauper. With the massive devaluation of the rouble after the collapse of communism, Russian pensions were decimated. Key retired KGB agents such as him found themselves suffering in harsh economic circumstances. The new KGB regime in Moscow decided to let Western journalists into Russia to interview former master-spies, such as Modin, who would command American dollar fees to make up in part for their diminished pension incomes. This was to be organised by the new wave of KGB spies, who believed they were aping Western capitalism by demanding commissions for the interviews. Having lived in England during twelve years of the 'hottest' period of the Cold War, from 1973 to 1985, I was intrigued (as many journalists were) to discover who was the Fifth Man in the Cambridge Ring, and investigate other espionage agents. In 1993, I arranged to interview Modin in Moscow. Face-to-face interviews took place in Modin's Moscow apartment on a daily basis over two weeks. I later wrote *The Fifth Man*, based on those and other interviews with KGB agents (it was published by Sidgwick & Jackson and Pan Macmillan in 1995). In 1996, I began researching a further member of the Cambridge Ring, American Michael Whitney

Straight, who had been recruited by Blunt. In the same year, I returned to Russia with British documentary filmmaker Jack Grossman; Modin agreed to the on-camera interviews for a $US1000 cash fee for his appearances in ten hours of filming over two days. Jack Grossman and I stayed at a hotel in Moscow's west and took a taxi a few kilometres to the KGB man's flat in an unprepossessing block. Modin was now a heavy-set man with a thick wave of white hair and a beard.

'He's the spitting image of Colonel Sanders,' Grossman whispered to me as he set up his camera.

Modin had by this time published his autobiography, *Mes camarades de Cambridge*, brought out by French publisher Laffont in 1994, after decades of advising his double agents to write their own stories. His decision to commit pen to paper himself was another way of earning quick money from eager Western publishers in France, England and the United States. Its 'revelations' would also keep Western investigators wandering aimlessly in an espionage labyrinth.

I asked the Russian about the special missions for George VI that Blunt had made from 1945 to 1947. Modin knew Blunt's assignment had been made public by British historian Hugh Trevor Roper (Lord Dacre) and elaborated on by a few journalists. But no-one had delved deeply into the reasons for the trips and what was recovered by Blunt for the archives at Windsor Castle.

'What was the correspondence about?' I asked.

'Royal matters,' Modin replied in his resonant, sometimes 'sing-song' Russian accent, 'some of them private.'

'Did they include correspondence between the Duke of Windsor and Hitler?'

'Oh, yes, of course. Much from him to the Nazis.'

'Can I see any of them?'

'That would be impossible. They are classified not for Western eyes.' Modin paused. 'I wish to tell you that I shall not give you any more information than Western intelligence already knows.'

'You are assuming I am linked to a Western agency?'

'I must.'

'It doesn't happen to be true but I understand your position,' I said. 'Anyway, it still puts me well ahead of the Western media pack.'

I probed about the Hitler correspondence. Modin kept blocking and avoiding the questions.

'You know, there is another line of investigation [for you] here,' Modin told me after fifteen minutes of getting nowhere. 'There are much more interesting royal letters that were passed to us by Blunt.'

'Can you tell me about any of them?'

Modin frowned and seemed to be thinking deeply.

'I can tell you about one that Blunt showed us to demonstrate his importance as a palace man.'

'As the king's art curator?'

'Yes, art curator.'

'Please . . .' I said, glancing at Grossman.

'The letter was written by Queen Victoria to her daughter. She confesses she had an affair before she was queen.'

I waited.

'That's all I can recall,' Modin said. 'I read some of the letters, but there were thousands.'

'So you could have blackmailed the royals?'

'Yes.'

'Did you ever try?'

'No,' Modin said with a vigorous shake of the head, 'we would not do it.'

With Grossman filming, I saw several other ex-KGB agents, including Vladimir Barkovsky, who had made a study of Blunt's material at KGB headquarters. Modin helped arrange the meeting and Barkovsky came to the Moscow Hotel at which we were staying. I waited for the Russian in the lobby. After a half-hour wait mid-morning in early October 1996, I noticed a lean, short older man in dark glasses. He wore a beige trench-coat and was carrying a black briefcase. I thought, 'This is the only person in the lobby who looks like a spy.' I approached the man and found it was indeed Barkovsky.

He was not as relaxed or polite as Modin but he was cooperative, explaining he needed the $US500 that he would be given for the half-hour interview to pay for a medical operation on his grandson.

'Our health system is not what it was,' he complained. 'I have to go private now and it costs.'

I asked him about the Victoria–Vicky correspondence.

'Yuri tells me you are interested in Victoria's letters to her daughter in 1860,' Barkovsky said reaching into his briefcase. 'I have copies of a sample of these letters. But I can't let you read them.'

Barkovsky shuffled photocopies of about ten letters, before he looked up and said: 'I am able to disclose a little information from one dated 25 July 1860 in which Victoria made a point of "confessing" a relationship before she met Albert. It concerned a member of the House of Lords who was in her royal court.'

'Does she say which lord?'

'I am not at liberty to divulge that.'

'But he was a member of her court?'

'Two courts, two monarchs.'

'Who was the other monarch?'

'That is for you to find out.'

'Are there more references to the "affair". . .?'

Barkovsky waved a letter from Victoria at Holyrood Castle, dated 7 August 1860.

'When was the letter written?'

Barkovsky looked at the letter.

'August seventh, 1860.'

'Is it possible to film any of these copies?' Grossman asked.

'No, I am sorry. If you discover the name of this lord, please do not divulge that I gave you this information. We have a rule of not disclosing the exact nature of espionage material. We have always paraphrased such material for the intended recipient. In this case, the letters are strictly banned. I am trusting in you because of your connection to Yuri Ivanovitch [Modin], who has found you most reliable.'

I finished the book on Straight, *Last of the Cold War Spies*, which was published by Da Capo—after lengthy correspondence with Straight himself—in 2005. Five years later I began an investigation into the veracity of the information in the Victoria–Vicky letters and discovered strong evidence of a relationship between Victoria and the thirteenth Lord Elphinstone. I then examined the Elphinstone archive at the British Library. It ran to 309 files. Library officials estimated that it would take six years intense work to devour them all. I spent several months in 2011 and 2012 cherry-picking relevant files, and discussed them with Grossman, telling him that I had established that Elphinstone and Victoria had had an affair *before* she became queen. I saw it as a cold case, like the television series.

'A cold case, yes,' Grossman agreed. 'Except you do not go back to a murder and a dead body. It's a state secret so it's probably well buried. Perhaps the best kept one in the history of the royals.'

'Yes,' I said, 'Queen Victoria's secret.'

NOTES

Ch. 1 A Princess in Peril

'The scales then fell...': Weintraub, *Victoria*, p.15.

Ch. 2 The Lover

'A more perfect gentleman...': *The Complete Peerage*, Elphinstone XIII, 1813, p. 60.

'lame and unable to stand...': Weintraub, *Victoria*, p. 88; reference to the love affair between Lord E and Victoria, in the UK *Dictionary of National Biography*; also *The Complete Peerage*, Elphinstone XIII, 1813, p. 60; Fraser, *The Elphinstone Family Book*, p. 41; Watson, *Kirkintilloch, Town and Parish 1894*.

'A romance hung...': Fraser, *The Elphinstone Family Book*, p. 486; Elphinstone Archive, British Library, Asian Section, Elphinstone [E] Archive, F309.

'very *new* in the world...' and 'Now they are quite gone...': Hibbert, *Queen Victoria*, pp. 38–44; Williams, *Becoming Queen*, pp. 228–36.

Ch. 3 Unsuitable Suitors

'extremely crushed and kept': Longford, *Victoria R.I.*, p. 240

Ch. 5 Transition to Monarchy

'How are you going on at Madras...': Orange to Lord E, Fraser, *The Elphinstone Family Book*, p. 487; E Archive; British Library, F87/309.

'I did not leave...': Lord E Diary, 30 November 1836, E Archive, British Library, F87/27.

'I wish to remain...': Royal Archive (RA), Windsor, Queen Victoria's Journal (QVJ), M7/14

'You are still very young...': RA, M7/52.

Ch. 6 Elphinstone in Exile: Victoria Victorious

'We were greeted by catamarans...': E Archive, British Library, Letters, F87/27, 6 March 1837; also Fraser, p. 304, *The Elphinstone Family Book*, F87/309.

'Her name is Husna Ahmed de Crepeney...' References to Husna in personal letters at the time spelt her surname 'de Crepeney'. Later references use various spellings, including the more conventional 'de Crespigny'.

'Your departure greatly affected the king...': Prince Hesse, 3 October, 1837. E Archive, British Library, Letters, F87/28; also Fraser, *The Elphinstone Family Book*, F87/309.

'we want a governor...': Kaye & Malleson, *History of the Indian Mutiny of 1857–8*, vol. 5, p. 287.

Ch. 7 The Governor's Distraction

'All the people here...': Longford, *Victoria R.I.*, p. 83.

'The queen always speaks most highly of you...': E Archive, British Library, Letters F87/44, Lord Falkland writing from 14 Curzon Street, London W1, 17 February 1838.

'I hear a new story...': E Archive, British Library, Letters, F87/44.

'This is really too bad...': Longford, *Victoria R.I.*, p. 83.

Ch. 8 Melbourne Munificent

'Such stories of knowledge...': Boyd, *A Mad, Bad and Dangerous People?*, p. 64.

Ch. 9 Crowned but Loveless

'An attachment between the two...': *The Asiatic Journal and Monthly Register for British and Foreigners in India*, December 1838, quoting *The Times*, London, 4 December, 1838.

'Whatever may be the cause of Lord E...': *The Times*, 13 December 1838; also Internet Archive: History 1793–1844, Europe 1827–1844; Volume 10, No. 42. (Report on press coverage of events of 1838.)

Ch. 10 The Fading Elph

'The Queen of Hearts...': *The Complete Peerage*, Elphinstone XIII, p. 60, (footnote d).

'We have derived from high sources...': *The Hobart Town Courier*, 17 October 1838.

'We have no doubt she is...': RA, QVJ, 2 February 1839.

Ch. 11 Victoria Faces the 'M' Word

'But I am but a poor...': RA, QVJ: 22 March 1839.

'I was [so much] accustomed...': RA, QVJ, 18 April 1839.

Ch. 12 Crisis of the Bedchamber

'considering the sacrifices...': Roxburgh Club, *Wellington Correspondence*, Duke of W to John Conroy, 6 July 1839.

'literally like a skeleton...': RA, QVJ, 27 June 1839

'Then again, I might like him...': Bolitho, *Albert, Prince Consort*, p. 40.

Ch. 13 Victoria's Proposal; Elphinstone's Compensation

'Albert is, in fact, fascinating...': Bolitho, *Albert, Prince Consort*, p. 40.

'He was not in love with her...': Strachey, *The Illustrated Queen Victoria*, p. 76.

'While I shall be untiring...': Strachey, *The Illustrated Queen Victoria*, p. 76.

'much animadversion': *The Newcastle Courier*, 6 November

1840. Also *The Hull Packet*, Hull, England, 16 April 1841.

'I am the sovereign...': RA, QVJ, 3 November 1839.

'I'll hang up my harp...': Watson, *Kirkintilloch, Town and Parish*, p. 42.

Ch. 14 Vicky's Birth: Elphinstone's Fever

'I cannot understand how anyone...': RA, QVJ, 2 November 1840,

'If my plagues...': RA, QVJ, 2 November 1840,

'In case of Victoria's death...': Bolitho, *Albert, Prince Consort*, p. 21.

'Three months ago...': Bolitho, *Albert, Prince Consort*, p. 21.

'Lord Elphinstone had a reputation...': Arbuthnol, *Memoirs of Rugby and India*, p. 67.

'We are happy in being able...': *The Times*, 11 July 1840.

'Elphinstone's excuse...': *The Hindu Times*, 2 May 1840.

'if he had not acted...': *The Hindu Times*, 2 May 1840.

Ch. 15 Bertie's Arrival: Lehzen's Departure

'Doctor Clark has mismanaged...': Longford, *Victoria R.I.*, p. 200.

'Lehzen is a crazy, common...': Longford, *Victoria R.I.*, p. 200.

Ch. 16 Lovers' Reunion

'the divinest thing in the world': Warwick, *Life's Ebb*, p. 34.

Ch. 17 The Perfect Butler

'Was he the wife...': Strachey, *The Illustrated Queen Victoria*, pp. 8–12.

'From resembling a foreign tenor...': Strachey, *The Illustrated Queen Victoria*, pp. 8–12.

'The husband was not so happy...': Strachey, *The Illustrated Queen Victoria*, pp. 8–12.

'Here, after four years, is the recognition...': Bolitho, *Albert, Prince Consort*, p. 85.

Ch. 21 On a high with the Highlanders

'The Queen wishes Lord Palmerston...': RA, QVJ: 18 October 1850.

'Besides Victoria, he presented...': Strachey, *The Illustrated Queen Victoria*, p. 8.

Ch. 25 Old Feelings, New Challenges in Bombay

'elegant [Indian] women in shortsatin...': E Archive, British Library, F87/104

Letter 27/1/1854, F87/104

'He brought to the office...': Kaye & Malleson, *History of the Indian Mutiny*, p. 2.

Ch. 26 Victoria Trumps Napoleon III

'You will be surprised...' and 'from the effects...': Fraser, *The Elphinstone Family Book,* p. 339.

Ch. 27 In the Barrel of a Gun

'Certainly the Prince of Wales...': Strachey, *The Illustrated Queen Victoria*, p. 204.

'I have been shamefully...': Fulford, *Dearest Child*, p. 134.

Ch. 28 Elphinstone Steps Up

'Elphinstone deserves the fullest praise...': Kaye & Malleson, *History of the Indian Mutiny*, pp. 288–9.

'From the very hour...': Kaye & Malleson, *History of the Indian Mutiny*, p. 260.

'Thanks to your admirable...': Fraser, *The Elphinstone Family Book*, p. 342.

'I am persuaded...': Kaye & Malleson, *History of the Indian Mutiny*, pp. 258–9.

'The column's march...': Kaye & Malleson, *History of the Indian Mutiny*, pp. 300–1.

Ch. 30 The British Prevail

'Only those who have enjoyed...': Kaye & Malleson, *History of the Indian Mutiny*, pp. 300, 301.

'feelings of horror...': Woodham-Smith,
Queen Victoria, p. 88.

Ch. 31 A 'Friend' in Trouble

'Lord Elphinstone also ought not to be left...': Weintraub,
Victoria, p. 261.

'demonstrated courage and resourcefulness...': Weintraub,
Victoria, p. 261.

'I felt a real pleasure in bearing...': Fraser, *The Elphinstone
Family Book*, p. 343.

Ch. 32 Last Writes

'Alas! Another most valuable...': Weintraub, *Victoria*, p. 261.

Ch. 33 Noble Intentions

'Thousand, thousand good wishes...': Roberts (ed.), *Letters
to Vicky*, p. 73.

Ch. 34 The End for Albert's Torment

'If you were to try to deny it...': Weintraub, *Edward the
Caresser*, p. 95.

Ch. 35 The Queen Has Gone Missing

'I never can, or shall, look at him...': Middlemas, *The Life
and Times of Edward VII*, p. 31.

'My dear Queen...': Hibbert, *The Royal Victorians*, p. 326.

Ch. 36 The Queen Revives; Disraeli Dazzles

'so lax and bad...': Weintraub, *Edward the Caresser*, pp. 140,
141.

'They may not dine out...': Longford, *Victoria R.I.*, p. 457.

'Everyone likes flattery...': Maurois, *Disraeli*, pp. 210–18.

Ch. 39 Victoria Up; Brown Down

'the sovereign and servant...': Grosvenor, 'Dear John' *History*

Today p. 78.

'He protected me so...': Grosvenor, 'Dear John' *History Today* p. 82.

Ch. 41 Victoria's New Passion

'Letters to her were signed...': Basu, *Victoria & Abdul*, p. 208.

'From the wisdom of businessmen...': Maurois, *King Edward and his Times*, p. 31.

Ch. 43 Symbolism over Invalidism

'I think it very dreadful that everyone was there...': Longford, *Victoria R.I.*, p. 707.

Ch. 44 Funeral for a Connoisseur

'a simple running down...': in Hibbert, *The Royal Victorians*, p. 501.

Ch. 45 Edward VII—Payback Time

'The new King did not want...': Basu, *Victoria and Abdul*, p. 167.

Ch. 48 The Problem with David

'His abdication was a severe loss...': Speer, *Inside the Third Reich*, p. 118.

BIBLIOGRAPHY

Arbuthnol, Sir Alexander, *Memoirs of Rugby and India,* T. Fisher, UK, 1910.

Aronson, Theo, *The King in Love: Edward VII's Mistress,* Corgi Books, UK, 1988.

Basu, Shrabrani, *Victoria & Abdul,* History Press, UK, 2011.

Bolitho, Hector, *Albert, Prince Consort,* Max Parrish, London, 1964.

Boyd, Hilton, *A Mad, Bad and Dangerous People? England 1783–1846,* Clarendon Press, Oxford, 2006.

Bradford, Sarah, *Elizabeth,* Heinemann, London, 1996.

Carter, Miranda, *Anthony Blunt: His Lives,* Macmillan, UK, 2002.

Chatwyn, Alys, *H.R.H. The Duchess of York,* London Book Co., London, 1953.

Clarke, John, and Jasper Ridley, ed. Antonia Fraser, *The Houses of Hanover and Saxe-Coburg-Gotha,* University of California Press, Berkeley, CA, 2000.

Clay, Catrine, *King, Kaiser, Tsar,* Walker & Company, New York, 2008.

Cokayne, George Edward, *Complete Peerage of England, Scotland, Ireland, Great Britian and the United Kingdom,* Nabu Press, London, 2010.

Costello, Peter, *Mask of Treachery*, William Morrow, New York, 1988.

Duke of Windsor, *A King's Story*, Cassell and Co., London, 1951.

Fraser, William, *The Elphinstone Family Book of the Lords Elphinstone, Balmerino and Coupar*, T & A Constable at the Edinburgh University Press, Edinburgh, 1897.

Fulford, Sir Roger, *Dearest Child: The Private Correspondence of Queen Victoria and the Princess Royal, 1858–1861*, Evans Brothers, UK, 1965.

—— *Hanover to Windsor*, The Fontana Library, Collins, London, 1960.

Grosvenor, Bendor, 'Dear John', *History Today*, 2005, vol. 55, no. 1.

Hibbert, Christopher, *Queen Victoria: A Personal History*, Da Capo Press, USA, 2000.

—— *The Royal Victorians*, J. B. Lippincott Company, New York, 1976.

Kaye, John, and G.B. Malleson, *History of the Indian Mutiny of 1857–8*, vols 1–5, Allen, London, 1889.

Logue, Mark, and Peter Conradi, *The King's Speech*, Quercus, UK, 2010.

Longford, Elizabeth, *Victoria R.I.*, Corgi Books, UK, 1964.

Mackenzie, Compton, *The Windsor Tapestry*, Rich & Cowan, UK, 1938.

Maurois, Andre, *Disraeli: A Picture of the Victorian Age*, Bodley Head, London, 1949.

—— *King Edward and his Times*, Cassell, London, 1933.

Middlemas, Keith, *The Life and Times of Edward VII*, Weidenfeld & Nicolson, London, 1972.

Perry, Roland, *The Fifth Man*, Sidgwick & Jackson, UK, 1994.

—— *Last of the Cold War Spies*, Da Capo Press, USA, 2005.

Potts, D. M., and W.T.M. Potts, *Queen Victoria's Gene: Haemophilia and the Royal Family*, The History Press, UK, 2010.

Roberts, Andrew, (ed.), *Letters to Vicky: The Correspondence between Queen Victoria and her Daughter Victoria, Empress of Germany, 1858–1901*, Folio Society, London, 2011.

Rose, Kenneth, *King George V*, Phoenix, UK, 1983.

Sinclair, David, *Queen and Country: Life of Elizabeth the Queen Mother*, J.M. Dent & Sons, UK, 1980.

Speer, Albert, *Inside the Third Reich*, Macmillan, New York, 1970.

Strachey, Lytton, *The Illustrated Queen Victoria*, Bloomsbury, UK, 1987.

—— *Queen Victoria*, Chatto & Windus, London, 1922.

Van der Kiste, John, *Sons, Servants and Statesmen: The Men in Queen Victoria's Life*, Sutton Publishing, UK, 2006.

Warwick, Frances, Countess of, *Life's Ebb*, William Morrow & Co., New York, 1929.

Watson, Thomas, *Kirkintilloch, Town and Parish*, John Smith & Sons, Glasgow, 1894, https://archive.org/details/kirkintillochtow00wats.

Weintraub, Stanley, *Edward the Caresser*, The Free Press, New York, 2011.

—— *Victoria: An Intimate Biography*, Plume, USA, 1992.

Wheeler-Bennett, John W., *King George VI*, Macmillan, London 1958.

Williams, Kate, *Becoming Queen*, Arrow Books, UK, 2009.

Wilson, A.N. *Our Times: The Age of Elizabeth II*, Farrar, Straus & Giroux, New York, 2008.

Woodham-Smith, Cecil, *Queen Victoria: Her Life and Times*, Cardinal, UK, 1975.

Ziegler, Philip, *Crown and People*, William Collins, UK, 1978.